Instructor Guide / Test Bank

ESSENTIALS
HUMAN ANATOMY & PHYSIOLOGY

NINTH EDITION

Asha Stephens
College of the Mainland

Patty Bostwick Taylor
Florence–Darlington Technical College

PEARSON

Benjamin
Cummings

San Francisco Boston New York
Cape Town Hong Kong London Madrid Mexico City
Montreal Munich Paris Singapore Sydney Tokyo Toronto

Senior Acquisitions Editor: Deirdre Espinoza
Project Editor: Sabrina Larson
Editorial Assistant: Shannon Cutt
Managing Editor: Wendy Earl
Production Editor: Leslie Austin
Compositor: Cecelia G. Morales
Proofreader: Martha Ghent
Cover Design: Riezebos Holzbaur Design Group
Senior Manufacturing Buyer: Stacey Weinberger
Marketing Manager: Gordon Lee

ISBN 0-321-53128-0
ISBN 978-0-321-53128-5
3 4 5 6 7 8 9 10—TCS—12 11 10
www.aw-bc.com

PREFACE ————————————————————

The Instructor Guide/Test Bank to accompany the Ninth Edition of *Essentials of Human Anatomy & Physiology* by Elaine N. Marieb features a wealth of information for the anatomy and physiology instructor.

Organization of this Guide

This guide is divided into two sections. The first section, the Instructor Guide, includes nine subsections for each chapter: Chapter Summary, Suggested Lecture Outlines, Key Terms, Lecture Hints, Transparencies/Media Manager Index, Answers to End of Chapter Review Questions, Classroom Demonstrations and Student Activities, and Multimedia. The second section, the Test Bank, contains sample test questions for each chapter.

Chapter Summaries. Chapter summaries give a brief synopsis of the material that is covered within the chapters. Each summary references the significance of the chapter in relation to the study of anatomy and physiology, and all major topics are highlighted in the order in which they appear.

Suggested Lecture Outlines. These outlines provide a quick overview of the chapter contents and include page references to the text.

Key Terms. These listings highlight all of the bold terms in each chapter.

Lecture Hints. Lecture hints provide useful information for creating lectures, including topics that are common student pitfalls, creative tips for clarifying difficult concepts with analogies and short demonstrations, and ideas for discussion topics that can add interest to the class. Key points emphasize the pedagogical relevance of each lecture hint.

Transparencies/Media Manager Index. This list details which figures in the chapter are available on the Media Manager and in the color transparency package. (Call your Benjamin Cummings representative for information on how to obtain these supplements.)

Answers to End of Chapter Review Questions. To assist students in studying, multiple-choice and short answer review questions appear at the end of each textbook chapter. This section also includes answers to the "Critical Thinking & Clinical Application" questions and page references pointing to where the answers can be found in the main text.

Classroom Demonstrations and Student Activities. The suggestions provided here address the need to have students actively involved in their learning. The activities run the gamut from participatory group activities to library research topics. Because most courses for this text do not have lab sessions, many of the demonstrations included here use models and simple laboratory equipment. Hopefully, these student-oriented activities will enable them to solidify their understanding or substantially expand it.

Multimedia. Completely revised and updated for this edition, this section contains listings of videotapes and software. Each title description includes the following information, when available, in the sequence indicated: title, distributor code, length of title, year of release, and format, as well as a brief description of the topics that are covered. If a listing is of particular interest, it is recommended that you check your own college's multimedia catalog. If the title is not available there, request it from the distributor listed. The distributors' addresses, phone numbers, and web addresses are listed in the Multimedia Resource Distributors' list that appears at the end of the Instructor Guide.

Multimedia Resource Distributors. This helpful list provides contact information for over 40 distributors of educational materials. The first part of this appendix provides a key to the media distributors that are referenced under Multimedia in the Instructor Guide.

Test Bank. The test bank contains questions in short answer, multiple-choice, true/false, matching, and essay formats. This test bank is intended to provide a foundation of test items of varying difficulty that can be used as written or modified to correlate with the personal focus of your own class. Page references to the main text are provided for each question.

I would like to express a tremendous "thank you" to project editor Sabrina Larson and editorial assistant Shannon Cutt of Benjamin Cummings for their patience and professionalism in completing this Instructor Guide. Both of these individuals were instrumental in working with me during this process, and I greatly appreciate all of their help and advice. I would also like to thank my husband, Brett, who is my constant source of support and love, and was always willing to stay up late with me while I was working. He has been my cheerleader and motivator on many occasions, and I can't thank him enough for all that he has done.

Finally, I would like to dedicate this Instructor Guide to my mother, Betty Samuel, who passed away much too young last year. She is greatly missed, and I know she would have loved to see me succeed by contributing to this work. She is my inspiration from which I draw strength and one of my first and best teachers.

Asha Stephens
College of the Mainland, Texas City, TX

I would like to thank Benjamin Cummings for the opportunity to work on this Test Bank. Shannon Cutt and Annie Bleecker, editorial assistants on this project, have provided much valuable guidance and assistance. I appreciate their efforts to ensure a successful product. I also want to extend a "thank you" to Deirdre Espinoza for establishing my role in this project. This project has provided me with a diversion to the rewards and challenges of teaching students at the two-year technical college level. How exciting that some of these questions could encourage a student of anatomy and physiology to critically think a little more about the marvel of the human body!

Patty Bostwick Taylor
Florence–Darlington Technical College, Florence, SC

CONTENTS

Part I Instructor Guide

Part II Test Bank

Instructor Guide

The Human Body: An Orientation

CHAPTER SUMMARY

Chapter 1 introduces and establishes the framework upon which all the other chapters are built. This chapter provides the necessary terminology so that instructor and students are all "speaking the same language." Marieb begins by defining the key terms *anatomy* and *physiology*, and then continues to describe the ways in which these key terms are interrelated. It is important that students realize that structure determines function, since that concept will help them to master the more difficult material in future chapters.

Levels of organization are presented next, beginning with the atomic level and continuing through to the highest level of organization, the human body. A brief overview of the various organ systems follows the discussion of the levels of structural organization, and the ways in which all the organ systems are interconnected into a working whole. This concept is further augmented by the discussion of the necessary life functions, since it is important for students to understand that each of the organ systems has several functions, and that any given function (e.g., excretion) is actually carried out by several organ systems working together to maintain appropriate balance within the living organism. This information leads to a discussion of homeostasis, and the disease states that occur when homeostatic mechanisms are out of balance for extended periods. Students appreciate the image of the dynamic body continually striving to maintain balance and equilibrium.

The final section of this chapter provides the basic terminology that will be used and expanded upon throughout the text. Directional terms help the student distinguish between relative terms such as proximal and distal, and thus help them understand the midline of the body as an axis point. Regional terms differentiate anterior and posterior body landmarks, divide the body into sections and planes, and identify the body cavities and their components. The anatomists' useful description of regions is also presented to round out the students' awareness of the ways in which the body can be physically and intellectually dissected.

SUGGESTED LECTURE OUTLINE

TEACHING TIP

Give word roots, prefixes, and suffixes to help students begin to build a language of biology. Have students make flash cards of the word parts, then combine them in different ways to make new terms. In discussing medical conditions, point out the use of these same word parts to form medical terms. Students are usually excited to see how quickly their vocabulary expands on their increasing knowledge of word parts.

I. AN OVERVIEW OF ANATOMY AND PHYSIOLOGY
(pp. 2–3)
    A. Anatomy (p. 2)
        1. Gross Anatomy
        2. Microscopic Anatomy
    B. Physiology (p. 2)
    C. Relationship Between Anatomy and Physiology (p. 2)

II. LEVELS OF STRUCTURAL ORGANIZATION (pp. 3–10)
    A. From Atoms to Organisms (pp. 3–4)
        1. Chemical Level
        2. Cellular Level
        3. Tissue Level
        4. Organ Level

5.   Organ System Level
6.   Organismal Level
B.   Organ System Overview (pp. 4–10; Figure 1.2)
1.   Integumentary System
2.   Skeletal System
3.   Muscular System
4.   Nervous System
5.   Endocrine System
6.   Cardiovascular System
7.   Lymphatic System
8.   Respiratory System
9.   Digestive System
10.   Urinary System
11.   Reproductive System

III.   MAINTAINING LIFE (pp. 10–12)
A.   Necessary Life Functions (pp. 10–11)
1.   Maintaining Boundaries
2.   Movement
3.   Responsiveness (irritability)
4.   Digestion
5.   Metabolism
6.   Excretion
7.   Reproduction
8.   Growth
B.   Survival Needs (pp. 11–12)
1.   Nutrients (food)
2.   Oxygen
3.   Water
4.   Body Temperature
5.   Atmospheric Pressure

IV.   HOMEOSTASIS (pp. 12–15)
A.   Homeostatic Control Mechanisms (pp. 12–13)
1.   Receptor
2.   Control Center
3.   Effector
4.   Negative Feedback Mechanisms
5.   Positive Feedback Mechanisms
B.   Homeostatic Imbalance (p. 15)

V.   THE LANGUAGE OF ANATOMY (pp. 15–22)
A.   Anatomical Position (p. 15)
B.   Directional Terms (p. 15; Table 1.1)
C.   Regional Terms (pp. 16–17; Figure 1.5)
1.   Anterior Body Landmarks
2.   Posterior Body Landmarks
D.   Body Planes and Sections (p. 17; Figure 1.6)
E.   Body Cavities (pp. 17–22)
1.   Dorsal Body Cavity
a.   Cranial Cavity
b.   Spinal Cavity

MEDIA TIP

The Universe Within (CBS; 60 min., 1995). Using micro-photography, NOVA presents the microworld of the human body.

2. Ventral Body Cavity
    a. Thoracic Cavity
    b. Abdominopelvic Cavity
       i. Abdominopelvic Quadrants
      ii. Abdominopelvic Regions
3. Open Body Cavities

KEY TERMS

abdominal cavity	frontal section	physiology
abdominopelvic cavity	homeostasis	plane
anatomical position	homeostatic imbalance	positive feedback
anatomy	integumentary system	mechanisms
atoms	irritability	receptor
cardiovascular system	lymphatic system	reproduction
cells	median section	reproductive system
control center	mediastinum	respiratory system
coronal section	metabolism	responsiveness (irritability)
cranial cavity	midsagittal (median) section	sagittal section
cross section	movement	section
diaphragm	muscular system	skeletal system
digestion	negative feedback	spinal cavity
digestive system	nervous system	thoracic cavity
dorsal body cavity	organ	tissues
effector	organ system	transverse section
endocrine system	organism	urinary system
excretion	pelvic cavity	ventral body cavity

Directional Terms

Superior (cranial or cephalad)	Posterior (dorsal)	Proximal
	Medial	Distal
Inferior (caudal)	Lateral	Superficial (external)
Anterior (ventral)	Intermediate	Deep (internal)

Anterior Body Landmarks

Abdominal	Coxal	Oral
Acromial	Crural	Orbital
Antebrachial	Deltoid	Patellar
Antecubital	Digital	Pelvic
Axillary	Femoral	Pubic
Brachial	Fibular	Sternal
Buccal	Frontal	Tarsal
Carpal	Inguinal	Thoracic
Cervical	Nasal	Umbilical

Posterior Body Landmarks

Calcaneal
Cephalic
Femoral
Gluteal

Lumbar
Occipital
Olecranal
Popliteal

Sacral
Scapular
Sural
Vertebral

Abdominopelvic Regions

Epigastric Region
Hypogastric (Pubic) Region
Left Hypochondriac Region
Left Iliac (Inguinal) Region

Left Lumbar Region
Right Hypochondriac
  Region
Right Iliac (Inguinal) Region

Right Lumbar Region
Umbilical Region

Open Body Cavities

Middle Ear Cavities
Nasal Cavity

Oral and Digestive Cavities
Orbital Cavities

LECTURE HINTS

1. To differentiate between anatomy and physiology, show models of various organs and discuss the way that structure determines function. A particularly good example is the digestive tract. Having the students see the digestive system as a single long tube from entrance to exit, with twists and turns along the way, helps them to visualize the correlation between anatomy and physiology.

   Key point: Anatomy and physiology are separate but closely related concepts. A slight change in anatomy, for example from a condition like sickle cell anemia, can have a significant effect on physiology.

2. Discuss the differences between microscopic and macroscopic (gross) anatomy, and their relevance to such specialties as pathology and microbiology.

   Key point: Point out to students that dissection is aimed at helping us to understand the functions of each of the various levels of organization, but that the body works as a whole and is consequently more complex than the simple sum of its component parts.

3. Starting with the concept of atoms joining to form molecules, have the students "build" a single organ system that then combines with other organs to form the living body.

   Key point: Every level of the system relies on the smooth workings of the level preceding it, and a malfunction at any level may have life-threatening consequences to the levels built upon it.

4. Discuss each of the fundamental life functions (e.g., digestion, metabolism) and have the students list all of the organ systems that contribute to this single function.

   Key point: It is important for students to understand that organ systems often have an obvious, primary function, but that all the systems are closely interrelated and impact one another in numerous ways, including ways not yet identified.

5. Ask the students to describe the physiological effects of working outside on a 100°F day, and compare that to being outside on a day that is below freezing. Outline the ways in which the body compensates for such variations in temperature and identify these mechanisms as homeostasis at work.

Key point: Point out to students that even though they may not be regularly exposed to extremes such as heatstroke or frostbite, the body is still in a constant state of flux, balancing between a range of "normal" values that is rarely static.

6. A simple, clear method of demonstrating negative feedback is to discuss the thermostat in the classroom. Students can easily understand the negative feedback system of the HVAC system at work.

   Key point: Negative feedback loops are the chief regulators of homeostasis under normal healthy conditions. A rise in any given value (e.g., blood pH, heart rate, blood pressure) precipitates a reaction to lower it, until such time as it becomes too low, causing negative feedback to initiate responses to raise it again.

7. Positive feedback is more difficult to understand than negative feedback. A brief explanation of the process of childbirth is usually the clearest way to present this concept in a context that most students are familiar with.

   Key point: Positive feedback loops are more rare than negative feedback loops. Positive feedback is reserved for events such as childbirth, which involve an ever-increasing buildup of responses that trigger the next response until they bring about the culmination of a major event. Like a nuclear reaction, positive feedback involves a series of chain reactions of ever-increasing magnitude.

8. Directional terms are best presented as opposites, with appropriate demonstrations for each. For example, anterior is easily distinguished from posterior, superior from inferior, etc. The most difficult set to distinguish seems to be proximal and distal. Use a set of examples that demonstrate their relationship, such as elbow to wrist (the elbow is *proximal* in this instance) compared with elbow to shoulder (the elbow is *distal* in this instance), to help clarify the concept.

   Key point: It is important for students to understand that proximal and distal terminology is used *relative to the midline of the body*.

9. Point out to students how the terms anterior/posterior and superior/inferior refer to different areas for bipeds and quadrupeds. Also point out that words are often combined to more accurately identify the relative position of a single structure.

   Key point: Just as more than one adjective can be used to describe a single noun, so can more than one directional term be used to describe a single structure.

10. Give definitions of word roots, prefixes, and suffixes to help students begin to build a language of biomedical terminology. Have students make flash cards of the word parts, then combine them in different ways to make new terms. In discussing medical conditions, point out the use of these same word parts to form medical terms. Students are usually excited to see how quickly their vocabulary expands based on their increasing knowledge of word parts.

    Key point: Increasing the students' understanding of word parts and the ways those word parts combine will greatly improve their understanding of the biological sciences and biomedical articles written in newspapers and magazines.

11. Emphasize that the language of anatomy is often redundant and that multiple terms exist for structures or events. These terms come from tradition (national origin, the discoverer, etc.) or were named in a more practical fashion, based on structure or function. Often both structural and functional names are given. Make sure students realize that it is difficult to master all of these terms quickly, and it can be frustrating as well, but that they can learn them more completely with experience.

    Key point: Science has its own language, as complex as English or any other language, and it takes time and concentrated effort to master.

12. Provide students with opportunities to verbalize material and use appropriate terminology that you have covered in your lecture. The unfamiliar terms students are introduced to will have more meaning if they pronounce them out loud. Encourage students to study verbally while practicing vocabulary and explaining concepts. Encourage students to explain processes or mechanisms in their own words whenever possible.

   Key point: As with any new language, practice is the key to development and long-term retention.

13. Most people correctly visualize a space when they hear the term cavity. Most body cavities, however, are potential spaces and are filled with viscera, tissues, and fluids. In addition to the dorsal body cavity and the ventral body cavity, mention other cavities such as the oral cavity, the nasal cavity, and the pericardial cavity.

   Key point: Explain that *potential space* is a space that exists, but that it may be filled, such as the abdominal cavity is filled with organs; an uninflated balloon also has a potential space that can be filled with air or fluid.

TRANSPARENCIES/MEDIA MANAGER INDEX

Figure 1.1	Levels of structural organization
Figure 1.2	The body's organ systems
Figure 1.3	Examples of selected interrelationships among body organ systems
Figure 1.4	The elements of a homeostatic control system
Figure 1.5	Surface anatomy: Regional terms
Figure 1.6	The anatomical position and planes of the body—median, frontal, and transverse with corresponding MRI scans
Figure 1.7	Body cavities
Figure 1.8	Abdominopelvic surface and cavity
Table 1.1	Orientation and Directional Terms
A Closer Look	Medical Imaging: Illuminating the Body
Focus on Careers	Dental Hygienist*

Indicates images that are on the Media Manager only.

ANSWERS TO IN CHAPTER QUESTIONS

Questions appear on p. 15

The wrist is <u>proximal</u> to the hand.

The breastbone is <u>anterior or ventral</u> to the spine.

The brain is <u>superior</u> to the spinal cord.

The thumb is <u>lateral</u> to the fingers.

ANSWERS TO END OF CHAPTER REVIEW QUESTIONS

Questions appear on pp. 23–25

Multiple Choice

1. d (p. 3)
2. a, b, c, d (pp. 12–13)
3. c (pp. 11–12)
4. superior, deep, proximal or lateral, proximal, medial, posterior (p. 15; Table 1.1)
5. e, c, i, f, h, a, b, d, g (pp. 16–17; Figure 1.5)
6. c (Table 1.1)
7. c (p. 20)
8. c (pp. 20–21; Figure 1.8)

Short Answer Essay

9. *Anatomy:* Study of the structure and shape of body parts and their relationship to one another. *Physiology:* Study of the function of the body or body parts, that is, how they work or operate. (p. 2)

10. See pp. 4–7, which summarize the body's organ systems. *Integumentary system:* Functions basically to protect. The integumentary system is an organ and an organ system. (Students may name sweat glands and the like, but this is not really necessary.) *Skeletal system:* Major role is to support the body and provide a framework on which the muscles can act to create movement; also protects by enclosing. Bones, ligaments. *Muscular system:* Major role is to promote body movement. Organs include the skeletal muscles. *Nervous system:* The body's fast-acting controlling and coordinating system; acts via electrical signals called nerve impulses. Brain, spinal cord, nerves. *Endocrine system:* The body's slower-acting controlling and coordinating system, which acts through chemicals called hormones. Pancreas, adrenals, thyroid, pituitary, parathyroid, thymus, pineal, ovaries (female), testes (male). *Cardiovascular system:* Basically a transport and delivery system for bringing adequate supplies of oxygen and nutrients to the body's cells and for getting rid of cell wastes. Heart, blood vessels, lungs. *Lymphatic system:* Collects fluid leaked from the cardiovascular system and returns it to the bloodstream. Houses cells involved in the immune response. Lymphatic vessels, lymph nodes, spleen, tonsils. *Respiratory system:* Exchanges respiratory gases, that is, takes in oxygen and releases carbon dioxide to the body exterior. Lungs, bronchi, bronchioles, trachea, nasal passages, pharynx, larynx. *Digestive system:* Breaks down ingested foods so that they can be absorbed into the bloodstream and thereby made available to the body's cells. Mouth (oral cavity), esophagus, stomach, small intestine, large intestine, rectum. *Urinary system:* Rids the body of nitrogenous wastes and regulates the acid-base, water balance, and electrolytes of the body fluids. Kidneys, ureters, bladder, urethra. *Reproductive system:* Produces sex (germ) cells so that reproduction of the individual can occur. Ovaries or testes, scrotum, penis, accessory glands, duct system (male), uterus, uterine tubes, vagina (female).

11. *Homeostasis:* A relatively stable condition of the body's internal environment that is maintained by various functional mechanisms despite changes in the external environment. (p. 12)

12. Aging, abnormal body functioning leading to illness and disease and/or death. (pp. 12 and 15)

13. Yes. No. (pp. 20–21)

14. Nose—anterior surface; calf—posterior surface; umbilicus—anterior surface; fingernails—posterior surface. (Figure 1.5)

15. Both subdivisions of the ventral body cavity—cardiovascular, circulatory, digestive, and muscular. Thoracic cavity only—respiratory. Abdominopelvic cavity only—reproductive and urinary. (pp. 20–21)

ANSWERS TO CRITICAL THINKING AND CLINICAL APPLICATION QUESTIONS

16. *Antecubital region:* He should have held out the anterior surface of his arm. (The antecubital region is the anterior aspect of the elbow. *Deltoid region:* He should have taken off his shirt to receive a shot in the shoulder region. *Sural:* His left calf was bruised. (pp. 16–17; Figure 1.5)

17. With age, body organs and control systems become less efficient at adapting to interior and exterior stressors. This drop in efficiency causes the internal environment to be less and less stable. Examples include: sweat glands become less active; decreased amounts of hormones are produced by endocrine glands; bones become weaker due to loss of bone mass; muscles start to atrophy; and decreased efficiency of the circulatory system. (See "Homeostatic Imbalance" sections in each chapter.)

18. Jennie's nerve is injured where her upper appendage attaches to the trunk (armpit). Torn ligaments are located in her neck and shoulder blade region. The broken bone is located in the right upper appendage between the shoulder and elbow. (pp. 16–17)

19. The doctors would probably use MRI because it has the highest resolving power to examine soft tissues such as the brain. Dense structures would not show up, so bones of the skull would not impair the view. (pp. 8–9)

20. Levels of calcium in the blood should increase as more parathyroid hormone (PTH) is secreted. This hormone is released in response to low levels of calcium in the blood; therefore, its functions include moving calcium out of storage (e.g., bones) and into the bloodstream, increasing calcium absorption in the intestines, and retaining calcium in the kidneys. These functions will increase blood calcium levels. (p. 13) (See also Chapter 9 for more information about the endocrine system functions.)

CLASSROOM DEMONSTRATIONS AND STUDENT ACTIVITIES

Classroom Demonstrations

1. Film(s) or other media of choice.

2. Dissect a freshly killed rat or a small preserved animal (e.g., a fetal pig) to demonstrate the various organ systems of the body. Point out at least two organs from each organ system and discuss their function. If dissection is not an option, there are several films that can be substituted (see Media section). In addition, Carolina Biological Supply Company offers plastinated dissected specimens and preserved dissected specimens that are mounted in clear acrylic containers.

3. Use a dissectible human torso model to point out the dorsal and ventral body cavities and the organs in each cavity.

4. Use a skeleton and human torso to show directional terms.

5. Demonstrate various pulse points, some of which the students will already be familiar with. Relating these pulse points to regional terminology will help the students understand their usage.

6. Arrange for the class to attend an autopsy (preferably after the material of Chapter 1 has been covered).

7. Decorate your classroom with posters and diagrams of body systems. Label with appropriate directional terms, regional terms, or terms related to body planes or body cavities.

8. Thin, plastinated sections of the human body can be purchased from Carolina Biological Supply Company and can be viewed with the naked eye, or projected on an overhead projector for viewing by the entire class. A 3-D overhead called ELMO has recently been reasonably priced for classroom use.

9. Create emergency room scenarios using terminology from Chapter 1. Have the students determine the location of the illness or injury.

Student Activities

1. Assume the anatomical position. Ask the students to comment on how that position differs from the "usual" standing position and to explain why knowing this position is important to precisely identify anatomical terms and physiological processes.

2. Remove all the organs from the ventral and dorsal body cavities of a human torso model. Ask for volunteers or assign students to return them to their proper anatomic location. As each organ is properly repositioned, have other students call out its name and organ system relationship.

3. Place a chair at center stage. Ask for a volunteer to come up and show how the chair would be cut along the sagittal, frontal, and transverse planes, and to choose which of these planes would yield a "usable" seat, providing an explanation for the choice made. (The explanation should also include the reasons the other options were not selected.)

4. To initiate a class discussion on the relative degree of protection of organs in the dorsal versus the ventral body cavity, ask the class a question such as, "Why do you think a dog instinctively curls over and protects its abdomen when that body region is approached (threatened by a blow, etc.) even playfully?" or "Two people have rapidly growing tumors. The tumor is in the dorsal cavity in one of these individuals and in the ventral cavity of the other. Which of these people will develop symptoms first, and why?"

5. Call out anatomical terms (buccal, femoral, etc.) and have the students (as a group) point out the named regions on their own bodies.

6. Have students find a series of landmarks on their own bodies, providing a list of landmarks for the students to locate. Use real-life examples to help the students better understand the terminology. For example, the list could include items such as "the location where a necktie is worn," "the location of a belly button piercing," and so on. Have the students do this in small groups so they can discuss the terms with each other and begin to develop camaraderie among the group.

7. Demonstrate the location of the radial, brachial, carotid, femoral, popliteal, and pedal pulses. Have students try to locate several pulse points on themselves and their fellow students.

8. Have students get into groups of four or five. List five root words on the board and have the student groups come up with as many terms as they can think of that incorporate those roots. The terms can be common English, biological, or medical in nature, as long as a root word is found in each. Allow them 15 minutes to compile their lists, then compare the terms of the various groups. Point out their increased vocabulary based on the knowledge of a relatively small number of roots.

9. To help the students understand negative feedback, ask them to explain how scratching an itch can be considered an example of negative feedback. Some students may be familiar with a TENS Unit which provides pain relief by continual electrical "scratching of an itch."

10. To encourage an understanding of organ system interrelationships, ask the students to comment on the functional relationships between muscles and bones, and between the respiratory and cardiovascular systems.

11. Use a simple battery-operated clock as an example to indicate the importance of relatively constant conditions on optimal functioning of any system. Ask the class to indicate what would happen if it was (a) immersed in water, (b) hit with a hammer, (c) heated until it was red-hot, and (d) had its battery removed. Then ask them what conditions would be best suited for the clock to operate properly, and ask them to provide a single term that describes those conditions (homeostasis).

12. Explore with the class the meaning of "alive." Use examples of animals exhibiting these characteristics on film or videodisc, and ask students to identify the characteristics being demonstrated. Or, allow students to develop a list of characteristics by discussing their own life needs. Are bacteria "alive" in themselves? (Yes.) Are viruses "alive" in themselves (No. Viruses need a fluid-filled host to be "alive.")

13. Student assignment for class discussion: Bring in an article from a popular magazine or newspaper describing an environmental problem(s), such as toxic waste disposal, pollution of the ocean, etc., that threatens their homeostasis, even survival. Be prepared to describe the problem and how it represents a threat to the body.

14. Discuss the changes in medical technology that have occurred over the lifetime of the students in your class. Have them speculate on what new technologies could emerge in the next decade, or even in the next century.

MULTIMEDIA

See page 182 for a listing of media distributors.

1. *Homeostasis* (FHS; 20 min., 1995, VHS, DVD). From *The New Living Body* series, live-action video, advanced imaging technology, and 3-D computer graphics show homeostatic mechanisms in the human body at work during a marathon.

2. *Human Biology* (FHS; 58 min., 1995, VHS, DVD). Twenty-one live-action video sequences provide an overview of human biology.

3. *Human Body: The Ultimate Machine* (CBS; 27 min., 2005, VHS, DVD). The body's major systems are described through footage of surgical procedures, microphotography, and 3-D animation.

4. *Introduction to the Body: Landscapes and Interiors* (FHS; 28 min., 1989, VHS, DVD). Introduction to the award-winning *The Living Body* series that shows the body's adaptability to diverse climates and other homeostatic triggers.

SOFTWARE

1. *A.D.A.M. Multimedia Package* (ADAM, BC; Win/Mac). Provides 500 anatomy and physiology graphics.
2. *A.D.A.M. InterActive Anatomy* (ADAM, BC; Win/Mac). Classic comprehensive database of the human body.
3. *InterActive Physiology 9-system suite* (ADAM, BC; Win/Mac). Educational package with CD-ROM modules to help students learn the difficult concepts of physiology.
4. *Explorations in Human Biology* (WNS; Win/Mac). A set of 15 interactive lessons.
5. *The Ultimate Human Body* (ED; Win/Mac). Exploration of the human body through three search paths.
6. *WARD's Radiographic Anatomy* (WNS; Win). Excellent collection of health-related images (CTs, MRIs, etc.), ideal for students interested in health careers.

Basic Chemistry

CHAPTER SUMMARY

Chapter 2 provides an overview of basic biological chemistry. Although this is often a topic students dread, it is necessary to convey the importance of physical chemistry reactions and biochemical metabolic pathways in physiology. This chapter begins with the fundamental concepts related to matter and energy, then proceeds to show the breakdown of matter into its components. A discussion of the periodic table reveals the way in which elements are arranged by properties, and provides a means for determining characteristics of certain elements based on their position on the periodic table. The four most abundant elements in all living organisms (i.e., carbon, oxygen, hydrogen, and nitrogen) are emphasized.

Atomic structure is presented next, and the planetary and orbital models provide a framework upon which students begin to build their understanding of atoms. Atomic number, atomic mass number, and atomic weight are discussed, followed by comments on the characteristics of isotopes and their role in health care assessment and management. The concepts presented about atomic structure lead naturally into a discussion of molecules and compounds. Chemical bonds and reactions are presented as a means by which molecules and bonds are continuously formed and destroyed. The differences between ionic, covalent, and hydrogen bonds are all discussed, as are synthesis and decomposition reactions.

The final section of this chapter provides an overview of biochemistry. The differences between organic and inorganic compounds are presented, along with applied examples of each. Water is noted to be the most abundant compound in the body, which helps students understand its role as the universal "solvent" of life. The reactions of acids and bases leads into the section about biochemical reactions in the body. The types of organic compounds (i.e., carbohydrates, lipids, proteins, and nucleic acids) further these concepts as students begin to see the importance of the proper utilization of these compounds in all body processes.

SUGGESTED LECTURE OUTLINE

I. CONCEPTS OF MATTER AND ENERGY (pp. 27–28)
   A. Matter (p. 27)
   B. Energy (pp. 27–28)
      1. Forms of Energy
         a. Chemical Energy
         b. Electrical Energy
         c. Mechanical Energy
         d. Radiant Energy
      2. Energy Form Conversions

II. COMPOSITION OF MATTER (pp. 29–34)
   A. Elements and Atoms (p. 29; Table 2.1)
      1. Major Elements
      2. Lesser Elements
      3. Trace Elements
   B. Atomic Structure (pp. 29, 31; Table 2.2)
      1. Subatomic Particles

TEACHING TIP

Discuss radioisotopes and their importance as a diagnostic tool in medicine. Students are usually familiar with scans that use contrast media such as iodine or barium, and they are often intrigued by the chemical implications of these tests.

MEDIA TIP

Basic Chemistry for Biology Students (HRM; 21 min., 1993). Excellent video for clarifying basic chemistry concepts.

2. Planetary and Orbital Models of an Atom
C. Identifying Elements (pp. 31–34)
   1. Atomic Number
   2. Atomic Mass Number
   3. Atomic Weight and Isotopes

III. MOLECULES AND COMPOUNDS (pp. 34–35)

IV. CHEMICAL BONDS AND CHEMICAL REACTIONS
(pp. 35–41)
   A. Bond Formation (pp. 35–39)
      1. Role of Electrons
      2. Types of Chemical Bonds
         a. Ionic Bonds
         b. Covalent Bonds
         c. Hydrogen Bonds
   B. Patterns of Chemical Reactions (pp. 40–41)
      1. Synthesis Reactions
      2. Decomposition Reactions
      3. Exchange Reactions
      4. Factors Influencing the Rate of Chemical
         Reactions

V. BIOCHEMISTRY: THE CHEMICAL COMPOSITION OF
LIVING MATTER (pp. 41–58)
   A. Inorganic Compounds (pp. 42–45)
      1. Water
         a. High Heat Capacity
         b. Polarity/Solvent Properties
         c. Chemical Reactivity
         d. Cushioning
      2. Salts
      3. Acids and Bases
         a. Characteristics of Acids
         b. Characteristics of Bases
         c. pH: Acid-Base Concentrations
   B. Organic Compounds (pp. 45–58)
      1. Carbohydrates
         a. Monosaccharides
         b. Disaccharides
         c. Polysaccharides
      2. Lipids
         a. Triglycerides
         b. Phospholipids
         c. Steroids
      3. Proteins
         a. Fibrous and Globular Proteins
         b. Enzymes and Enzyme Activity
      4. Nucleic Acids
         a. Nucleotides
         b. Deoxyribonucleic Acid (DNA)
         c. Ribonucleic Acid (RNA)
      5. Adenosine Triphosphate (ATP)

KEY TERMS

-ase
acids
active sites
adenosine disphosphate (ADP)
adenosine triphosphate (ATP)
amino acids
atomic mass
atomic mass number
atomic number
atomic symbol
atomic weight
atoms
bases
buffers
catalyst
carbohydrates
chemical energy
chemical reactivity
cholesterol
compound
covalent bonds
cushioning
decomposition reactions
dehydration synthesis
deoxyribonucleic acid (DNA)
disaccharides
electrical energy

electrolytes
electron shells
electrons
elements (e^-)
energy
energy levels
exchange reactions
fatty acids
fibrous (structural) proteins
functional proteins
globular proteins
glucose
glycerol
high heat capacity
hydrogen bonds
hydrolysis
inorganic compounds
ionic bonds
ions
isotopes
kinetic energy
lipids
matter
mechanical energy
molecules
monosaccharide
monounsaturated
neutral fats
neutralization reaction
neutrons (n^0)

nucleic acids
nucleotides
omega-3 fatty acids
orbital model
organic compounds
periodic table
pH
phospholipids
planetary model
polarity (solvent) properties
polysaccharides
polyunsaturated
potential energy
proteins
proton acceptors
proton donors
protons (p^+)
radiant energy
radioactivity
radioisotopes
ribonucleic acid (RNA)
salt
saturated
steroids
structural proteins
synthesis reactions
trans fats
triglycerides
unsaturated
valence shell

LECTURE HINTS

1. Students benefit from the presentation of chemistry through a variety of sources. The 21-minute video, *Basic Chemistry for Biology Students*, provides an excellent visual summary of the material and helps them grasp the basics.

   Key point: There isn't enough time in this course to present chemistry in significant depth, and yet students need a solid understanding of the basic concepts. Keeping the material as clear and straightforward as possible helps to decrease their frustration.

2. Remind students of the levels of structural organization, starting with the atom. Explain the relevance of chemistry to this hierarchy and reiterate that higher levels of complexity are dependent upon the smooth workings of preceding, less complex, levels.

   Key point: Since chemistry seems abstract to students, they often fail to understand its importance until that connection is made for them. Providing clear examples of some of the chemical reactions we use to sustain life (e.g., IV therapy, medication administration) helps them to put chemistry into its proper applied perspective.

3. Emphasize the fact that energy is not created or destroyed, but can be converted from one form to another. Use food as an example, starting with electromagnetic radiation

from the sun and ending with the chemical bonds of an ATP molecule in a human muscle cell.

Key point: It is important for students to understand that energy is never lost, it is just found in different forms, some of which we can capture and others of which, at this point, we cannot.

4. Use the periodic table as a tool to discuss atoms and elements, and continue to use it while presenting the mechanics of bond formation. Work through a few examples (e.g., sodium reacting with chlorine) then have the students work through several combinations of elements contained within the same columns.

   Key point: Once the students see how the elements react based on their valence electrons, they begin to form a clearer picture of the chemical properties of the elements.

5. Use as many visual aids as you can to demonstrate bonding patterns between atoms. Ball-and-stick models or cutouts for the board will work well.

   Key point: The more experience students have with forming molecules and compounds in model form, the better their understanding of the various bond formations.

6. Explain the tendency of elements with less than 4 electrons in their valence shell to want to *lose* those electrons, while elements with more than 4 electrons in their valence shell will want to *gain* electrons, all in the name of achieving "stability." Further explain that it is when there are 4 electrons in the valence shell that the element doesn't want to gain or lose electrons, but is willing at that point to *share* electrons. Note that only a few elements (the noble gases) come equipped with a stable valence shell and that prolonged excess of highly reactive unstable molecules within the body upsets homeostasis and may cause chronic diseases.

   Key point: The entire field of organic chemistry is dependent upon these principles. Carbon has the capacity to form not only single bonds, but also double and triple bonds, making it a very versatile element. Without the property of carbon to share electrons, life on Earth would be entirely different or not existent at all. It is important to emphasize that humans are carbon-based organisms, as are all living things on our planet.

7. Ionic bonds form when electrons are transferred from one atom to another. In covalent bonds, electrons are shared among the atoms of the molecule and are 18 times stronger than ionic bonds.

   Key point: The fact that a covalent bond is 18 times stronger is the "take home" concept when comparing the two bonds.

8. Make sure students understand that hydrogen bonds can be formed between molecules or can be formed within a molecule. Use water as an example of intermolecular hydrogen bonding and proteins for intramolecular bonding.

   Key point: Hydrogen bonds, although weak, are important for holding DNA and large proteins together, as well as for holding water molecules together. The fact that only weak hydrogen bonds join these base pairs together within the middle of the DNA molecule and very strong covalent bonds join the sugar-phosphate backbones is very important because the DNA molecule is enabled to split apart and replicate. This discovery by Watson and Crick forever changed the world of biological thinking and is one main reason why Watson and Crick won the Nobel Prize.

9. Discuss surface tension to explain the outcome of hydrogen bonds. Students have usually seen insects "walk on water" and appreciate gaining an understanding of why this is possible.

Key point: Until they can "see" the effects of millions of hydrogen bonds holding water together, it is difficult for students to understand their importance.

10. Emphasize the fact that the larger the pH number, the smaller the concentration of hydrogen ions and thus the larger the relative concentration of hydroxy ions and more alkaline the solution, whereas the smaller the pH number, the larger the concentration of hydrogen ions and thus the more acidic the solution.

    Key point: Students frequently confuse this point. It is important to point out that each change of 1 pH unit represents a tenfold change in hydrogen-ion concentration.

11. Discuss the importance of maintaining pH in different regions of the body. Use pH values of blood and gastric juice to illustrate two different environments in the body, and explain how enzymes in one area may not work in another area.

    Key point: Explain how chemical reactions (and therefore, cell functions) cannot function properly outside of their normal pH range. This concept will be important later when discussing the respiratory buffer system in Chapters 13 and 15.

12. Construct a flowchart to help students identify molecular formulas for carbohydrates, lipids, and proteins. For example, if H:O = 2:1, the molecule is a carbohydrate. Then, if the carbohydrate has 3–7 carbons and exists in a single ring or a single chain, it is a monosaccharide. Then, put cutout pictures of various examples of carbohydrates, lipids, or amino acids on the board and ask students to classify them using the chart.

    Key point: It is important to help students visualize organic compounds and their component parts. This will be particularly relevant later when students begin analyzing anabolism and catabolism.

13. Many students learn that proteins are important because they are enzymes. Emphasize all the roles that proteins play in the human body.

    Key point: Since proteins account for over 50% of organic matter in the body, it is valuable for students to understand the wide variety of functions that proteins play, from formation of enzymes to construction of body substances.

14. Discuss the role of enzymes in catalyzing reactions. Explain that enzymes work in a lock-and-key method. The particular three-dimensional shape (active site) of the enzyme determines what substrate they "fit" with chemically. Note that the "key" is not used up on a single reaction, but can, in fact, be used over and over.

    Key point: Visualizing the three-dimensional shape of enzymes helps students understand what happens when proteins (enzymes) are denatured such as when body temperature is excessively elevated. Without intact binding sites, enzymes cannot perform their designated function.

15. Discuss radioisotopes and their importance as a diagnostic tool in medicine. Students are usually familiar with scans, which use contrast media such as iodine or barium, and they are intrigued by the chemical implications of these tests.

    Key point: Increasing the students' understanding of basic chemistry helps them begin to see its relevance to other areas of life, including medicine.

16. Adipose tissue cells shrink or swell like sponges depending on how much fat (triglyceride) is deposited within them. Fat represents stored "potential energy" and is mobilized out into the bloodstream where it travels to skeletal muscles and is utilized for energy during exercise. Future chapters will build on this information.

    Key point: Fat tissue is not metabolically active tissue whereas skeletal muscle is. Thus, the stored energy within the fat must first be mobilized into the bloodstream in order to travel to other cells such as skeletal muscle to be used for energy.

TRANSPARENCIES/MEDIA MANAGER INDEX

Figure 2.1	The structure of an atom
Figure 2.2	Atomic structure of the three smallest atoms
Figure 2.3	Isotopes of hydrogen
Figure 2.4	Properties of a compound differ from those of its atoms
Figure 2.5	Chemically inert and reactive elements
Figure 2.6	Formation of an ionic bond
Figure 2.7	Formation of covalent bonds
Figure 2.8	Molecular models illustrating the three-dimensional structure of carbon dioxide and water molecules
Figure 2.9	Hydrogen bonding between polar water molecules
Figure 2.10	Patterns of chemical reactions
Figure 2.11	Dissociation of a salt in water
Figure 2.12	The pH scale and pH values of representative substances
Figure 2.13	Carbohydrates
Figure 2.14	Dehydration synthesis and hydrolysis of a molecule of sucrose
Figure 2.15	Lipids
Figure 2.16	Amino acid structures
Figure 2.17	General structure of (a) a fibrous protein and (b) a globular protein
Figure 2.18	Simple diagram illustrating denaturation of a functional protein molecule such as an enzyme
Figure 2.19	Structure of DNA
Figure 2.20	ATP—structure and hydrolysis
Figure 2.21	Three examples of how ATP drives cellular work
Table 2.1	Common Elements Making Up the Human Body
Table 2.2	Subatomic Particles
Table 2.3	Atomic Structures of the Most Abundant Elements in the Body
Table 2.4	Factors Increasing the Rate of Chemical Reactions
Table 2.5	Representative Lipids Found in the Body
Table 2.6	Representative Groups of Functional Proteins
A Closer Look	DNA Electrophoresis*
Focus on Careers	Food Technologist*

Indicates images that are on the Media Manager only.

ANSWERS TO END OF CHAPTER REVIEW QUESTIONS

Questions appear on pp. 61–63

Multiple Choice

1. a, c, d (pp. 29, 31–32)
2. a, c, e (p. 33)

3. a, b, c, d, e (p. 42)
4. c, e (Figure 2.12)
5. b, c (pp. 49–50, 54)
6. d (p. 49)
7. a, b, c, d, e (p. 55)
8. c (p. 55)
9. a (Table 2.1)

Short Answer Essay

10. Chemistry is basic to an understanding of anatomy and physiology because our bodies, everything in our environment, and everything we take into our bodies are all chemical substances. (p. 27)

11. Energy has no mass and does not occupy space. It can only be defined by its effect on matter. Energy is defined as the ability to do work or put matter into motion. (pp. 27–28)

12. When energy is active (doing work), it is called kinetic energy. Potential energy is an inactive form where energy is stored (e.g., ATP). All forms of energy have both kinetic and potential work capacities. (p. 28)

13. Chewing food—mechanical energy; vision—light energy and electrical energy (of a nerve impulse); bending the fingers—mechanical energy; breaking ATP bonds—chemical energy. (p. 28)

14. Both lead and gold are elements. Elements are the unique building blocks of matter and have a definite number of protons in their nuclei that cannot be transformed into one another. (p. 29)

15. Carbon (C), hydrogen (H), nitrogen (N), and oxygen (O) make up the bulk of living matter. Nitrogen is found chiefly in proteins and nucleic acids. (pp. 29–30)

16. All atoms contain equal numbers of protons and electrons, meaning that the positive and negative charges are balanced. With balanced charges, the atom is neutral. (p. 29)

17.

Particle	Position in Atom	Charge	Mass
Proton	Nucleus	+	1 amu
Neutron	Nucleus	None	1 amu
Electron	Orbital around the nucleus	–	0

(Table 2.2)

18. The heaviest isotopes of elements are usually radioisotopes because they are unstable and often decompose to become more stable. Spontaneous deterioration of an (unstable) atom by emission of particles or energy from the nucleus = radioactivity. (p. 33)

19. A molecule is a combination of two or more atoms held together by chemical bonds. (p. 34)

20. Ionic bonds form when electrons are transferred from one atom to another. (pp. 35–36)

21. Hydrogen bonds are fragile bonds formed when hydrogen atoms bonded to one molecule (or one part of a single molecule) are attracted by electron-hungry atoms of other molecules (or other atoms of the same molecule). They are important to the body because they not only hold water molecules together, but also play a major role in determining the three-dimensional shape (and therefore, function) of proteins and DNA. (p. 39)

22. This statement is false. A polar molecule is formed only when the atoms of the molecule are different and have different electron-attracting abilities. Oxygen gas contains two oxygen atoms and is therefore nonpolar. (pp. 37–38)

23. Argon has a full valence shell so it will not readily donate or accept electrons, meaning that it does not combine easily with other elements. Oxygen does not have a full valence shell (it only has 6 electrons in its outermost shell), so it can accept (share) electrons when combining with other elements. (pp. 35–36)

24. $2 Hg + O_2 \longrightarrow 2 HgO$; synthesis.

    $Fe^{2+} CuSO_4 \longrightarrow FeSO_4 + Cu^{2+}$; exchange.

    $HCl + NaOH \longrightarrow NaCl + H_2O$; exchange.

    $HNO_3 \longrightarrow H^+ + NO_3^-$; decomposition.

    (pp. 40–41)

25. Inorganic compounds, with a few exceptions such as CO_2, are noncarbon-containing: water, salts, acids, and bases. Organic compounds are carbon-containing: carbohydrates, lipids, proteins, and nucleic acids. (pp. 42–52, 54–55)

26. An electrolyte is a chemical substance that ionizes and dissociates in water, and is then able to conduct an electrical current. (p. 43)

27. pH is a measure of hydrogen ion concentration in solution. Blood is slightly basic. (p. 44)

28. A pH of 3.3 is ten times more acidic than a pH of 4.3. (p. 44)

29. *Monosaccharides:* simple sugars, basic units of carbohydrates; examples are glucose, fructose, and galactose. *Disaccharides:* two simple sugars bonded together; examples are sucrose, lactose, and maltose. *Polysaccharides:* many simple sugars bonded together; examples are starch and glycogen. *Carbohydrates* are the major energy fuel for producing ATP in body cells. (pp. 45–46)

30. Neutral fats consist of three fatty acid chains joined to a glycerol backbone; they insulate and cushion the body and provide stored energy fuel. Phospholipids consist of two fatty acids and a phosphorus-containing group attached to glycerol; they are part of all cell membranes. Steroids are flat structures made of four interlocking rings. They, particularly cholesterol, form the basis of steroid hormones, vitamin D, and bile salts. (pp. 46–49)

31. The R-group is different for each amino acid, giving each type unique properties. (Figure 2.16 gives a diagrammatic representation of these structures.) (p. 49)

32. Structural proteins are basically fibrous or linear proteins that have secondary structure; keratin, collagen, and elastin are examples. Functional proteins are globular or spherical proteins (having tertiary structure); examples are enzymes, some hormones, antibodies, and hemoglobin. (pp. 50–52)

33. An enzyme is a biological catalyst. Enzymes increase the rate of chemical reactions by holding the reaction molecules in the proper position(s) to interact. (pp. 52, 54)

34. High body temperature and acidosis interfere with enzyme activity by destroying the three-dimensional structure that is essential for binding substrate and enzyme. (p. 50)

35. The structural unit of nucleic acids is the nucleotide. The major classes of nucleic acids are DNA and RNA. DNA is a double-stranded helix of nucleotides; its bases are A, G, C, and T, and its sugar is deoxyribose. RNA is single-stranded; its bases are A, G, C, and U, and its sugar is ribose. DNA is the genetic material that carries instructions for protein synthesis; RNA carries out DNA's instructions. (pp. 54–55)

36. ATP is the immediate source of chemical energy for all body cells. (p. 55)

37. Surface tension (caused by hydrogen bonds) prevents water molecules "stacked" slightly above the glass from spilling over. (p. 39)

38. All salts are electrolytes and thus have the ability to conduct electrical currents within fluid solutions such as the blood. If electrolyte balance were to become severely disturbed by excessive salt water intake, virtually all life-sustaining physiological functioning would slow down and eventually cease, as all biochemical processes require a fluid medium where salt concentration is maintained within a relatively narrow range. Excessive salt water consumption will also elevate blood pressure as increased salinization within the bloodstream will draw more fluid into the blood vessels via osmosis. For this reason, excessive salt intake is often associated with cardiovascular disease because it increases arterial blood pressure "from the inside out." (p. 43)

ANSWERS TO CRITICAL THINKING AND CLINICAL APPLICATION QUESTIONS

39. If the antibiotic binds to the enzyme region that normally bonds to reactants, the bacterial enzyme's function will be blocked. The bacteria may die as a result, meaning that the person may get better. (pp. 51–52)

40. pH is defined as the measurement of the hydrogen ion concentration in a solution. The normal blood pH is between 7.35 and 7.45. Severe acidosis is critical because blood comes in contact with nearly every body cell and can adversely affect the cell membranes, kidney functions, muscle contraction, and neural activity. Hemoglobin, an iron-containing protein in red blood cells that carries oxygen, may also be affected by the more acidic pH level. When this change happens, then oxygen delivery to the tissues will be decreased or stopped completely, which leads to impaired cell functioning all over the body. (pp. 44–45)

41. Neutral fats are found in deposits under the skin and surrounding organs. One of their functions is to insulate the body and prevent heat loss. Evelyn is thin and feels cold because she has less insulation, so she loses heat more readily than Barbara, who retains heat because she has more insulating body fat. (pp. 47 and 49; Table 2.4)

42. Proteins will be greatly affected by high temperatures. Protein structure is held together by fragile hydrogen bonds that can easily be broken with excess heat. If protein structure is not maintained, it cannot function properly. Without proper protein structure, extensive cell and tissue damage could occur. (p. 50)

CLASSROOM DEMONSTRATIONS AND STUDENT ACTIVITIES

Classroom Demonstrations

1. Film(s) or other media of choice.

2. Demonstrate to the students how the amount of energy increases in atoms that have more electrons (and more electron orbitals). Under a fume hood, add small particles of lithium, sodium, and potassium to water in a glass beaker or Petri dish. Students can observe the length of time before the substance reacts, how long it reacts, and how bright the flame will be depending on the number of electrons each element has in their orbitals.

3. Use the periodic table of elements to show the ionic bonding of sodium and chlorine to form salt. Have the students then diagram the ionic bonding of potassium chloride, potassium bromide, and similar salts, using the periodic table as a guide.

4. Use the periodic table of elements to show the covalent bonding of carbon and methane. Have the students then diagram other organic compounds using the periodic table as a guide.

5. Show the video, *Double Helix*, on one of the first lab days. It is an excellent BBC production that presents the drama, humor, and intrigue of the discovery of DNA. Students always love it, and they come away with a new respect for the work of those involved in a discovery that often goes unnoticed, most particularly the work of Rosalyn Franklin.

6. Demonstrate the structure of simple molecules with ball-and-stick models.

7. Obtain two strings of dissimilar pop-it beads. Put the beads together to demonstrate a synthesis reaction, and take them apart to demonstrate a decomposition reaction. Take a bead from each different chain and put them together to illustrate an exchange reaction.

8. Use a Slinky to demonstrate denaturation of an enzyme. Tie colored yarn on the Slinky at two sites that are widely separated, and then coil and twist the Slinky upon itself to bring the two pieces of yarn next to each other. Identify the active site where the yarn pieces are located. Then remind students that when the hydrogen bonds holding the enzyme (or functional protein) in its specific 3-D structure are broken, the spherical structure (and the active site) is destroyed, by allowing the Slinky to resume its helical shape. (Best done when protein and enzyme structure has been discussed.)

9. Use a 3-D model of a portion of DNA to demonstrate its units and overall structure.

10. Discuss the important role of cholesterol in the body, and then describe the consequences of high circulating levels in the bloodstream. Explain the difference between LDL (low density lipoprotein—"bad" cholesterol) and HDL (high density lipoprotein—"good" cholesterol). Examine the role of each type with respect to cardio-vascular disease.

Student Activities

1. Have the students draw Bohr models of the elements most important to organic chemistry to clarify their understanding of the arrangement of electrons in shells.

2. Have the students draw electron dot models (Lewis structures) of various molecules to help further their understanding of ionic and covalent bonds.

3. Construct three-dimensional models of various organic molecules, such as glucose, proteins, and lipids.

4. Show the students a model of DNA. Have them build several nucleotides from construction paper or blocks, and then attempt to join the nucleotides into a helical shape. Present the shape of the helix as a "twisted ladder," with strong sugar and phosphate covalent bonds making up the side supports while nitrogenous bases attached by weak hydrogen bonds form the rungs.

5. Ask students to name all the foods containing saturated fats and all those containing unsaturated fats that they have eaten in the last 24 hours.

6. Bring in materials or objects that are composed of common elements (e.g., a gold chain, a piece of coal, a piece of copper pipe, a cast iron skillet). Also provide examples of common compounds, such as water, table salt, vinegar, and sodium bicarbonate. Ask students to define atom, element, and compound, and explain how an atom and a molecule of a compound differ.

7. Provide wide-range pH paper or use pH meters and beakers containing (a) distilled water, (b) vinegar, (c) sodium bicarbonate solution, and (d) aqueous solutions of egg white, lemon juice, and ammonia. Ask students to determine the pH of each solution and to indicate whether it is acidic, neutral, or basic. Use this exercise as a lead-in to a discussion of common acids and bases and the importance of pH homeostasis in the body.

8. Using lemon juice to represent the acidic environment of the stomach, compare the amounts needed of various antacid remedies that would be used to treat acid indigestion and neutralize the lemon juice. Add measured amounts of each product to the lemon juice and determine which product works the fastest to neutralize the acid using pH meters or pH paper.

9. Student assignment for class discussion: Find examples of the uses of radioisotopes in popular articles or journals, and be prepared to discuss the advantages and disadvantages of radioisotope use in medicine.

10. Bring students to an imaging lab where they can see examples of radioisotope use in medicine, and talk to a technologist and/or doctor about nuclear medicine.

11. Have your students answer the following questions to demonstrate their understanding of how to select appropriate equipment and technology:

    Mrs. Newkirk has some wonderful news to share with her family. She had a test at her doctor's office, and it was determined that in a few months, twins will be joining the family! Which test, which uses medical technology, provided this information?

    A. Cholesterol screening
    B. Ultrasound*
    C. EEG
    D. Arthroscopy

    Nick is running hard, trying to score the winning run. He slides into home base just in time, but feels a popping in his wrist. Amid the cheers he is holding his aching wrist with his other hand, and the coach puts ice on it and sends him to the emergency room. The doctor orders a test to find out if there is a fracture. What is the name of this test that uses medical technology?

    A. Phlebotomy
    B. X ray*
    C. Stress test
    D. EKG

12. Show a ten-minute clip of *Jurassic Park* or *Science at War: Fritz Haber* and engage the students in a class discussion.

MULTIMEDIA

See page 182 for a listing of media distributors.

1. *The Atom Revealed* (FHS; 50 min., 1993, VHS, DVD). Journeys into the atomic structure of substances that make up our world.

2. *Chemical Bonding* (FHS; 18 min., 2000, VHS, DVD). From *Chemistry: The Standard Deviants Core Curriculum*, this video presents Lewis structures and the Octet Rule and its exceptions.

3. *Double Helix* (FHS; 107 min., 1987, VHS, DVD). Exceptional Hollywood-style film (starring well-known actor Jeff Goldblum) that captures all the drama of the discovery of DNA.

4. *The Elements* (WNS; 60 min., 1997, VHS, DVD). Traces the evolution of chemistry to the development of the periodic table.

5. *Jurassic Park* (127 min., 1993, VHS, DVD). A fictional story of how a wealthy entrepreneur creates a theme park featuring living dinosaurs from prehistoric DNA. Scientifically sound arguments lead to interesting class discussions on the possibility of dinosaur cloning today, and the resulting ethical and ecological ramifications of bringing back extinct species. This MCA Universal City Studios film is rated PG-13 and is available at most national chain video distribution stores.

6. *Unlocking the Secrets of Life* (FHS; 50 min., 1993, VHS, DVD). Presents the atomic structure of living things, showing how DNA governs the manufacture of proteins.

SOFTWARE

1. *CyberEd's Biochemistry: The Chemistry of Life* (CE, LP; Win/Mac). Covers atoms, elements, molecules, chemical bonds, chemical formulas, and essential organic and inorganic compounds.

Cells and Tissues

CHAPTER SUMMARY

Chapter 3 is the transition chapter between microscopic and macroscopic anatomical study. Students are asked to examine the microscopic structure of an individual cell, then to intellectually build those individual cells into body tissues that perform specialized functions.

First, the anatomy of a *generalized* cell is presented. It is important to start with a generalized cell (i.e., one that has all the representative parts of all cells) in order for students to gain a clear understanding of the basic components of cells. From that basis, they are then able to discern which structures are essential to every cell and which structures are variable depending upon function of any *specific* cell or group of cells. The components contained within the nucleus, plasma membrane, and cytoplasm are discussed, followed by an explanation of the various organelles which enable life to be sustained. The structure and function of ribosomes, smooth and rough endoplasmic reticulum, Golgi apparati, lysosomes, peroxisomes, mitochondria, cytoskeleton, and centrioles are presented.

A discussion of cell diversity follows a presentation of the anatomical structure of the cells' component parts. This is the point at which students learn to differentiate between an *average* or *generalized* cell and any *specific* cell (e.g., they begin to understand the similarities as well as the necessary differences between blood cells, bone cells, etc.). Cell physiology is presented next, with an explanation of both active and passive transport processes, followed by a discussion of cell division. A brief explanation of protein synthesis and the role of genes in DNA transcription and translation is presented to make the replication picture complete.

The final section of this chapter presents body tissues and their functions. Epithelial, connective, muscle, and nervous tissues are differentiated, followed by an overview of the developmental aspects of cells and tissues.

SUGGESTED LECTURE OUTLINE

PART I: CELLS (pp. 65–88)

I. OVERVIEW OF THE CELLULAR BASIS OF LIFE (pp. 65–66)

II. ANATOMY OF A GENERALIZED CELL (pp. 66–76)
- A. The Nucleus (p. 67)
  1. Nuclear Envelope
  2. Nucleoli
  3. Chromatin
- B. The Plasma Membrane (pp. 67–69)
  1. Structure
  2. Specializations of the Plasma Membrane
     - a. Microvilli
     - b. Membrane Junctions
       - i. Tight Junctions
       - ii. Desmosomes
       - iii. Gap Junctions

TEACHING TIP

Present phagocytosis (cell eating) and bulk-phase endocytosis (pinocytosis, or cell drinking) by first identifying their word parts. Explain that both processes are part of endocytosis, where the cell brings substances ***inside***. Be sure that students understand that bulk-phase endocytosis is not just taking in water, but is in fact a means of bringing in extracellular fluid and the dissolved substances within that fluid.

MEDIA TIP

Voyage Inside the Cell (FHS; 15 min., 1999). With computer-generated images and instructive narrative, the viewer is taken on a journey inside a living cell.

   C. The Cytoplasm (pp. 69–74)
      1. Structure
      2. Cytoplasmic Organelles
         a. Mitochondria
         b. Ribosomes
         c. Endoplasmic Reticulum (ER)
            i. Rough ER
            ii. Smooth ER
         d. Golgi Apparatus
            i. Secretory Vessels
         e. Lysosomes
         f. Peroxisomes
         g. Cytoskeleton
            i. Intermediate Filaments
            ii. Microfilaments
            iii. Microtubules
         h. Centrioles
         i. Other Structures in Specialized Cells
            i. Cilia
            ii. Flagella
   D. Cell Diversity (pp. 74–76)
      1. Cells That Connect Body Parts
      2. Cell That Covers and Lines Body Organs
      3. Cells That Move Organs and Body Parts
      4. Cell That Stores Nutrients
      5. Cell That Fights Disease
      6. Cells That Gathers Information and Controls Body Functions
      7. Cells of Reproduction
III. CELL PHYSIOLOGY (pp. 76–88)
   A. Membrane Transport (pp. 76–79, 81–83)
      1. The Fluid Environment
      2. Passive Transport Processes: Diffusion and Filtration
         a. Diffusion
            i. Simple Diffusion
            ii. Osmosis
            iii. Facilitated Diffusion
         b. Filtration
      3. Active Transport Processes
         a. Active Transport
         b. Vesicular Transport
            i. Exocytosis
            ii. Endocytosis
               (1) Phagocytosis
               (2) Pinocytosis
               (3) Receptor-Mediated Endocytosis
   B. Cell Division (pp. 83–88)
      1. Cell Life Cycle
      2. Preparations: DNA Replication

3. Events of Cell Division
   a. Mitosis
      i.   Prophase
      ii. Metaphase
      iii. Anaphase
      iv. Telophase
   b. Cytokinesis
C. Protein Synthesis (pp. 86–88)
   1. Genes: The Blueprint for Protein Structure
   2. The Role of RNA
   3. Transcription
   4. Translation

PART II: BODY TISSUES (pp. 88–101)

I. EPITHELIAL TISSUE (pp. 88–93)
   A. Functions (pp. 88–89)
   B. Special Characteristics of Epithelium (p. 89)
   C. Classification of Epithelium (pp. 89–93)
      1. Simple Epithelia
         a. Simple Squamous Epithelium
         b. Simple Cuboidal Epithelium
         c. Simple Columnar Epithelium
         d. Pseudostratified Columnar Epithelium
      2. Stratified Epithelia
         a. Stratified Squamous Epithelium
         b. Stratified Cuboidal and Stratified Columnar Epithelia
         c. Transitional Epithelium
      3. Glandular Epithelium
         a. Endocrine Glands
         b. Exocrine Glands

II. CONNECTIVE TISSUE (pp. 93–97)
   A. Functions (p. 93)
   B. Common Characteristics of Connective Tissue (p. 93)
      1. Variations in Blood Supply
      3. Extracellular Matrix
   C. Extracellular Matrix (pp. 93–94)
   D. Types of Connective Tissue (pp. 94–97)
      1. Bone (Osseous)
      2. Cartilage
         a. Hyaline
         b. Fibrocartilage
         c. Elastic Cartilage
      3. Dense Connective Tissue (Dense Fibrous Tissue)
      4. Loose Connective Tissue
         a. Areolar Tissue
         b. Adipose Tissue
         c. Reticular Connective Tissue
      5. Blood

III. MUSCLE TISSUE (pp. 97–99)
  A. Types of Muscle Tissue (pp. 97–99)
    1. Skeletal Muscle
    2. Cardiac Muscle
    3. Smooth (Visceral) Muscle

IV. NERVOUS TISSUE (p. 98)
  A. Neurons
  B. Supporting Cells

V. TISSUE REPAIR (WOUND HEALING) (pp. 100–101)
  A. Regeneration
  B. Fibrosis
  C. Events in Tissue Repair

PART III: DEVELOPMENTAL ASPECTS OF CELLS AND TISSUES (pp. 101 and 104)

I. DEVELOPMENTAL ASPECTS (pp. 101 and 104)
  A. Cell Division
  B. Amitotic Cells
  C. Aging Process
  D. Cell and Tissue Modification
    1. Neoplasm—Benign or Malignant
    2. Hyperplasia
    3. Atrophy

KEY TERMS

adipose tissue
anaphase
anticodon
apical surface
areolar tissue
atrophy
basement membrane
blood
bone
cardiac muscle
cartilege
cells
cell division
cell life cycle
centrioles
centromere
chromatid
chromatin
chromosomes
cilia
cleavage furrow

codons
columnar epithelium
concentration gradient
connective tissue
connexons
cytokinesis
cytoplasm
cytosol
cytoskeleton
dense connective (fibrous) tissue
deoxyribonucleic acid (DNA)
desmosomes
diffusion
edema
elastic cartilage
endocrine glands
endocytosis
endoplasmic reticulum (ER)
enzymes

epithelial tissue (epithelium)
exocytosis
extracellular matrix
facilitated diffusion
fibrocartilage
fibrosis
filtration
flagella
free radicals
gap junctions
gene
generalized cell
gland
goblet cells
golgi apparatus
hyaline cartilage
hyperplasia
inclusions
intermediate filaments
interphase
interstitial fluid

interstitial fluid ligaments
intracellular fluid
lysosomes
membrane junctions
messenger RNA (mRNA)
   molecules
metaphase
microfilaments
microtubules
microvilli
mitochondria
mitosis
mitotic spindle
mucosae
mucous membranes
muscle tissues
neoplasm
nervous sustem
nervous tissue
neurons
nuclear envelope
nuclear pores
nucleoli
nucleus
organelles
osmosis

passive transport
peroxisomes
phagocytosis
pinocytosis
plasma membrane
pressure gradient
prophase
pseudostratified
receptor-mediated
   endocytosis
regeneration
reticular connective tissue
ribonucleic acid (RNA)
ribosomal RNA (rRNA)
ribosomes
rough ER
secretion
secretory vesicles
selective permeability
serous membranes (serosae)
simple diffusion
simple epithelium
simple squamous epithelium
skeletal muscle
smooth ER
smooth (visceral) muscle

solutes
solute pumps
solution
solvent
stratified columnar
   epithelium
stratified cuboidal
   epithelium
stratified epithelium
stratified squamous
   epithelium
stroma
supporting cells
telophase
tendons
tight junctions
tissues
transitional epithelium
transcription
transfer RNA (tRNA)
   molecules
translation phase
transport vesicles
triplet
vesicular transport

LECTURE HINTS

1. Emphasize that the cell described in this chapter is a *generalized* cell and that there are many cells in the body that have a different structure. Mature red blood cells, for example, are anucleate and round, while skeletal muscle cells are multinucleate and elongated. Stress that it is the specialized structure of these cells that determines their ability to perform specific life-sustaining functions.

   Key point: It is important for students to first understand the variety of components found in cells. From there, students begin to understand that all cells have *some* of the components, but few cells have *all* the components, and that it is the cell's function that prescribes which components will be present. Relate to students that overall health of a cell is dependent on the weakest link in the chain, and that malfunctioning of one critical organelle can cause the entire cell to die.

2. Show transparencies of many different types of cells and ask the students to identify the similarities as well as differences between the cells.

   Key point: This helps students begin to visualize the structures of the cells and to learn which cells have certain components and why.

3. Differentiate between centrioles and centromeres, as this is an area that students frequently find confusing. Stress to students that mitosis is division of the cell nucleus and that serious mutations can result when prophase, metaphase, anaphase, and telophase do not progress properly.

Key point: The centromeres hold the chromatids together, while the centrioles direct the assembly of the mitotic spindle upon which the chromosomes migrate during anaphase.

4. Give a brief explanation of mitosis vs. meiosis to help students understand that mitosis is the method by which a body (somatic) cell constantly produces identical daughter cells, whereas meiosis is part of the reproductive process of gametes (sex cells are discussed in Chapter 16).

   Key point: Students frequently confuse these two processes and it is important to clarify their differences from the beginning.

5. Discuss cancer as mitosis "gone wild."

   Key point: Once students understand that all body cells have a limited life span and need to continuously replace themselves, they begin to understand that an imbalance in the replication process can have devastating effects.

6. Teach students the mnemonic device, "I Passed My Algebra Test," to help them learn the stages of mitosis in order. Point out that interphase is not part of mitosis since interphase includes the daily activities of the cell while mitosis is nuclear division.

   Key point: Explain that cells live out the bulk of their lives in interphase, which is not a dormant phase as was previously thought, but is the time from within which the DNA content of a cell must precisely double. Cells then form two identical daughter cells by going through prophase, metaphase, anaphase, and telophase during mitotis.

7. Although the stages of the cell cycle are described as discrete events, students should see that they represent a continuous process. Video segments that show the cell cycle in action will help students to better visualize this process.

   Key point: Explain to students that the phases of mitosis follow one after another in a continuous flow, but that they are presented in segments for better understanding.

8. Explain to students that cytokinesis begins during mitosis and is not a separate process that occurs after mitosis is complete.

   Key point: Show students how cytokinesis begins during anaphase when the chromosomes pull apart and the cell changes shape. Cytokinesis ends after telophase, once the nuclear division is complete.

9. Differentiate between intracellular and extracellular fluid. Explain that extracellular fluid, or fluid found *outside* the cell, is also called interstitial fluid because it is located in the spaces between the cells. Discuss how a buildup of this fluid would lead to edema following an injury or during chronic sedentary living.

   Key point: Having a clear understanding of the location of body fluids will help students to understand the homeostatic mechanisms involved in fluid balance.

10. The terms *hypertonic*, *hypotonic*, and *isotonic* should be broken into their roots so that their meanings are immediately obvious to the student. For example, hypertonic means excessive tension, therefore water is drawn *into* a hypertonic solution. Hypotonic, on the other hand, means deficient tension, therefore water passes *out* of a hypotonic solution. Since isotonic means equal tension, an isotonic solution is homeostatically balanced.

    Key point: It is important for students to have a clear understanding of these terms and their significance in the body's water balance. The terms hypertonic, hypotonic, and isotonic can refer to either intracellular or extracellular fluid.

11. Discuss the application of different intravenous solutions in health care. Identify various types of solutions as hypertonic, hypotonic, or isotonic (D_5W, 1/2 NS, and NS).

    Key point: Presenting real-world applications helps students better understand the importance of these concepts.

12. Explain osmosis, or the diffusion of water, in detail. Students are frequently confused by the fact that water moves into an area of high solute concentration. Point out that it is easier for water molecules to move than for solutes to move across semipermeable membranes, thus water's role is to dilute the solution until equilibrium is reached. Water is a very polar molecule enabling polar solutes to be dissolved within it.

    Key point: Being able to visualize the shift of fluids within the body is particularly necessary in understanding the activities of the urinary and cardiovascular systems. Water is absolutely essential to life as we know it and the search for past or present life on other planets always revolves on the evidence of water.

13. Discuss the concentration gradient and the idea that when molecules move *down* the gradient, they are involved in passive transport processes, whereas molecules moving *up* the gradient are involved in active transport processes.

    Key point: The role of the concentration gradient in active and passive transport processes is a significant concept for students to master.

14. Present phagocytosis (cell eating) and bulk-phase endocytosis (pinocytosis, or cell drinking) by first identifying their word parts. Explain that both processes are part of endoctytosis, where the cell brings substances *inside*. Be sure that students understand that bulk-phase endocytosis is not just taking in water, but is in fact a means of bringing in extracellular fluid, including the dissolved substances within that fluid.

    Key point: Students sometimes confuse cell drinking with simple water intake and it is important to clarify that the process is more complex than that.

15. Show transparencies of various tissues and point out the similarities and differences so that students can identify the tissue types based on their characteristics.

    Key point: The various tissue types appear confusing at first but become clearer as their key characteristics are noted.

16. Relate to students that *hyperplasia* describes an increase in the total number of fibers within a body tissue or organ. Contrast for students that *hypertrophy* describes the increase in size of existing cells as compared to *atrophy,* which describes the decrease in size of existing cells, with neither hypertrophy nor atrophy describing any changes in the total number of fibers.

    Key point: A weight lifter exhibits skeletal muscle hypertrophy during chronic strength training, whereas the reverse condition of skeletal muscle atrophy occurs when training load is reduced. Hyperplasia of skeletal muscle does not occur even during intense conditioning, although there is a possibility that athletes who dangerously abuse anabolic steroids may exhibit some hyperplasia.

TRANSPARENCIES/MEDIA MANAGER INDEX

Figure 3.1   Anatomy of the generalized animal cell nucleus

Figure 3.2   Structure of the plasma membrane

Figure 3.3   Cell junctions

Figure 3.4   Structure of the generalized cell

Figure 3.5   Synthesis and export of a protein by the rough ER

Figure 3.6   Role of the Golgi apparatus in packaging the products of the rough ER

Figure 3.7   The cytoskeleton

Figure 3.8   Cell diversity

ANSWERS TO END OF CHAPTER REVIEW QUESTIONS

Questions appear on pp. 106–108

Multiple Choice

1. a (p. 68)
2. c (p. 69)
3. a, b, d (p. 68)
4. e (p. 73)
5. c (p. 72)
6. a, c (pp. 76–77)
7. b (p. 90)
8. b (p. 90)
9. a (p. 97)
10. a (p. 97)
11. a, b, d, e (p. 98)
12. c (pp. 102, 104)
13. b (pp. 82–83)

Short Answer Essay

14. *Cell:* The basic living unit of structure and function. (p. 65)

    Organelle: Literally, little organ. An intracellular structure that performs a specific function for the cell. (p. 69)

15. All cells are able to metabolize, divide, grow, respond to stimuli, digest nutrients, move, and excrete wastes. (p. 76)

16. DNA is the storehouse of the cell's genetic instructions, which specify protein structure. DNA is contained in the chromatin. Nucleoli are sites of ribosome formation. (p. 67)

17. The plasma membrane is composed of a double layer of lipids (phospholipids and cholesterol), with proteins floating in the lipid. Some of the proteins have attached sugar groups (glycoproteins). The plasma membrane serves as a selectively permeable barrier that contains cell contents, and functions in membrane transport and cell-to-cell interactions. (pp. 67–68)

18. The cytosol is a semitransparent fluid that not only suspends cell organelles and inclusions, but also contains water, nutrients, and a variety of solutes. The cytosol functions to transport materials around the cell. Inclusions are chemical substances that may or may not be present, depending on the cell. They are nonfunctioning units and are usually stored nutrients or cell products (e.g., lipid droplets, glycogen granules, pigments, etc.). (p. 69)

19. *Mitochondria:* The major sites of ATP synthesis in the cell. (pp. 70–71) *Ribosomes:* Protein synthesis. (p. 71) *Endoplasmic reticulum:* Intracellular transport of proteins made on the ribosomes (rough ER) or formation of lipids/steroids. (pp. 71–72) *Golgi apparatus:* Packaging of proteins for export from the cell. (pp. 72–73) *Lysosomes:* Breakdown of "worn-out" cell organelles or ingested foreign materials, such as bacteria. (p. 73) *Centrioles:* Structures that direct the formation of the mitotic spindle during cell division; form bases of cilia and flagella. (p. 73) *Peroxisomes:* Detoxify harmful chemicals, such as alcohol and free radicals. (p. 73) *Cytoskeleton:* Formed of microtubules and different types of filaments that construct the internal framework of the cell and promote cellular movements. (p. 73)

20. *Diffusion:* The movement of particles from an area of higher concentration to an area of lower concentration as a result of their kinetic energy; a passive process. (p. 76) *Osmosis:* The diffusion of water through a semipermeable or selectively permeable membrane. (p. 77) *Simple Diffusion:* The unassisted diffusion of solutes through a semipermeable or selectively permeable membrane. (p. 77) *Filtration:* The passage of solutes and solvent through a membrane from an area of higher hydrostatic pressure to an area of lower hydrostatic pressure. (pp. 77–78) *Solute pumping:* The movement of substances across a membrane by a solute pump, a "carrier" protein present in cell membrane. Requires that ATP be used and usually occurs against concentration and electrical gradients. (pp. 78–79) *Exocytosis:* A mechanism by which substances are moved from the cell interior to the extracellular space as a vesicle fuses with the plasma membrane. (p. 81) *Endocytosis:* A means by which fairly large extracellular molecules or particles are engulfed and enter cells. (pp. 81–82) *Phagocytosis:* Endocytosis of relatively large particles. (p. 82) *Pinocytosis:* Invagination of plasma membrane which encloses extracellular fluids containing protein or fat. (p. 82) *Receptor-mediated endocytosis:* Specific target molecules are taken into a cell when specific receptor proteins bind to the cell membrane. (pp. 82–83)

21. *Passive process:* The size of the pores and whether the substance is soluble in the lipid (fat) portion of the membrane. (p. 77) *Active process:* Whether the proper carrier proteins (pumps) are present in the membrane and in what amounts. (pp. 78–79)

22. Hypertonic solutions cause cells within them to become crenated (shrunken) as water leaves by osmosis. Hypotonic solutions cause cells to become swollen as water enters them from an area of higher water concentration. If there is a substantial difference in water concentration, the cell will burst (lyse) as excessive water enters it. Isotonic solutions have the same water/solute concentrations as cells; thus no structural changes occur. (pp. 80–81)

22. The DNA helix uncoils and the hydrogen bonds holding the bases together are broken by enzymes. Each freed nucleotide strand then acts as a model for building a complementary strand from DNA nucleotides. This process occurs during interphase, before the start of cell division. (p. 83; Figure 3.14)

24. *Mitosis:* Nuclear division. Divided into the phases of prophase, metaphase, anaphase, and telophase. Mitosis is important because it provides cells needed for growth and body repair. (pp. 83, 85–86; Figure 3.15)

25. The spindle acts as a scaffolding or attachment site for the chromosomes during mitotic division. (p. 84)

26. If the cells of an organ are amitotic, the cells that repair any damage to that organ will restore its structure but not necessarily its ability to function. For example, when heart cells die, they are replaced by connective tissue cells (scar tissue), which are unable to contract as do heart muscle cells. Likewise, damaged nerve cells are replaced by scar tissue, which is unable to transmit electrical signals. When tissue repair occurs by regeneration (mitosis of the same type of cells), normal function is restored. (pp. 100–101)

27. DNA contains numerous genes, which provide the specific instructions for building proteins; that is, each three-base sequence along the gene indicates the precise amino acid that is to appear in the protein at that relative position. RNA carries out DNA's instructions and sees that the protein is built. Messenger RNA carries the "message" outside the nucleus to a ribosome. Transfer RNA transports amino acids to the ribosome, and ribosomal RNA forms part of the ribosome, or protein synthesis site. (pp. 86–88)

28. *Tissue:* A group of cells similar in structure and function. The four major tissue types are epithelial, connective, muscle, and nervous. Connective tissue is the type most widely distributed in the body. (pp. 88, 93)

29. Epithelial tissues share a number of common characteristics. They tend to form continuous sheets, and the membranes always have one free edge or surface. The lowest surface rests on a basement membrane. It is avascular and regenerates well. Its most important functions are protection, absorption, filtration, and secretion. For example, the external epithelium (epidermis) protects against bacterial, chemical, and thermal damage; that of the respiratory system has cilia, which sweep debris away from the lungs; that of the digestive system is able to absorb substances; in the kidneys epithelium absorbs and filters; and secretion is the specialty of glands. (pp. 88–89)

30. Ciliated epithelium is found in the respiratory system, where it acts to prevent debris from entering the lower respiratory passageways. It is also found in the reproductive system, where it acts to move sex cells along the duct passageways. (p. 90)

31. Connective tissues are usually characterized by a large amount of extracellular *matrix*, which is secreted by the living cells and variations in vascularization. Connective tissues serve to connect, support, protect, and repair other body tissues. The functions of connective tissue are best explained by its matrix; that is, when connective tissue is a cushioning tissue, the matrix is soft and pliable; when the connective tissue is meant to support or give strength to the body, the matrix is hard/strong. (pp. 93–94)

32. a. Areolar (p. 97); b. Bone. (p. 94)

33. Muscle tissue contracts (shortens) to produce movement. (p. 97)

34. *Skeletal:* Attached to the skeleton and providing for gross body movement. *Smooth:* Found in the walls of internal organs and providing for the movement of substances (e.g., urine, food) through internal body tracts. *Cardiac:* Forms the heart, which propels blood through the blood vessels. When a muscle type is said to be involuntary in action, this means that one cannot consciously control its action. (p. 98)

35. During fibrosis, the destroyed tissue is replaced with dense connective tissue, which forms scar tissue. Tissue repaired in this way can lose some functionality. For example, when cardiac muscle is damaged, it cannot be regenerated, so fibrosis occurs and a scar forms. This region is no longer able to contract, so it will affect how the heart pumps blood. In tissue regeneration, destroyed tissue is replaced by the same type of cells. Regeneration is more desirable because no scar tissue forms and the cells retain their functional ability. (p. 100)

36. *Atrophy:* A decrease in the size of a body organ or body part as a result of the loss of normal stimulation (exercise or nerve stimulation). (p. 104)

ANSWERS TO CRITICAL THINKING AND CLINICAL APPLICATION QUESTIONS

37. *Vincristine:* Anything that damages the mitotic spindle interferes with cell division and, thus, would prevent proliferation of the cancer cells. (p. 84) *Adriamycin:* If messenger RNA cannot be made, proteins cannot be made either. All cells must have essential proteins such as enzymes to function properly. (pp. 86–88)

38. Lysosomal destruction releases acid hydrolases into the cytoplasm, killing the cell. When the cell lyses, inflammation is triggered. Hydrocortisone controls the unpleasant effects of inflammation by stabilizing the lysosomes, thus reducing cell death and the resultant inflammation. (p. 73)

39. Cartilage heals much slower than bone and other tissues because it lacks the blood supply necessary for the healing process. (p. 93)

40. Only the liver will fully recover because it is composed of epithelial tissue, which has the ability to completely regenerate. The injured areas of the heart and the brain grow back as scar tissue and thus do not regenerate to the previous functional capacity. (pp. 100–101)

41. *Hyperplasia:* enlargement of body tissues or organs due to an increase in cell number. This reaction occurs when there is a local irritant or condition that stimulates the cells. *Dysplasia:* abnormal development of tissues or organs. *Neoplasia:* an abnormal cell mass that proliferates without control. Kareem does not have cancer (malignant neoplasm) because the doctor stated that there was no evidence of neoplasia on his lip. (p. 104)

CLASSROOM DEMONSTRATIONS AND STUDENT ACTIVITIES

Classroom Demonstrations

1. Film(s) or other media of choice.
2. Use a cell model to demonstrate the various organelles and cell parts.
3. Use transparencies to demonstrate the structure of a cell and the cell's organelles.
4. Use microscope slides to show the differences between various cell types.
5. Use models of the events of mitosis to support your class presentation of cell division.
6. Walk through the phases of mitosis using transparencies and show a corresponding video demonstrating the continuous process in motion.
7. Have students look at prepared microscope slides of animal (e.g., whitefish blastula) and plant (e.g., *Allium* root tip) cells undergoing various mitotic phases.

8. Have students link cutouts of base pairs, similar to what Watson and Crick do in the video the *Double Helix*.

9. Provide models of nucleotides for students to disassemble and reassemble into various nucleotide sequences. Note that a change in even a single base pair will completely change the resultant protein. Use the example of sickle-cell anemia to illustrate this concept.

10. Bring in various IV solutions and discuss their uses in health care. Examples include mannitol (isomotic diuretic), $D_5$1/2NS (hypotonic), and normal saline (isotonic).

11. Set up a simple osmometer before class and have students observe the fluid level in the tube from time to time. Put glucose solution in a dialysis sac and tie the sac tightly to a length of glass tubing. Secure the glass tubing to a ring stand with a clamp. The glucose-containing dialysis sac should be immersed in distilled water in a beaker. Use this demonstration to support your discussion of osmosis and how knowledge of fluid dynamics is critical to health care.

Student Activities

1. Have students draw a large-scale *generalized* cell, with all organelles clearly labeled.

2. Have students look at several cell types and draw what they see. Ask them to identify all the structures they see. Point out similarities and differences, and ask them to guess the various functions based on structure.

3. Use models of RNA and DNA to illustrate their differences.

4. List a string of nucleotides on the board. Indicate this represents an original DNA sequence. With the students, walk through the corresponding mRNA sequence that would result from transcription. Next, list the nucleotide chain that results from translation, and emphasize that this will code for a specific protein. With all three lists still on the board, point out that the translated strand is identical in sequence to the original DNA segment with the exception that all thymine molecules are replaced by uracil molecules. Liken this process to making a picture from a negative of an original scene.

5. Have students name any examples of diffusion, osmosis, and filtration they can think of from their daily lives.

6. Have students prepare a wet mount of their own cheek cells so that they determine what tissue type they collected.

MULTIMEDIA

See page 182 for a listing of media distributors.

1. *A Journey Through the Cell* (FHS; 25 min. each, 1997, VHS, DVD). A two-volume set that combines live-action footage, computer graphics, and animation to explore cell structure and function.

2. *After Darwin: Genetics, Eugenics, and the Human Genome* (FHS; 2 parts, 49 min. and 46 min., 1999, VHS, DVD). Award-winning documentary about the history of genomic research, including the Human Genome Project, cloning, and gene patenting.

3. *Cancer and Metastasis* (FHS; 38 min., 1995, VHS, DVD). This video studies the biological processes by which cancer develops and metastasizes.

4. *Double-Helix* (FHS; 107 min., 1987, VHS, DVD). Exceptional film (starring well-known actor Jeff Goldblum) that captures all the drama of the discovery of DNA.

5.   *Hand-Me-Down Genes: An Introduction to Genetics* (FHS; 2 parts, 25 min. and 28 min., 1997, VHS, DVD). A two-part series covering "How Genes Work" and "Family Patterns."

6.   *Human Biology* (FHS; 58 min., 1995, VHS, DVD). Twenty-one live action video sequences provide an overview of the human biology.

7.   *Human Body: The Ultimate Machine* (CBS; 27 min., 2005, VHS, DVD). The body's major systems are described through footage of surgical procedures, microphotography, and 3-D animation.

8.   *The Universe Within: An Incredible Voyage into the Microworld of the Human Body* (NIMCO; 60 min., 1995, VHS). Using microphotography, NOVA presents the microworld of the human body.

9.   *Voyage Inside the Cell* (FHS; 15 min., 1999, VHS, DVD). With computer-generated images and instructive narrative, the viewer is taken on a journey inside a living cell.

SOFTWARE

1.   *Cyber Ed's BioChemistry: The Chemistry of Living Things* (CE, LP; Win/Mac). Teaches the basics of biochemistry through molecular models, animation, photographs, and narratives.

2.   *The Cell: Structure, Function, and Process* (HRM; Win/Mac). Introduces the microscopic world of the cell and explores various cell processes.

3.   *Inside the Cell* (CE; Win/Mac). 3-D graphics illustrate cellular organization and recent advancements in cellular biology.

4.   *Introduction to Cells: The Structure of the Cell* (IM; Win/Mac). Provides an introduction to the cell and describes cell structure and function.

5.   *Osmosis Lab* (IM; Win/Mac). Studies osmosis by controlling numerous variables and discusses hypertonic, hypotonic, and isotonic solutions.

6.   *WARD's Epithelial Cells, Smart Slides* (WNS; Win/Mac). Students view epithelial cells as they would appear through a microscope.

7.   *WARD's Histology Collection* (WNS; Win/Mac). Microscopic images of 384 slides that explore microanatomy of the organ systems.

Skin and Body Membranes

CHAPTER SUMMARY

Chapter 4 builds upon the cell and tissue information presented in Chapter 3. Students have already gained an understanding of the similarities and differences between cells, and also have a working knowledge of the various types of tissues in the body. Continuing with the theme of increasing levels of organization, the next logical step is recognizing that various tissues combine together to form organs, such as membranes, that have specific functions. Types of membranes are discussed first, with explanations provided as to the similarities and differences between cutaneous, mucous, serous, and synovial membranes.

The next section of the chapter delves into the mechanics of the integumentary system, which students easily identify as their skin, and which they have just learned is also a special type of epithelial membrane known as a cutaneous membrane. Because a majority of the body is water, the skin prevents you from dripping all over the ground as you sit in class. The many functions of the skin are often taken for granted, and this is a good opportunity for students to learn that as the largest organ of the body, skin has a multitude of functions. The structure of the skin is presented, detailing the layers and components of the epidermis as well as the dermis. Skin color in its various manifestations, both normal and abnormal, are explained.

Accessory structures of the skin are discussed next. Cutaneous glands (sweat and sebaceous), hair and hair follicles, and nails are all presented. Finally, an overview of homeostatic imbalances affecting skin are outlined, including the effects of infections and allergies, burns, and skin cancers. The chapter closes on an explanation of the developmental aspects of the skin and body membranes, and students particularly enjoy learning about the skin's aging processes and what they can do to delay that process.

SUGGESTED LECTURE OUTLINE

I. CLASSIFICATION OF BODY MEMBRANES
    (pp. 110–113)
    A. Epithelial Membranes (pp. 110–112)
        1. Cutaneous Membrane
        2. Mucous Membranes
        3. Serous Membranes
    B. Connective Tissue Membranes (p. 112)
        1. Synovial Membranes

II. THE INTEGUMENTARY SYSTEM (SKIN)
    (pp. 113–127)
    A. Functions of the Integumentary System
        (pp. 114–115)
    B. Structure of the Skin (pp. 115–118)
        1. Epidermis
        2. Dermis

TEACHING TIP

Point out the role of melanin in acting as a "natural sunscreen." Discuss the fact that dark-skinned people seldom have skin cancer due to melanin's effectiveness at preventing extreme sunburn and mutation in surface skin cells. Also point out that tanning is the body's built-in protective mechanism that leads to increased melanin production and thus protection from UV radiation.

MEDIA TIP

Melanoma: Winning the Battle Against Skin Cancer (FHS; 17 min., 1996). Examines the problem of skin cancer from its roots in chronic overexposure to the sun to treatment that prevents recurrences.

    C. Skin Color (pp. 118–119)
       1. Pigments
       2. Emotions
    D. Appendages of the Skin (pp. 119–123)
       1. Cutaneous Glands
          a. Sebaceous (Oil) Glands
          b. Sweat Glands
       2. Hair and Hair Follicles
          a. Hairs
          b. Hair Follicles
       3. Nails
    E. Homeostatic Imbalances of the Skin (pp. 123–127)
       1. Infections and Allergies
          a. Athlete's Foot
          b. Boils and Carbuncles
          c. Cold Sores
          d. Contact Dermatitis
          e. Impetigo
          f. Psoriasis
       2. Burns
       3. Skin Cancer
          a. Basal Cell Carcinoma
          b. Squamous Cell Carcinoma
          c. Malignant Melanoma

III. DEVELOPMENTAL ASPECTS OF SKIN AND BODY MEMBRANES (p. 127)
    A. Fetal and Infant Stages
    B. Adolescence
    C. Aging

KEY TERMS

ABCD rule	full-thickness burns	papillary layer
apocrine glands	hair follicles	partial-thickness burns
arrector pili	hairs	pericardium
Athlete's foot	hypodermis	peritoneum
body membranes	impetigo	pleura
boils (carbuncles)	integument	psoriasis
burn	integumentary system	reticular layer
cold sores	keratin	rule of nines
contact dermatitis	keratinization	sebaceous glands
cutaneous membrane	keratinocytes	sebum
dermal papillae	matrix	second-degree burns
dermis	melanin	serous fluid
eccrine glands	melanocytes	serous membrane (serosa)
epidermis	mucous membrane	skin
epithelial membranes	(mucosa)	skin appendages
exocrine glands	mucus	stratum basale
first-degree burns	nail	stratum corneum

stratum granulosum
stratum lucidum
stratum spinosum

subcutaneous tissue
  (hypodermis)
sudoriferous glands
sweat

sweat glands (sudoriferous)
synovial membranes
third-degree burns

LECTURE HINTS

1. Show slides of various types of skin sections. Emphasize that the diagrams of skin in the text are *idealized* pictures, and that skin varies at different regions of the body with age, sex, and race.

    Key point: It is often difficult at first for students to "see" all of the different structures found in skin when looking at actual cross sections, as compared to structures represented in diagrams. The more samples they see, the better their understanding of what they are seeing. Microscopic slides of various healthy and diseased skin tissues are not always as nice as the presentations in textbooks.

2. Students are always interested in discussing the skin as a thermoregulatory organ. Ask students to discuss changes in their skin on hot and cold days, or when they have a fever. Remind them of behavioral changes as well, such as curling up under a blanket when sleeping on a cold night or stretching out without a cover on a hot night. Discuss the effects of alcohol consumption on skin color and body temperature regulation.

    Key point: Skin is an excellent thermoregulator that is frequently taken for granted until discussed in detail.

3. Discuss the fact that humans all have roughly the same number of melanocytes, and that skin color is based on genetic determination of the *activity* of the existing melanocytes, not on numbers. Point out the natural selection process at work, where there is increased melanin production (size and number of melanin granules) in those exposed to more UV radiation and decreased melanin production in those exposed to less UV radiation.

    Key point: Students are often surprised by the fact that there are similar numbers of melanocytes among people of different ethnic groups, and that it is simply production of melanin that accounts for skin color differences.

4. Point out the role of melanin in acting as a "natural sunscreen." Discuss the fact that dark-skinned people seldom have skin cancer due to melanin's effectiveness. Also point out that tanning is the body's built-in protective mechanism that leads to increased melanin production and thus protection from UV radiation. Conventional tanning booths are not consistent in the amounts and types of light radiating out of their bulbs, and have not consistently proven to be a healthy way to enhance the protectiveness of skin from the sun.

    Key point: It is important for students to understand that melanin plays an important role in body protection. It often helps to point out that people with albinism, who are genetically unable to produce melanin, have to be extremely cautious about exposure to the sun.

5. Discuss all of the factors involved in skin color, including the amounts and kinds of pigment present, the amount of carotene present, the amount of oxygen bound to hemoglobin, and emotional stimuli.

    Key point: It is important for students to understand that many factors are at play in determination of relatively permanent and temporary skin color, and that some of the factors are externally induced.

6. Differentiate between types of sweat glands, pointing out that sweat produced by eccrine glands is primarily water, whereas sweat produced by apocrine glands contain fatty acids and proteins. Note that sweat produced by the latter type of sweat glands provides a food source for bacteria living on the skin, and it is a by-product of those bacteria that accounts for the unpleasant odor associated with sweat. Sweat produced by eccrine glands is an odorless substance that actually inhibits bacterial growth.

    Key point: Students usually don't realize there are two distinct types of sweat glands producing two distinct products that have separate functions.

7. Discuss differences in hair types. Hair that has an oval shaft is smooth and silky whereas hair that is flat and ribbonlike is curly or kinky. Students enjoy learning about what makes their hair have the characteristics it has, and appreciate the mechanisms involved in trying to change their hair type by "perming" and other methods. Have students examine normal-colored and artificially-colored hair under a microscope.

    Key point: This is an area students enjoy discussing and it provides a valuable opportunity for the appreciation of genetic variety.

8. Use a variety of diagrams to help students understand the terms visceral and parietal. Point out that *visceral* refers to the viscera, or the organ itself, whereas *parietal* refers to the sac an organ sits in.

    Key point: It is important for students to understand that there are distinct coverings to the organs, and that this pattern of having a visceral as well as parietal covering will be found numerous times as we study various organs.

9. As a point of interest, note that although vitamin D is produced in the skin and is converted from its inactive to active form by sunlight, it is activated by the kidneys. Functioning kidneys are key to vitamin D availability in the body, thus premature infants with unstable kidneys are at risk for developing rickets and other related diseases.

    Key point: This is a good opportunity to point out the interplay between body systems and to note their interrelationships in maintaining homeostasis.

10. In this chapter, students learn that burns are classified according to depth and/or amount of surface area affected. Emphasize that there are other factors to consider, such as the type of burn (electrical, chemical, etc.), area of the body burned (chest, face, hands, etc.), and the person's age. Include the value of stem cells found in the accessory skin organs for healing and tissue regeneration.

    Key point: When discussing the consequences of serious burns, refer to the functions of the integument. Loss of skin leads to loss of protection against infection, loss of water, etc.

11. Discuss sunburn in relation to the degree of burn and the long-term potential for skin cancer. Most students have had at least one serious bout with sunburn and are eager to know the implications.

    Key point: Sunburn that involves blistering is a second-degree burn that requires treatment to prevent infection. Concerning skin cancer, students appreciate knowing what to look for and value the ABCD rule as a good tool for recognizing melanoma.

12. There are over a thousand different disorders related to homeostatic imbalances of the skin. It is helpful to discuss some of the more common skin disorders, such as acne, athlete's foot, cold sores, and psoriasis, as well as some of the exanthematous skin eruptions, including chicken pox and measles.

    Key point: The significance of homeostatic imbalance related to the skin is often quite clear to students, since many have had some form of skin disorder during their lifetime.

13. Discuss the physiology behind alopecia (baldness).

    Key point: Students are interested in the condition of alopecia and enjoy learning more about its causes, including heredity, pathology, and injury. One of the few things that boys can really blame on their mothers is male pattern baldness.

TRANSPARENCIES/MEDIA MANAGER INDEX

Figure 4.1	Classes of epithelial membranes
Figure 4.2	A typical synovial joint
Figure 4.3	The epidermis of thick skin
Figure 4.4	Skin structure
Figure 4.5	Photograph of a deep (stage III) decubitus ulcer
Figure 4.6	Photomicrographs of cutaneous glands
Figure 4.7	Structure of a hair and hair follicle
Figure 4.8	Scanning electron micrograph showing a hair shaft emerging from a follicle at the skin surface
Figure 4.9	Structure of a nail
Figure 4.10	Cutaneous lesions
Figure 4.11	Burns
Figure 4.12	Photographs of skin cancers
Table 4.1	Functions of the Integumentary System
A Closer Look	Tattoos*
Focus on Careers	Medical Transcriptionist*
Systems in Sync	Homeostatic Relationships Between the Integumentary System and Other Body Systems

Indicates images that are on the Media Manager only.

ANSWERS TO END OF CHAPTER REVIEW QUESTIONS

Questions appear on pp. 131–132

Multiple Choice

1. c (pp. 110, 112)
2. b, e (p. 112)
3. c, e (p. 120)
4. c (p. 121)
5. a, c, d (pp. 121, 127)
6. d (pp. 122–123)
7. c (pp. 119–121)
8. a (pp. 117–118, 121–122; Figure 4.4)
9. 1-e, 2-d, 3-f, 4-b, 5-g, 6-c (pp. 115, 117–118, 119–120)

Short Answer Essay

10. Synovial membrane. (p. 112)

11. Chemical (e.g., acids and bases), mechanical (pressure, trauma), bacterial (via the acid mantle), desiccation (via the waterproofing keratin), UV, and thermal. (pp. 114–115)

12. When the amount of UV radiation reaching the skin increases (as when sitting in the sun), the melanocytes in the skin begin to produce increased amounts of protective melanin (a brown pigment), which is deposited in the epidermal skin layers to protect the basal cells from the damaging effects of UV radiation. (p. 117)

13. *Decubitus ulcer:* A localized breakdown of the skin and underlying tissues resulting from continuous pressure causing a lack of blood supply to the area. (p. 118)

14. Perspiration (water, salt, and sometimes protein/lipid substances) from sweat glands; sebum (fatty substances and broken cells) from sebaceous glands. (pp. 119–120)

15. All temperature-regulating functions of the skin are controlled by the nervous system. Under conditions of high external temperature, blood is allowed to flush into the skin capillary net so that heat radiates from the body surface. At the same time, sweat glands produce perspiration, which evaporates from the skin surface so that more body heat is dissipated by evaporation and convection. With low external temperatures, blood is prevented from entering the skin capillary system, and thus radiation to the body exterior is prevented and perspiration does not occur. This mechanism restricts the blood to deeper tissues and maintains the core temperature of the body. (pp. 118, 120)

16. *Blackhead:* An accumulation of dried sebum and bacteria in a sebaceous gland. (p. 119)

17. Arrector pili are small bands of smooth muscle cells attached to a hair follicle that pull the hair (follicle) into an upright position when they contract. They are activated by cold or fright. (p. 122)

18. Squamous cell carcinoma arises from the stratum spinosum layer of the epidermis. (p. 126)

19. This is a result of a delayed-action gene that (eventually) causes the nonproduction of melanin. (p. 127)

20. It dries, thins (leading to the increased possibility of bruising), has less elasticity, and loses subcutaneous fat tissue. (p. 127)

21. No. Very fine hairs are formed but they are colorless and many do not actually emerge from the follicle. (p. 127)

ANSWERS TO CRITICAL THINKING AND CLINICAL APPLICATION QUESTIONS

22. *Cyanosis:* A blue cast to the skin and mucosae. Its presence indicates a lack of oxygen in the surface blood vessels. (pp. 118–119)

23. There is a decrease in insulatory aloility of the skin due to the lack of adipose tissue in the subcutaneous layer. (pp. 115, 127)

24. His long-term exposure to UV radiation in sunlight is considered to be a risk factor related to the development of skin cancer. In addition, moles or pigmented spots that show (a) asymmetry, (b) border irregularity, (c) color variation, and (d) a diameter greater than 6 mm are all signs of a possible malignant melanoma. He should seek immediate medical attention. If it is a malignant melanoma, the chance for survival is not high, but early detection increases survival rates. (pp. 125–126)

25. The orange color might be due to carotene deposited in the stratum corneum and sub-cutaneous tissue. Carotene is found in orange vegetables such as carrots and in deep yellow and leafy green vegetables. (p. 118)

26. Keratin found in cells of the stratum corneum is a water-repellent protein. Its presence prevents water intake from the ambient environment. (p. 115)

27. It is likely that Mr. Bellazono has squamous cell carcinoma induced by sun exposure. (p. 127)

28. Fat-soluble drugs are usually absorbed more rapidly than water-soluble drugs, due to the lipophilic nature of the plasma membrane. As well, the extracellular space contains glycolipids, which would allow fat-soluble drugs to pass easily. (p. 117)

29. In a sunburn, usually large areas of the skin surface have been burned. The tissue comprising the epidermis is stratified squamous epithelium, meaning that there are many layers of flat cells joined in sheets. As a result, large sheets tend to peel after a sunburn. (p. 115)

30. Intradermal injections allow drugs to be absorbed more rapidly because the dermal layer contains blood vessels while the epidermis does not. (pp. 115, 118)

CLASSROOM DEMONSTRATIONS AND STUDENT ACTIVITIES

Classroom Demonstrations

1. Film(s) or other media of choice.
2. Demonstrate the structure of the skin using a 3-D model.
3. Thrust your fist into a flaccid balloon to demonstrate the relationship between the parietal and visceral layers of a serosa. Note that you can blow up a balloon by blowing air into it or by placing it in an airtight container and sucking out all the air around the balloon.
4. Use a human torso model to show the body location of the mucous and serous membranes.
5. Show slides or transparencies of selected skin disorders.
6. Bring a paramedic into the classroom to discuss the treatment of burn injuries.

Student Activities

1. Have a small fan operating. As students file into the classroom, spray their arm or hand with water (a simple window-cleaner spray bottle may be used as the "sprayer"). Ask them to describe their sensations as the water evaporates and to explain why evaporation of water (sweat) from the skin surface is important to body homeostasis. Stress that calories of heat are only released from the body as liquid sweat turns into gas.

2. Indicate to the class that many animals (snakes, insects, and lobsters, for instance) shed their skin periodically. Ask them to comment on how humans compare in this aspect.

3. Student assignment for class discussion:

   a. Look up the current drug treatment for baldness in the medical library (minoxidil).

   b. Find references in current journals to the damaging effects of sunlight on the skin, and be prepared to describe the difference in the A and B types of UV rays relative to skin damage.

c. Examine the effects of using sunscreen, including the meaning of SPF values and the duration of its effectiveness.

4. Show students a picture of a heavily-wrinkled person. Ask them to list all of the factors that might have contributed to the skin deterioration. Discuss the research that led to the use of retinoic acid for the treatment of photo-aged skin.

5. Provide magnifying lenses. Have the students use them to scrutinize their skin and the mucosa of a classmate, and then describe important differences visible in these two types of covering epithelia.

6. Provide small glass plates and instruct students to observe the change in the color of their skin while pressing the heel of their hand firmly against the glass. Ask them to explain the reason for the color change and what would happen to their skin cells if the pressure was prolonged.

7. Student assignment for class discussion: Look up the signs and symptoms of basal cell carcinoma and malignant melanoma for class discussion.

8. Student assignment for class discussion: Have students research and report on FDA regulations for the classification of cosmetics and drugs.

9. Look at shafts of hair and shavings of nails under a microscope. Point out that even though these substances are dead, they are a good indicator of health or disease caused by dietary insufficiency or other homeostatic imbalances.

10. Discuss how hair and nails are used in forensic analysis.

MULTIMEDIA

See page 182 for a listing of media distributors.

1. *Skin* (FHS; 20 min., 1995, VHS, DVD). From *The New Living Body* series, this video shows the detailed internal structure of the skin using high-quality computer graphics.

2. *Tissue Engineering: Custom-Made Organs on Demand* (FHS; 22 min., 1999, VHS, DVD). Tissue engineering is explored, including applications in burn victims and diabetics.

SOFTWARE

1. *Cross-Sectional Anatomy Tutor* (FHS; Win). Interactive, instructional program correlates normal cross-sectional anatomy with radiographic images from CT and MRI images.

2. *The Pathology Atlas* (FHS; Win/Mac). Extensive database of pathology images with associated medical information.

3. *Medical Images Library* (FHS; Win/Mac). Over 12,000 images showing visual manifestations of disease, medical treatment, and health care practices.

The Skeletal System

CHAPTER SUMMARY

The skeletal system is one of the body systems that students enjoy studying most. Naming the bones is, at first, a challenge, then rapidly becomes a source of confidence as students develop their identification skills. Learning about the dynamic nature of bones also dispels many preconceived ideas that students may have about bones resembling dead twigs or remaining unchanged over time.

This chapter begins with an overview of the many functions of bones, including their role in support, protection, and movement of the body, as well as in the storage of nutrients and in blood cell formation. Next, bones are classified as long, short, flat, or irregular, each made up of either spongy or compact bone, or a combination of both to meet unique body needs. The macroscopic (gross) anatomy of a long bone provides a conceptual image of bone structure, and the microscopic anatomy helps students to begin to understand the complexity of bone and the reasons for its dynamic nature. The principles of bone ossification, growth, and remodeling are explored, along with the role of calcium and vitamin D in keeping bones strong and healthy. The various types of bone fractures and their resultant medical corrections are also presented to round out the students' understanding of some common bone disorders.

In the final sections of Chapter 5, the 206 named bones that make up the axial and appendicular skeletons are presented, and their major projections and depressions are identified. The differences observed in the fetal skeleton, along with other developments throughout the life span are introduced, are examined and explained. A discussion of articulations found in the body follows the bone identification section, and the types of joints and their related inflammatory disorders.

SUGGESTED LECTURE OUTLINE

I. BONES: AN OVERVIEW (pp. 134–144)
   A. Functions of the Bones (pp. 134–135)
      1. Support
      2. Protection
      3. Movement
      4. Storage of Nutrients
      5. Blood Cell Formation
   B. Classification of Bones (p. 135)
      1. Composition
      2. Classification According to Shape
         a. Long Bones
         b. Short Bones
         c. Flat Bones
         d. Irregular Bones
   C. Structure of a Long Bone (pp. 135–140)
      1. Gross Anatomy
      2. Microscopic Anatomy

TEACHING TIP

Students are fascinated by the differences between male and female skeletons. Have two articulated skeletons, one of each gender, available to point out the differences as they are presented in lecture, and discuss the information that skeletons provide in forensic medicine.

MEDIA TIP

Bones and Joints (FHS; 20 min., 1995). From *The New Living Body* series, this video introduces the topics of movement, the structure and function of joints, bone growth, and the effects of chronic exercise versus sedentary living on bone health.

D. Bone Formation, Growth, and Remodeling (pp. 140–142)
E. Bone Fractures (pp. 142–144)
   1. Types of Fractures
   2. Treatment of Fractures
   3. Repair of Fractures

II. AXIAL SKELETON (pp. 144–158)
  A. Skull (pp. 145–150)
    1. Cranium
      a. Frontal Bone
      b. Parietal Bones
      c. Temporal Bones
      d. Occipital Bone
      e. Sphenoid Bone
      f. Ethmoid Bone
    2. Facial Bones
      a. Maxillae
      b. Palatine Bones
      c. Zygomatic Bones
      d. Lacrimal Bones
      e. Nasal Bones
      f. Vomer Bone
      g. Inferior Conchae
      h. Mandible
    3. The Hyoid Bone
    4. Fetal Skull
  B. Vertebral Column (Spine) (pp. 150–157)
    1. Vertebral Characteristics
    2. Cervical Vertebrae
    3. Thoracic Vertebrae
    4. Lumbar Vertebrae
    5. Sacrum
    6. Coccyx
  C. Thoracic Cage (pp. 157–158)
    1. Sternum
      a. Manubrium
      b. Body
      c. Xiphoid Process
    2. Ribs
      a. True Ribs
      b. False Ribs
      c. Floating Ribs

III. APPENDICULAR SKELETON (pp. 158–166)
  A. Bones of the Shoulder Girdle (pp. 158–160)
    1. Clavicle (Collarbones)
    2. Scapulae (Shoulder Blades)
  B. Bones of the Upper Limbs (pp. 160–162)
    1. Arm
      a. Humerus

      2. Forearm
          a. Radius
          b. Ulna
      3. Hand
          a. Carpals
          b. Metacarpals
          c. Phalanges
  C. Bones of the Pelvic Girdle (pp. 162–164)
      1. Coxal (Hip) Bones
          a. Ilium
          b. Ischium
          c. Pubis
  D. Bones of the Lower Limbs (pp. 164–166)
      1. Thigh
          a. Femur
      2. Leg
          a. Tibia
          b. Fibula
      3. Foot
          a. Tarsal Bones
              i. Talus and Calcaneus
          b. Metatarsals
          c. Phalanges

IV. JOINTS (pp. 166–174)
  A. Functional Categories of Joints (pp. 166–168)
      1. Synarthroses
      2. Amphiarthroses
      3. Diarthroses
  B. Structural Categories of Joints (pp. 168–172)
      1. Fibrous Joints
      2. Cartilaginous Joints
      3. Synovial Joints
      4. Types of Synovial Joints Based on Shape
          a. Plane Joint
          b. Hinge Joint
          c. Pivot Joint
          d. Condyloid Joint
          e. Saddle Joint
          f. Ball-and-Socket Joint
  C. Homeostatic Imbalances of Joints (pp. 172–174)
      1. Bursitis
      2. Osteoarthritis (OA)
      3. Rheumatoid Arthritis (RA)
      4. Gouty Arthritis

V. DEVELOPMENTAL ASPECTS OF THE SKELETON
    (pp. 174–176)
  A. Fetal Development
  B. Infant and Child Development
  C. Adolescent Development
  D. Osteoporosis—Chronic Bone-Thinning Disease from
      Hormone Deficiency or Inactivity in Elderly

KEY TERMS

acetabulum
acromioclavicular joint
acromion
alae
alvelolar margin
amphiarthroses
anatomical neck
anterior border
anterior superior iliac spine
appendicular skeleton
articular cartilage
articulations (joints)
atlas
axis
axial skeleton
ball-and-socket joint
body
bone markings
bone remodeling
bony callus
bony thorax
bursae
calcaneus
canaliculi
capitulum
carotid canal
carpal bones
carpus
cartilaginous joints
central (Haversian) canals
cervical vertebrae
clavical
compact bone
condyloid joint
coracoid process
coronoid fossa
coronoid process
coronal suture
coxal bones
cranium
cribriform plates
cristagalli curvatures
diaphysis
diarthroses
deltoid tuberosity
dens
epiphyseal line
epiphyseal plate
epiphysis

external auditory meatus
facial bones
false pelvis
false ribs
femur
fibrocartilage callus
fibrous articular capsule
fibrous joints
fibula
fissures
flat bones
floating ribs
fontanels
foramen magnum
foramen ovale
glenoid cavity
greater/lesser trochanters
greater sciatic notch
gluteal tunerosity
Haversian system (osteon)
hematoma
hinge joint
humerus
hyoid bone
iliac crest
ilium
inlet
intercondylar fossa
internal acoustic meatus
interosseous membrane
interotrochanteric line
intertubercular sulcus
intervertebral discs
irregular bones
ischial spine
ischial tuberosity
ischium
joints
joint cavity
jugular foramen
jugular notch
lacunae
lamboid suture
lamellae
lateral epicondyles
lateral malleolus
lateral/medial condyles
long bones
lumbar vertebrae

manubrium (body and
   xiphoid) process
mastoid process
maxillary bones
medial/lateral condyles
medial malleolus
median sacral crest
medullary cavity (yellow
   marrow)
metacarpals
metatarsals
nasal conchae
obturator foramen
occipital condyles
olecranon fossa
olecranon process
optic canal ossification
ossa coxae
osteoblasts
osteoclasts
osteocytes
osteoporosis
outlet
palatine processes
paranasal sinuses
patellar surface
pectoral (shoulder) girdle
pelvic girdle
perforating (Sharpey's)
   fibers
perforating (Volkmann's)
   canals
periosteum
phalanges
pivot joint
plane joint
posterior superior iliac spine
primary curvatures
pubic bone
pubic symphysis
radial groove
radial tuberosity
radioulnar joints
radius
red marrow
reinforcing ligaments
ribs
sacral canal
sacral hiatus

sacroiliac joint
sacrum
saddle joints
sagittal suture
scapulae
secondary curvatures
sellaturcica
short bones
sinuses
skeletal system
skull
sphenoid sinuses
spongy bone
squamous sutures
sternal angle

sternum
styloid process
superior orbital fissure
suprasoapular notch
surgical neck
sutures
synarthroses
syndesmoses
synovial joints
talus
tarsal bones
tarsus
tendon sheath
tibia
tibial tuberosity

thoracic cage
thoracic vertebrae
trochlea
trochlear notch
true ribs
true pelvis
transverse processes
ulna
vertebrae
vertebral arch
vertebral column
vertebral foramen
xiphisternal joint
zygomatic process

LECTURE HINTS

1. Students are fascinated by the differences between male and female skeletons. Have two articulated skeletons, one of each gender, available to point out the differences as they are presented in lecture, and discuss the information that skeletons provide in forensic medicine, such as how the hyoid bone can provide evidence as to homicide or suicide upon autopsy.

   Key point: There are significant differences not only between the skeletons of males and females, but also between athletes and sedentary people, young and old people, etc., and discussing some of these differences will help students to conceptualize the dynamic nature of bones.

2. Emphasize the dynamic and ready-healing nature of bones and the fact that bones are highly vascular, with this rich blood supply accounting for why "if you are going to break something, break a bone." Also point out that bone material is constantly being produced and reabsorbed for the purpose of calcium balance, and to accommodate functional and gravitational stress. Explain that moderate weight-bearing exercise will stimulate bone supercompensation and may delay the development of chronic diseases such as osteoporosis. Discuss the consequences of little or no weight bearing, such as with people who are wheelchair-dependent or bed-ridden.

   Key point: The dynamic nature of bones cannot be overemphasized. In this chapter, students learn valuable information about the long-term health of bones and what they can do to delay or prevent osteoporosis, arthritis, and other homeostatic imbalances.

3. Students are surprised to hear that ossification is incomplete at birth. Share a timetable of ossification with students and point out that babies crawl and walk at the time that is physiologically right for them, in part based on bone development. Also discuss greenstick fractures and their occurrence in young people whose bones are still developing.

   Key point: Ossification and bone growth and development are processes that continue into early adulthood.

4. Use a flexible, articulated skeleton to demonstrate the location of bones and their markings as you discuss them in lecture.

   Key point: It is important for students to actually see the location of the bones and touch either real bones or plastic models as they hear about each of them individually.

5. Use a skull that has been sectioned transversely to demonstrate the location of the interior bones of the skull as you discuss them during lecture.

   Key point: The interior bones of the skull are the most difficult to identify and this helps students to visualize their locations within the skull.

6. Identify the risk factors for chronic conditions such as osteoporosis and arthritis, and discuss preventative measures, current treatments, and future therapies for these conditions.

   Key point: Osteoporosis and arthritis are major health concerns in our aging population and this discussion gives students a frame of reference for understanding the causes and treatments for this condition.

7. Identify the placement and functions of the fontanels in fetal and infant skull development. Explain that fontanel means "little fountain" and is related to the fact that a baby's pulse is palpable at these "soft spots." This allows the skull to compress slightly during birth and the brain to grow during late pregnancy and early infancy. Note: This is why fontanels are so important. It also can provide a health indicator since a depressed fontanel could indicate dehydration while a raised fontanel could indicate increased cranial pressure.

   Key point: Students may be familiar with the location of at least the anterior fontanel and may be interested to learn of the others.

8. Spend time discussing the Haversian system. Students may find this topic confusing, but it is an important concept for them to understand since it directly relates to the dynamic nature of bones, particularly during growth and healing.

   Key point: Haversian systems, with their interlinked canals and transportation systems, provide living bone cells with the nutrients necessary for growth and healing following overuse or trauma, as well as a means of removing toxic metabolic wastes so as to keep bones healthy.

9. Discuss the various joint disorders that students are familiar with, as well as their causes and treatments.

   Key point: Joints hold bones together and provide mobility. They are the site of numerous disorders due to overuse and, at times, abuse, and it is valuable for students to appreciate their fragility as well as their complexity.

10. Discuss ruptured intervertebral disks and explain the pathology behind this disorder.

    Key point: This is often the first time that students have actually seen the vertebral column and the way it is designed to protect the spinal column. Discussing what happens when a disk "leaks" into surrounding tissues helps students to understand the severity of the disorder.

11. Emphasize the differences between osteoclasts (bone destroyers) and osteoblasts (bone formers), and explain why a dynamic balance between them is necessary.

    Key point: As new bone is formed, which is a constant process, old bone is destroyed. This represents homeostatic balance using negative feedback loops at their finest.

12. Discuss *cleft palate* and the surgical correction of this condition.

    Key point: Even though the maxilla appears to be one bone, it is really two bones fused at the midline. Any disruption in the fusion during fetal life results in a cleft, which severely impedes an infant's ability to suck in critical nutrition.

13. Explain the root words of the various bones as they are presented (e.g., the manubrium of the sternum means "handle of a sword"; scapula means "spade").

Key point: Building upon the students' vocabulary by providing definitions of word parts helps them to learn the names of all 206 bones more easily and will make muscles easier to locate and describe in Chapter 6.

14. The number of vertebrae within each region of the vertebral column denotes where each region begins and ends. Explain to students that while a normal human has seven cervical vertebrae, he or she will have eight cervical nerves. This is important to remember when the spinal nerves are discussed in Chapter 7.

    Key point: Vertebrae are singular and the spinal nerves are in pairs. Also, the first cervical nerve branches are superior to the first cervical vertebrae.

15. Discuss the impact of bone structure for muscle attachment.

    Key point: By understanding the role of bone shape in muscle attachment (and therefore, body movement), students can be better prepared for the muscular system in Chapter 6.

TRANSPARENCIES/MEDIA MANAGER INDEX

Indicates images that are on the Media Manager only.

ANSWERS TO END OF CHAPTER REVIEW QUESTIONS

Questions appear on pp. 179–181

Multiple Choice

1. a, b, d (p. 135; Figure 5.1)
2. d (p. 139)
3. b (p. 140)
4. d (p.145)
5. a, b, c, d, e (pp. 145–149)
6. d (p. 160; Figure 5.6)
7. d (p. 155)
8. b, c, e (p. 164)
9. b (p. 160, 164)
10. b (p. 175)
11. 1-a, b; 2-a; 3-a; 4-a; 5-b; 6-c; 7-c; 8-a; 9-c (pp. 168–172)
12. a-1; b-2; c-3; d-1; e-2; f-1 (Table 5.1)

Short Answer Essay

13. Forms the body's internal structural framework (provides support). Anchors skeletal muscles and allows them to exert force to produce movement. Protects by enclosing (skull, thorax, and pelvis). Provides a storage depot for calcium and fats. Site of blood cell formation. (pp. 134–135)

14. *Yellow marrow:* Substance composed of fat found in the medullary cavity of long bones in adults. (p. 136) Spongy bone looks cancellous, whereas compact bone appears to be solid, smooth, and dense. (p. 135)

15. Bone is highly vascularized and thus heals rapidly. Cartilage has poor vascularization and depends on diffusion for its nutrient supply; thus, it heals slowly or poorly, if at all. (pp. 139–140)

16. PTH plays a significant role in calcium homeostasis. When blood calcium levels begin to drop, PTH activates the osteoclasts of bone. As the bone matrix is broken down, ionic calcium is released to the blood. Mechanical forces acting on bones determine where calcium can safely be removed or where more calcium salts should be deposited to maintain bone strength. In areas where there are bulky muscles, bone needs to be thicker and form large projections for muscle attachment. (pp. 140–142)

17. Compression and comminuted fractures are particularly common in the elderly. Greenstick fractures (incomplete fractures) are more common in children because their bone matrix contains relatively more collagen and is more pliable. (p. 142; Table 5.2)

18. Two each: Temporal and parietal bones. One each: Occipital, frontal, sphenoid, and ethmoid bones. (pp. 145–147)

19. Joint between the mandible and temporal bone (temporomandibular joint). (p. 149)

10. *Chin:* Mandible. *Cheekbone:* Zygomatic. *Upper jaw:* Maxilla. *Eyebrow ridges:* Frontal. (pp. 145, 149)

21. The fetal skull has (a) much larger cranium-to-skull size ratio, (b) foreshortened facial bones, and (c) fontanelle or unfused (membraneous) areas. (pp. 149–150)

22. Cervical: 7 vertebrae; thoracic: 12 vertebrae; lumbar: 5 vertebrae. (pp. 150–151)

23. See Figure 5.14 (p. 151) and Figure 5.16 (p. 154).

24. To cushion the vertebrae and absorb shocks. Also, they allow movement and flexibility of the spinal column (e.g., laterally). A slipped disc (or herniated disc) occurs when an intervertebral disc bulges outward (protrudes) or ruptures, putting pressure on the spinal cord and/or spinal nerves. As a result, a person may feel numbness and excruciating pain in the affected area. (p. 151)

25. Sternum, ribs (attached to the vertebral column posteriorly). (p. 157)

26. A floating rib is a false rib. Floating ribs are easily broken because they have no anterior (sternal) attachment (direct or indirect) and thus have no anterior reinforcement. (pp. 157–158)

27. Clavicle and scapula. (pp. 158–160)

28. Humerus, radius, carpals. (pp. 160–161; Figure 5.6)

29. Ilium, ischium, pubis. The ilium is the largest. The ischium has the "sit-down" tuberosities. The pubis is most anterior. (pp. 162–164)

30. Femur, patella, fibula/tibia, tarsals, metatarsals, phalanges. (pp. 164–166; Figure 5.6)

31. *Synarthrotic:* Essentially immovable, generally fibrous. *Amphiarthrotic:* Slightly movable, generally cartilaginous. *Diarthrotic:* Freely movable, synovial. (pp. 166, 168–170; Table 5.3)

32. The articulating ends of bones in a synovial joint are covered with articular cartilage and are separated by a cavity that contains synovial fluid. Synovial joints are enclosed by a fibrous connective tissue capsule lined with a smooth synovial membrane. Reinforcing ligaments may reinforce the fibrous capsule, and bursae and tendon sheaths may cushion tendons where they contact bone. (p. 170; Figure 5.29)

33. Professor Rogers is incorrect. The foramen magnum allows nerves connecting the brain and spinal cord to pass through, whereas the esophagus allows food to pass from the mouth to the stomach. (p. 145)

34. Diaphysis. (p. 139; Figure 5.3)

35. Factors that keep bones healthy: physical stress/use (most important), proper diet (e.g., calcium). Factors that cause bones to become soft or atrophy: Disuse, hormone imbalances, loss of gravitational and movement stress. (pp. 175–176)

ANSWERS TO CRITICAL THINKING AND CLINICAL APPLICATION QUESTIONS

36. The youngster had more organic material in her bones, allowing them to bend, while her grandmother's bones are completely calcified, having little organic material, and also probably thin due to osteoporosis. (pp. 140–142)

37. No; the palatine bones are posterior to the palatine processes of the maxillae. If the palatine processes do not fuse, then the palatine bones remain unfused as well. (p. 149)

38. Most likely the paranasal sinuses on the right side of the face. (p. 149; Figure 5.10)

39. Most likely osteoporosis, a condition common in older women. A decline in bone mass, particularly in the spine and neck of the femur, increases the probability of fractures. (p. 175)

40. Dislocation. The head of the humerus has been forced out of its normal position in the glenoid cavity. (p. 170)

41. This might be a spiral fracture. (p. 142; Table 5.2)

42. The epiphyseal line seen in fully grown adult bone is the remnant of the epiphyseal plate found in young, growing bone. (pp. 140, 174; Figure 5.4)

43. The joint between the temporal bone and the mandible (temporomandibular joint). (p. 149)

44. The thoracic region of the vertebral column would show abnormal curvature in scoliosis. (p. 154)

CLASSROOM DEMONSTRATIONS AND STUDENT ACTIVITIES

Classroom Demonstrations

1. Film(s) or other media of choice.

2. Use an articulated skeleton to (a) indicate the protective and supportive aspects of bones, (b) identify individual bones, and (c) identify the security aspects of various body joints.

3. Use a prepared long bone to demonstrate the structural aspects of a *typical* long bone.

4. Use a femur or humerus cut longitudinally to reveal the inner structures of a long bone.

5. Use a disarticulated skull to demonstrate more clearly the individual skull bones and to show the fragile internal structure of bones containing sinuses (e.g., ethmoid, sphenoid, etc.).

6. Use a fetal skeleton to emphasize the changes in skull and body proportions that occur after birth. Point out that initially the skeleton is formed primarily of hyaline cartilage rather than bone, and that ossification is the process that replaces the cartilage with bone.

7. Obtain X rays of the abnormal spinal curvatures lordosis (lateral view), scoliosis (posterior view), and kyphosis. Explain the position that each abnormal curvature can be viewed from and the basic scoliosis examination provided by most school nurses.

8. Show a video on the techniques of arthroscopic surgery.

9. Obtain X-rays of different fracture types so that students can better visualize these injuries.

Student Activities

1. Have students look at a full set of disarticulated vertebrae. Ask them to identify which are cervical, thoracic, lumbar, sacral, and coxal. Point out the differences between the groups and explain the reasons for those differences.

2. Have students examine the differences between the axis and atlas vertebrae, and relate their structure to their location and function in the vertebral column.

3. Have students get into groups of four or five. Provide a list of bones and major markings and ask the students to manually touch and identify each item on an articulated skeleton (have a skeleton provided for each group). Repeat this exercise over several days and as many times as possible.

4. Using a disarticulated skeleton, hold up various bones and have students try to classify them as long, short, flat, or irregular.

5. Have students try to identify right and left side bones using the scapula, humerus, pelvic girdle, and femur from a disarticulated skeleton.

6. Have students look at microscopic cross sections of bone. Ask them to draw and label as many of the parts of the Haversian system as they can.

7. Look at the first-, second-, and third-degree lever actions of various bones and discuss the movements associated with these actions.

8. Have students write down the nutritional components of milk and milk products (they can bring in empty milk cartons for reference). Discuss why and how dairy products "help build strong bodies." Have students list other foods that would provide similar nutrients.

9. Have the students make flash cards of bones and bone markings to help in their memorization of these terms.

10. Look at examples of the various types of joints and ask students to identify their type, such as synarthroses or diarthroses.

MULTIMEDIA

See page 182 for a listing of media distributors.

1. *The Anatomy of the Ankle and Foot* (FHS; 17 min., 1999, VHS, DVD). This video examines the major weight-bearing joint, the ankle, along with the bones of the foot and ankle. Common foot and ankle injuries are covered.

2. *The Anatomy of the Hand* (FHS; 14 min., 1999, VHS, DVD). This program demonstrates the opposable nature and other functions of the hand.

3. *The Anatomy of the Knee* (FHS; 15 min., 1999, VHS, DVD). The intricate nature of the knee joint is examined, as well as some of the most common knee injuries.

4. *The Anatomy of the Shoulder* (FHS; 17 min., 1999, VHS, DVD). This program shows the range of motion that the ball-and-socket joint of the shoulder is capable of and explains the technical specifications involved.

5. *Bones and Joints* (FHS; 20 min., 1995, VHS, DVD). From *The New Living Body* series, this video introduces the topics of movement, the structure and function of joints, bone growth, and the effects of chronic exercise versus sedentary living on bone health.

6. *The Exercise and Nutrition Connection* (FHS; 26 min., 1996, VHS, DVD). Shows how nutrition and exercise affect the body.

7. *The Human Skeletal System* (IM; 23 min., 2001, DVD). This video explains the functions and components of the human skeletal system.

8. *Movements at Joints of the Body* (FHS; 40 min., 1997, VHS, DVD). This three-part series demonstrates various body movements using live subjects and features a self-quiz with teacher instructions.

9. *Skeletal System: The Infrastucture* (FHS; 25 min., 1998, VHS, DVD). This program explores the skeletal system, with an emphasis on its importance in providing structure and support for the body.

10. *The Talking Skull: Forensic Anthropology* (FHS; 26 min., 1998, VHS, DVD). Part of the *Medical Detectives* series, this video shows the use of forensic techniques to identify the bones and hair of a murder victim.

SOFTWARE

1. *WARD's Radiographic Anatomy* (WNS; Win). Excellent collection of health-related images (CTs, MRIs, etc.).

The Muscular System

CHAPTER SUMMARY

The muscular system presents challenges similar to those in the skeletal system in that this system requires both the conceptualization of complex mechanisms and the memorization of numerous terms. Providing students with a list of criteria used in the naming of muscles helps them overcome their anxieties and helps them view the task as manageable.

This chapter begins with an overview of muscle types. Skeletal, smooth, and cardiac muscle are discussed, and their differences as well as similarities in microscopic appearance and level of conscious control are emphasized. The applied anatomy of a muscle is presented, from the endomysium that covers a single muscle fiber to the epimysium that covers an entire muscle. The functions of muscle are explored, including movement, maintenance of posture, joint stabilization, and heat generation.

The next section of the chapter discusses the microscopic anatomy of skeletal muscle, followed by an overview of the mechanism of muscle contraction. The sliding filament mechanism is often confusing to students, but the explanation of muscle responses to various levels of stimulation, muscle fatigue and its relationship to available oxygen, and the types of muscle contractions help to clarify this concept.

In the final sections of the chapter, the "5 Golden Rules" of skeletal muscle activity are presented to help students comprehend muscle movements and their related interactions. First, the types of body movements generated by muscles are explained. Then a basic list of criteria for naming muscles is provided to ensure that students understand the logic involved in the naming of most muscles. Finally, the most important of the more than 600 muscles of the human body are presented, along with their points of origin and insertion as well as function.

SUGGESTED LECTURE OUTLINE

I. OVERVIEW OF MUSCLE TISSUES (pp. 183–187)
   A. Muscle Types (pp. 183–186)
      1. Skeletal Muscle
      2. Smooth Muscles
      3. Cardiac Muscle
   B. Skeletal Muscle Functions (p. 187)
      1. Producing Movement
      2. Maintaining Posture
      3. Stabilizing Joints
      4. Generating Heat

II. MICROSCOPIC ANATOMY OF SKELETAL MUSCLE (pp. 187–189)

III. SKELETAL MUSCLE ACTIVITY (pp. 189–198)
   A. Stimulation and Contraction of Single Skeletal Muscle Cells (pp. 189–194)
      1. The Nerve Stimulus and the Action Potential

TEACHING TIP

While discussing each specific muscle, point out the word parts in the muscle name to emphasize why it was named that way. For example, the sternocleidomastoid originates on the sternum and clavicle (cleido) and inserts on the mastoid process of the temporal bone. The sartorius is named for the Latin *sartor*, or tailor, and is the muscle used for the cross-legged sitting position once used by tailors.

MEDIA TIP

Muscular System: The Inner Athlete (FHS; 25 min., 2000). From *The Human Body: Systems at Work* series, this program looks at the many roles played by muscle in our everyday lives.

2. Mechanism of Muscle Contraction: The Sliding Filament Theory

   B. Contraction of a Skeletal Muscle as a Whole (pp. 194–198)

      1. Graded Responses

         a. Muscle Response to Increasingly Rapid Stimulation

            i. Muscle Twitches

            ii. Complete Tetanus

            iii. Incomplete Tetanus

         b. Muscle Response to Stronger Stimuli

      2. Providing Energy for Muscle Contraction

         a. Direct Phosphorylation of ADP by Creatine Phosphate

         b. Aerobic Respiration

         c. Anaerobic Glycolysis and Lactic Acid Formation

      3. Muscle Fatigue and Oxygen Debt

      4. Types of Muscle Contractions—Isotonic and Isometric

      5. Muscle Tone

      6. Effect of Exercise on Muscles

IV. MUSCLE MOVEMENTS, TYPES, AND NAMES (pp. 198–206)

   A. Five Golden Rules of Muscle Activity (p. 198)

   B. Types of Body Movements (pp. 198–202)

      1. Common Movements

         a. Flexion

         b. Extension

         c. Rotation

         d. Abduction

         e. Adduction

         f. Circumduction

      2. Special Movements

         a. Dorsiflexion and Plantar Flexion

         b. Inversion and Eversion

         c. Supination and Pronation

         d. Opposition

   C. Interactions of Skeletal Muscles in the Body (p. 202)

   D. Naming Skeletal Muscles (pp. 202 and 204)

      1. Direction of the Muscle Fibers

      2. Relative Size of the Muscle

      3. Location of the Muscle

      4. Number of Origins

      5. Location of the Muscle's Origin and Insertion

      6. Shape of the Muscle

      7. Action of the Muscle

   E. Arrangement of Fascicles (pp. 204–206)

V. GROSS ANATOMY OF SKELETAL MUSCLES (pp. 206–219; Figures 6.21–6.22; Tables 6.3–6.4)

   A. Head and Neck Muscles (pp. 206–207)

      1. Facial Muscles

         a. Frontalis

         b. Orbicularis Oculi

         c. Orbicularis Oris

       d. Buccinator
       e. Zygomaticus
   2. Chewing Muscles
       a. Masseter
       b. Temporalis
   3. Neck Muscles
       a. Platysma
       b. Sternocleidomastoid
B. Trunk Muscles (pp. 207–210)
   1. Anterior Muscles
       a. Pectoralis Major
       b. Intercostal Muscles
       c. Muscles of the Abdominal Girdle
          i. Rectus Abdominis
          ii. External Oblique
          iii. Internal Oblique
          iv. Transversus Abdominis
   2. Posterior Muscles
       a. Trapezius
       b. Latissimus Dorsi
       c. Erector Spinae
       d. Quadratus Lumborum
       d. Deltoid
C. Muscles of the Upper Limb (pp. 210–211)
   1. Muscles of the Humerus That Act on the Forearm
       a. Biceps Brachii
       b. Brachialis
       c. Brachioradialis
       d. Triceps Brachii
D. Muscles of the Lower Limb (pp. 211–215)
   1. Muscles Causing Movement at the Hip Joint
       a. Gluteus Maximus
       b. Gluteus Medius
       c. Iliopsoas
       d. Adductor Muscles
   2. Muscles Causing Movement at the Knee Joint
       a. Hamstring Group
          i. Biceps Femoris
          ii. Semimembranosus
          iii. Semitendinosus
       b. Sartorius
       c. Quadriceps Group
          i. Rectus Femoris
          ii. Vastus Muscles
   3. Muscles Causing Movement at the Ankle and Foot
       a. Tibialis Anterior
       b. Extensor Digitorum Longus
       c. Fibularis Muscles
       d. Gastrocnemius
       e. Soleus

VI. DEVELOPMENTAL ASPECTS OF THE MUSCULAR SYSTEM (p. 221)
   A. Embryonic Development
   B. Aging Effects
      1. Hypertrophy
      2. Atrophy
   C. Homeostatic Imbalances
      1. Muscular Dystrophy
      2. Myasthenia Gravis

KEY TERMS

abduction
acetylcholine (ACh)
actin
action potential
adduction
adductor muscles
aerobic
aerobic respiration
all-or-none
antagonists
aponeuroses
axon
axon terminals
biceps brachii
biceps femoris
brachialis
brachioradialis
brevis
cardiac muscle
circular
circumduction
convergent
creatine phosphate (CP)
cross bridges
dark (A) bands
deltoid
dorsiflexion/plantar flexion
endomysium
endurance
epimysium
erector spine
eversion
extension
extensor digitorum longus
external oblique
fascicle
fibularis muscles

fixators
flexion
fusiform
gastrocnemius
gluteus maximus
gluteus medius
graded responses
hamstring group
iliopsoas
insertion
internal oblique
inversion
involuntary
isometric contractions
isotonic contractions
latissimus dorsi
light (I) bands
longus
motor unit
muscle fatigue
muscle fibers
muscle tone
muscle twitches
myofibers
myofibrils
myofilaments
myosin
neuromuscular junctions
neurotransmitter
occipitalis
opposition
origin
oxygen deficit
parallel
pennate
perimysium
prime mover

pronation
quadratus lumborum
quadriceps group
rectusabdominis
rectus femoris
resistance exercises
rotation
sarcolemma
sarcomeres
sarcoplasmic reticulum (SR)
sartorius
semimembranosus
semitendinosus
skeletal muscle fibers
sliding filament mechanism
smooth muscle
soleus
striated muscle
supination
synaptic cleft
synergists
tendons
tertius
tetanus (fused/complete)
tetanus
   (unfused/incomplete)
thick filaments
thin filaments
tibialis anterior
triceps brachii
transversus abdominis
trapezius
unfused (incomplete)
   tetanus
vastus muscles
voluntary muscle

LECTURE HINTS

1. Emphasize the increasing levels of organization that lead to a complete muscle. At the sub-cellular level, discuss the organelles, such as the myofibrils that are in turn composed of even smaller myofilaments. At the cellular level, discuss the multinucleated structure of a single muscle cell (a myofiber) which is wrapped in its protective sheath, the endomysium. At the next level, describe the fascicle, which is composed of several sheathed muscle fibers wrapped in their own protective covering, the perimysium. And finally, point out that a bundle of fascicles are wrapped by another protective covering, the epimysium, to form the compete muscle.

   Key point: This increasing level of organization follows the concepts we have been discussing since Chapter 1 and helps students understand the consistency of the pattern.

2. Use transparencies and/or slides and microscopes to have students look at each of the muscle types (cardiac, smooth, and skeletal) while discussing their similarities and differences.

   Key point: It is important for students to understand that each muscle type has a structure relevant to its function, and that, for example, cardiac muscle is different from the other two types because of its specific role as a continuously contracting circulatory pump.

3. Spend extra time on the sliding filament mechanism, first discussing the new terminology relevant to the process, then applying that terminology to the way the mechanism works. Use the example of a rowboat moving through water, with the oars pulling the boat along with each stroke, to help clarify the concept. Note that Huxley's Sliding Filament Theory is very unique in that other scientists have not improved his explanation of muscle contraction even after seven decades of research.

   Key point: This topic is often one of the most confusing aspects of the muscular system for students to understand, and spending the extra time helps in clarification.

4. Another difficult concept for students is the action between a neuron and all the skeletal muscle cells it stimulates. Discuss a motor unit and the activity at the neuromuscular junction. Be sure that students understand the interplay between the nervous system and the muscular system, which results in muscle activity.

   Key point: Clarifying this interplay now will help greatly as students begin to study the nervous system in greater detail in the following chapter. Note that a skeletal muscle cannot contract unless it is stimulated by a motor nerve (even if you beat it with a hammer).

5. Explain that the "all-or-none" law of muscle physiology can be likened to a light switch. It is either on or off, nothing in between. Point out that this law applies to an *individual* muscle cell and *not the whole muscle*, thus providing a muscle with the ability to generate a graded response.

   Key point: This is often difficult for students to visualize until it is explained that a muscle is made up of thousands of muscle cells, and if only few of them contract to their full capacity, the overall response is still going to be minimal.

6. Discuss disorders of the neuromuscular junction, such as the effects of botulism and snake venom.

   Key point: These are real-world examples that help consolidate the concepts of synaptic imbalance for the students.

7. Discuss the use of botulinum toxin in botox injections. Explain why this toxin can be injected but not ingested.

   Key point: Many students are familiar with this procedure and enjoy learning the science behind it.

8. Students enjoy learning about muscle fatigue and oxygen debt. Nearly everyone has experienced the short-lived muscle fatigue that follows a new exercise routine, and this presents a good opportunity to explain the mechanism involved. Students appreciate learning that the soreness will last until the oxygen debt has been "paid back" and the accumulated lactic acid has been converted into ATP and creatine phosphate reserves. Note that delayed muscle soreness after prolonged endurance events such as a marathon is not due to lactic acid accumulation as blood lactate levels return to normal a few minutes after finishing the race.

   Key point: This is a great opportunity for students to apply some of their newly gained knowledge to an everyday occurrence.

9. Provide students with several examples of the muscle movement of prime movers and their opposing movements by antagonists. Also discuss the role of synergists and fixators in each of the movements.

   Key point: This helps students see that for every muscle action there is a counterbalancing reaction. It also clarifies the point that muscles can only *pull* and that the opposing action requires *pull* from another muscle. Diseases of the neuromuscular system become evident when an agonist muscle is not appropriately balanced by its antagonist.

10. While discussing each specific muscle, point out the word parts in the muscle name to emphasize why it was named that way. For example, the sternocleidomastoid originates on the sternum and clavicle (cleido) and inserts on the mastoid process of the temporal bone. The sartorius is named for the Latin *sartor*, or tailor, and is the muscle used for the cross-legged sitting position once used by tailors.

    Key point: There is a logical basis for the naming of most muscles. The name often provides clues to location, shape, size, origin, insertion, and/or action, which will help students tremendously in the memorization process.

11. Point out to students that although there are more than 600 muscles in the human body, they will only be asked to memorize a select group of the most important ones. Provide them with a list of the muscles that they are responsible for memorizing.

    Key point: A one-semester course is simply not long enough for students to learn all of the muscles of the human body. For students choosing to go on into a field such as medicine, an upper level anatomy and physiology course series will be part of their future curriculum.

12. Discuss disorders of the muscular system such as muscular dystrophy, fibromyalgia, and myasthenia gravis.

    Key point: Students have usually heard about these conditions and appreciate learning about their underlying pathology.

13. Have a physical therapist speak to the class about rehabilitation to muscles after surgery, an illness, an injury, or a disease condition.

    Key point: Students can learn the application of muscle movements in the medical field.

TRANSPARENCIES/MEDIA MANAGER INDEX

Figure 6.1   Connective tissue wrappings of skeletal muscle

Figure 6.2   Arrangement of smooth and cardiac muscle cells

Indicates images that are on the Media Manager only.

ANSWERS TO END OF CHAPTER REVIEW QUESTIONS

Questions appear on pp. 224–226

Multiple Choice

1. c, e (pp. 192–193; Figure 6.7)
2. a (p. 190; Figure 6.5)
3. c (p. 198)
4. b (p. 199)

5. a, b, c, d (p. 204)
6. a, b (pp. 209 and 214)
7. a, b, d (pp. 211–214; Figure 6.19)
8. a, b, d (pp. 210–211; Tables 6.3 and 6.4)

Short Answer Essay

9. To contract or shorten. To cause movement. (p. 183)

10. *Skeletal muscle:* Long, cylindrical, banded (striated), multinucleate cells; attached to bones and crossing joints; forms the "flesh" of the body and is responsible for all voluntary movement. *Cardiac muscle:* Branching, striated cells containing a single nucleus; interdigitate with one another at tight junctions called intercalated disks; found only in the heart, arranged in spiral bundles; contraction of the heart propels blood into the blood vessels. *Smooth muscle:* Fusiform, uninucleate cells; generally found in cell layers (or sheets) arranged at right angles to one another (one running longitudinally and the other circularly) within the walls of hollow organs; causes substances to move through internal body tracts (digestive, urinary, reproductive, and the like). (pp. 183–186; Table 6.1)

11. Skeletal and cardiac muscle. (Table 6.1)

12. They protect, reinforce, and strengthen the delicate muscle tissue. Endomysium, perimysium, and epimysium. (p. 185)

13. Tendons attach muscle to bone. (p. 185)

14. *Neuromuscular junction:* The junction of a motor neuron's axon terminals and the sarcolemma of a muscle cell. (p. 189)

    Motor unit: One motor neuron and all the muscle cells it stimulates. (p. 189)

    Tetanus: The smooth, sustained contractions of a muscle with no evidence of relaxation. (p. 194)

    Graded response: Different degrees of contraction in response to different levels of stimulation (changes in both the rate and strength of stimuli). (p. 194)

    Aerobic respiration: Metabolic pathways that use O_2 to generate ATP. (p. 195)

    Anaerobic glycolysis: Metabolic pathway that breaks down glucose into pyruvic acid (without using O_2) to generate ATP. (p. 195)

    Muscle fatigue: The inability of a muscle to contract even though it is still being stimulated; usually a result of a lack of oxygen and the accumulation of acids in the muscle tissue. (pp. 195–197)

    Neurotransmitter: A chemical substance released by a neuron when the nerve impulse reaches its axon terminals. (p. 189)

15. Acetylcholine is released; it diffuses through the synaptic cleft and attaches to receptors on the sarcolemma; sarcolemma permeability to sodium ions increases briefly; sodium ions rush into the muscle cell, changing the electrical conditions of the resting sarcolemma; action potential is initiated and sweeps over the entire sarcolemma eventually reaching the sarcoplasmic reticulum deep inside the cell; calcium ions are released from the sarcoplasmic reticulum; attachment of calcium ions to the thin filaments exposes binding sites for myosin. Myosin cross-bridges bind to actin, triggering the sliding of the myofilaments; contraction occurs. (pp. 189–190)

16. *Isotonic contractions:* Muscle tension remains the same, and the muscle shortens. *Isometric contractions:* Muscle tension increases, and the muscle does not shorten. (p. 197)

17. Muscle tone is a state of continuous, partial contraction of muscles resulting from discontinuous but systematic stimulation by the nervous system. A muscle without tone is paralyzed (unable to contract) and becomes flaccid and can eventually atrophy. (p. 197)

18. *Origin:* Immovable (or less movable) end. *Insertion:* Movable end; when contraction occurs, the insertion moves toward the origin. (pp. 198–199)

19. Flexion, extension, abduction, adduction, rotation, circumduction, pronation, supination, inversion, eversion, dorsiflexion, plantar flexion. (pp. 199–202; Figure 6.13)

20. A prime mover is a muscle that has major responsibility for causing a particular movement; for example, the gastrocnemius is the prime mover of plantar flexion. Synergist muscles aid prime movers by causing the same movement (but less effectively) or by stabilizing joints or bones over which the prime mover acts; for example, the peroneus muscles (which promote plantar flexion) are synergists of the gastrocnemius muscle. The tibialis anterior muscle causes dorsiflexion of the foot; thus, the gastrocnemius (prime mover for plantar flexion) is its antagonist. (p. 202)

21. Chewing food, grinding your teeth, or just opening and closing the jaw. *Frontalis:* covers the frontal bone; allows you to raise your eyebrows and wrinkle your forehead. *Orbicularis oculi:* found in circles around eyes; functions to close eyes, squint, blink, and wink. *Orbicularis oris:* circular muscle of the lips; closes mouth and protrudes lips (kissing motion). *Buccinator:* runs horizontally across the cheek and inserts into the orbicularis oris; flattens cheek and aids in chewing. *Zygomaticus:* extends from corner of mouth to cheekbone; raises corners of mouth upward. *Temporalis:* overlies the frontal bone; closes jaw. (p. 207; Table 6.3)

22. Trapezius muscles. (pp. 209–210; Tables 6.3–6.4)

23. Anteriorly, the pectoralis major. Posteriorly, the latissimus dorsi. (pp. 208 and 210; Tables 6.3 and 6.4)

24. *Prime mover:* Biceps brachii. *Antagonist:* Triceps brachii. (p. 204; Tables 6.3 and 6.4)

25. The four muscles (or muscle pairs) are arranged so their fibers run in different directions, much as sheets of different wood grains are compressed together to make plywood. Like plywood, the abdominal wall musculature is extremely strong for its thickness; it is well constructed for its function as an abdominal girdle. (pp. 208–209)

26. *Hamstrings:* Extend hip and flex knee. (Table 6.4) *Quadriceps:* Flex hip (rectus femoris only) and extend knee. (p. 207; Table 6.3)

27. *Gastrocnemius:* Plantar flexion. (p. 214; Table 6.4)

28. Muscles that are exercised regularly are healthy (with increased endurance), firm and free of superficial fat, and perhaps larger in size (depending on the type of exercise). Resistance-type exercises, such as weight lifting, cause muscles to hypertrophy to meet the increased demands placed on them. Muscles that are not used will atrophy (lose mass) and become weak. (pp. 197–198)

29. With aging, skeletal muscle tissue mass decreases and the relative amount of connective tissue in the muscles increases, causing the muscles to become sinewy. As the muscles decrease in mass, they also decrease in strength. Loss in muscle mass may be partially prevented by regular exercise. (p. 221)

30. He or she should engage in aerobic training. Training aerobically increases the amount and activity of enzymes within the aerobic metabolic pathways to make ATP for repeated muscular contractions whereas anaerobic training increases the amount and activity of enzymes within the glycolytic metabolic pathways. Muscles that are stronger, more resistant to fatigue, and flexible are the result of aerobic types of exercise. (pp. 197–198)

ANSWERS TO CRITICAL THINKING
AND CLINICAL APPLICATION QUESTIONS

31. Deltoid, gluteus maximus, gluteus medius, vastus lateralis, and rectus femoris. The vastus lateralis and rectus femoris is used more often for babies because their arm and hip muscles are poorly developed. (pp. 210–214; Figures 6.18–6.19)

32. He ruptured his Achilles tendon, which attaches the gastrocnemius to the heel bone. This accounts for the gap between the calf and the heel, as well as the inability to plantar flex the foot. (p. 214)

33. Any muscle that inserts on the clavicle-trapezius. The muscles of her arm would also be immobilized by the sling. (pp. 207–210)

34. Eric's oxygen intake has not been adequate to keep his muscles supplied with the oxygen they needed to support prolonged aerobic activity. His heavy breathing will supply oxygen to repay the oxygen debt. His muscle cells were relying on aerobic metabolism, and their oxygen consumption led to breathlessness. When the oxygen ran out, anaerobic metabolism took place, leading to lactic acid accumulation, short-term muscle fatigue, and muscle soreness. (pp. 195–197)

35. The neurotransmitter acetylcholine diffuses across the neuromuscular synaptic cleft and stimulates skeletal muscle contraction under the influence of calcium ions. Complete or partial blocking of acetylcholine-specific protein receptors on the sarcolemma membrane would cause muscle relaxation. (pp. 189–190)

36. Abnormal lateral curvature of the spine is scoliosis. It is caused by unequal muscle pull on the spine. The rectus abdominis, external and internal obliques flex the vertebral column. The latter two also rotate the trunk and bend it laterally. (pp. 208–209)

37. Rigor mortis sets in soon after death as lack of breathing suspends oxygen-driven ATP generation in the mitochondria. ATP is used to break the linkage between actin and myosin, so without ATP, the myosin-actin cross bridges remain attached. (Figure 6.8) (pp. 189–197)

CLASSROOM DEMONSTRATIONS AND STUDENT ACTIVITIES

Classroom Demonstrations

1. Film(s) or other media of choice.

2. Use models to compare the three types of muscle tissue and point out the unique structural characteristics of each.

3. Use a model to demonstrate the sliding filament mechanism, or make your own model out of disk-shaped Styrofoam pieces placed on pickup sticks to represent Z lines on myofilaments.

4. Show a model of the neuromuscular junction to help students conceptualize the interplay between the muscular and nervous systems.

5. Demonstrate the difference between isotonic and isometric exercises, and discuss the way isometric, or resistance, exercises differ from aerobic, or endurance, types of exercise.

6. Demonstrate muscle contraction (twitch contractions, summation, and tetanus) using a simple myograph or kymograph apparatus and the gastrocnemius muscle of a frog.

Student Activities

1. Divide the class into small groups. Have students demonstrate to each other the differences between various types of body movements, such as flexion, extension, abduction, and adduction. Be sure that they try these movements with different groups of muscles, including muscles of the hands, arms, and legs.

2. Call out an action, and ask students to provide the name of the muscle or muscles responsible for that action. Students can also be challenged to identify the antagonists and synergists when given the name of a muscle.

3. Have students work in pairs as follows: One attempts to contract a particular muscle, while the partner provides resistance to prevent that movement. In this way, the muscle will produce its maximal "bulge." Each student should palpate muscles being examined in both the relaxed and contracted states. For example, the "demonstrator" can attempt to flex his or her elbow while the person providing the resistance holds the forearm to prevent its movement. The biceps brachii on the anterior arm will bulge and be easily palpated.

4. Have students obtain information on the procedures used to build muscle mass and how those procedures accomplish that goal. Also discuss atrophy as a result of wearing a cast on a broken limb or from prolonged hospitalization with minimal activity and discuss what can be done about it.

5. Have the students attempt to pick up objects in the classroom that have been permanently installed. Point out that this represents an isometric activity, where muscle length stays the same despite force applied. Next, have the students pick up a loose object and note what happens to the muscle during isotonic activity.

6. Provide articulated skeletons to students in small groups. Ask the students to point out the origins and insertions of various muscles, as well as the movement that each muscle generates.

MULTIMEDIA

See page 182 for a listing of media distributors.

1. *Muscle and Bone* (AMB, NIMCO; 30 min., 1994, VHS, DVD). From the *Body Atlas* series, this video looks at the interrelationship of muscle and bone in movement.

2. *Muscles* (FHS; 20 min., 1995, VHS, DVD). From *The New Living Body* series, this video introduces the widespread nature of muscle tissue in the body and looks at the complex movements involved in the exercise of rowing.

3. *Muscular System at Work: The Inner Athlete* (FHS; 25 min., 1998, VHS, DVD). From *The Human Body: Systems at Work* series, this program looks at the many roles played by muscle in our everyday lives.

SOFTWARE

1. *Body Works* (WNS; Win). An economical CD of anatomy and physiology.

2. *InterActive Physiology 9-System Suite* (ADAM, BC; Win/Mac). Offers lucid, interactive exploration of some of the more difficult concepts of muscle physiology.

The Nervous System

CHAPTER SUMMARY

The nervous system is the body's fast-acting master controller. It monitors changes inside and outside the body, integrates sensory input, and effects an appropriate feedback response. In conjunction with the slower-acting endocrine system, which is the body's second important regulating system, the nervous system is able to constantly regulate and maintain homeostasis within narrow limits. This chapter looks at both the structural and functional classifications of the nervous system, first separately and then as an integrated whole, to help students conceptualize the complexity of this system.

First, this chapter describes the structure and function of nervous tissue. The types and activities of the supporting cells are discussed, followed by a complete description of the anatomy of a neuron. Neurons are then classified as either afferent (sensory), efferent (motor), or association neurons, and the role of each type is presented. Discussion of the physiology of nerve impulses is next, focusing on the two functional properties of neurons, *irritability* and *conductivity*. Both of these properties are explored, and the mechanisms involved within simple and more complex reflex arcs are explained to help clarify application of these principles.

The next section of the chapter presents the central nervous system and its components. The structure and function of the cerebral hemispheres, diencephalon, brain stem, cerebellum, and spinal cord are explored, followed by a discussion of the protection provided to the CNS by the meninges and cerebrospinal fluid. A discussion of some of the more common brain dysfunctions showcases their variability and provides interesting starting points for classroom discussions.

The final section of this chapter examines the peripheral nervous system, beginning with the cranial and spinal nerves, followed by a discussion of the differences between the somatic and autonomic nervous systems. The autonomic nervous system is then further subdivided into its sympathetic and parasympathetic divisions, and the "fight-or-flight" mechanism of the sympathetic division is compared to the "resting and digesting" mechanism of the parasympathetic division. Finally, the developmental aspects of the nervous system are presented, along with a discussion of some of the more common congenital complications, such as cerebral palsy and spina bifida.

SUGGESTED LECTURE OUTLINE

I. ORGANIZATION OF THE NERVOUS SYSTEM
   (pp. 229–230)
   A. Structural Classification (p. 229)
      1. Central Nervous System (CNS)
         a. Brain
         b. Spinal Cord
      2. Peripheral Nervous System (PNS)
         a. Nerves
         b. Ganglia

TEACHING TIP

Describe saltatory conduction, in which a nerve impulse leaps from node to node, as being similar to flying cross-country with quick stops in between as compared to traveling the entire distance by car. Saltatory conduction is significantly faster than continuous conduction, and nerve impulses traveling on myelinated fibers are faster than those traveling on unmyelinated fibers.

B. Functional Classification (pp. 229–230)
  1. Sensory (Afferent) Division
  2. Motor (Efferent) Division
     a. Somatic (Voluntary) Nervous System
     b. Autonomic (Involuntary) Nervous System (ANS)

II. NERVOUS TISSUE: STRUCTURE AND FUNCTION (pp. 230–242)
  A. Supporting Cells in the CNS (pp. 230–232)
    1. Astrocytes
    2. Microglia
    3. Ependymal
    4. Oligodendrocytes
  B. Supporting Cells in the PNS
    1. Schwann Cells
    2. Satellite Cells
  C. Neurons (pp. 232–242)
    1. Anatomy
       a. Cell Body Processes
          i. Dendrites
          ii. Axons
       b. Myelin Sheaths
       c. Terminology
    2. Classification
       a. Functional Classification
          i. Sensory (Afferent) Neurons
          ii. Motor (Efferent) Neurons
          iii. Interneurons (Association Neurons)
       b. Structural Classification
          i. Multipolar
          ii. Bipolar
          iii. Unipolar
    3. Physiology
       a. Nerve Impulses
       b. Reflexes
          i. Somatic
          ii. Autonomic

III. CENTRAL NERVOUS SYSTEM (pp. 242–258)
  A. Functional Anatomy of the Brain (pp. 242–248)
    1. Cerebral Hemispheres (Cerebrum)
       a. Cerebral Cortex
       b. Cerebral White Matter
       c. Basal Nuclei
    2. Diencephalon (Interbrain)
       a. Thalamus
       b. Hypothalamus
       c. Epithalamus

MEDIA TIP

The Nervous System (IM; 24 min., 1993). Details the job of the nervous system, revealing its control over all bodily activity.

       3. Brain Stem
          a. Midbrain
          b. Pons
          c. Medulla Oblongata
          d. Reticular Formation
       4. Cerebellum

  B. Protection of the Central Nervous System
    (pp. 248–252)
      1. Bony Enclosures
      2. Meninges
         a. Dura Mater
         b. Arachnoid Mater
         c. Pia Mater
      3. Cerebrospinal Fluid (CSF)
      4. The Blood-Brain Barrier

  C. Brain Dysfunctions (pp. 252–255)
      1. Traumatic Brain Injuries
         a. Concussions
         b. Contusions
         c. Intracranial Hemorrhage
         d. Cerebral Edema
      2. Cerebrovascular Accidents (CVA)—Stroke
         a. Paralysis
         b. Aphasias
         c. Transient Ischemic Attack (TI)

  D. Spinal Cord (pp. 255–258)
      1. Gray Matter of the Spinal Cords and Spinal Roots
      2. White Matter of the Spinal Cord

IV. PERIPHERAL NERVOUS SYSTEM (pp. 258–270)
  A. Structure of a Nerve (p. 258)
  B. Cranial Nerves (pp. 258–262; Figure 7.24; Table 7.1)
  C. Spinal Nerves and Nerve Plexuses (p. 262; Figures
    7.25 and 7.26; Table 7.2)
  D. Autonomic Nervous System (pp. 262–273)
      1. Somatic and Autonomic Nervous Systems
         Compared
      2. Anatomy of the Parasympathetic Division
      3. Anatomy of the Sympathetic Division
      4. Autonomic Functioning
         a. Sympathetic Division
         b. Parasympathetic Division

V. DEVELOPMENTAL ASPECTS OF THE NERVOUS
  SYSTEM (pp. 272–275)
  A. Embryonic and Fetal Brain Development: Normal
    and Abnormal
      1. Cerebral Palsy
      2. Hydrocephalus
      3. Anencephaly
      4. Spina Bifida
  B. Premature Infants
  C. Childhood and Adolescent Brain Development

D. Aging
   1. Orthostatic Hypertension
   2. Arteriosclerosis
   3. Senility

KEY TERMS

action potential (nerve impulse)
afferent division
arachnoid mater
arachnoid villi
arteriosclerosis
astrocytes
autonomic nervous system (ANS)
autonomic reflexes
axons
axon hillock
axon terminals
basal nuclei (ganglia)
bipolar neurons
blood-brain barrier
brain stem
Broca's area
cauda equina
cell body
central canal
central nervous system (CNS)
central sulcus
cerebellum
cerebral aqueduct
cerebral cortex
cerebral hemispheres
cerebral peduncles
cerebral white matter
cerebrospinal fluid (CSF)
cerebrum
choroid plexus
collateral ganglion
columns
corpora quadrigemina
corpus callosum
cranial nerves
cutaneous sense organs
depolarization
dendrites
diencephalon (interbrain)
dorsal root ganglion
dorsal column

dorsal rami
dura matter
endoneurium
efferent division
endoneurium
ependymal cells
epineurium
epithalamus
falx cerebri
fascicles
fissures
frontal lobe
fourth ventricle
ganglia
glia
graded potential
gray matter
gyri
hypothalamus
integration
interneurons (association) neurons
involuntary nervous system
lateral column
limbic system
lobes
mammilary bodies
medulla oblongata
meninges
microglia
midbrain
mixed nerves
motor (efferent) nerves
motor (efferent) neurons
motor homunculus
motor output
multipolar neuron
myelin
myelin sheath
nerve
nervous system
neural tube
neurilemma
neurofibrils

neuroglia
neuron (nerve cell)
neurotransmitters
nissl substance
nodes of Ranvier
nuclei
occipital lobe
oligodendrocytes
orthostatic hypotension
parasympathetic division
parietal lobe
perineurium
peripheral nervous system (PNS)
pia mater
pineal body
pituitary gland
plexuses
polarized
pons
postganglionic axon
preganglionic axon
primary motor area
processes
proprioceptors
pyramidal (corticospinal) tract
ramus communicans
receptors
reflex arcs
reflexes
reticular activating system (RAS)
reticular formation
repolarization
satellite cells
schwann cells
senility
sensory
sensory (afferent) nerves
sensory homunculus
sensory input
sensory (afferent) neurons
somatic nervous system

somatic reflexes
somatic sensory area
speech area
spinal cord
splanchnic nerves
subarachoid space
sulci
sympathetic chain (trunk)

sympathetic chain ganglion
sympathetic division
synapse
synaptic cleft
temporal lobe
tentorium cerebelli
terminal ganglion
thalamus

tracts
unipolar neurons
ventral column
ventral rami
ventricles
voluntary nervous system
white matter

LECTURE HINTS

1. Before going into depth, outline the general organization of the nervous system on the board, comparing the central nervous system (the brain and spinal cord) to the peripheral nervous system (the cranial and spinal nerves). Further outline the two divisions of the peripheral nervous system, the sensory and motor divisions, followed by the two subdivisions of the motor division, the somatic (voluntary) and autonomic (involuntary) nervous systems. Give a brief description and a specific example of the distinct role of each division.

   Key point: Point out that any attempt to divide the nervous system into discrete sections is done strictly to help us understand the workings of this complex system, and that the divisions are man-made for simplification purposes only.

2. Discuss the neuroglia as the "glue that holds the nervous system together." These supporting cells are frequently ignored in favor of the "star" (i.e., the functional neuron), and it is wise to emphasize their importance early.

   Key point: Although the functional unit of the nervous system is the neuron, the neuroglia provide them with support, protection, access to nutrients, and numerous other life-sustaining services.

3. Use transparencies or images from the Instructor's Resource CD-ROM to present the basic anatomy of a *typical* neuron. Point out to students that neurons come in a variety of shapes and sizes, and that we are looking at a representative sample to help us visualize commonalities.

   Key point: It is important for students to first understand the general structure of a neuron before they learn of the many variations that are possible.

4. To help students understand the importance of the myelin sheath, discuss multiple sclerosis and its effects. Point out that the types of abilities that are lost are dependent upon the position of the sclerotic patches within the nervous system, and thus accounts for the wide range of disability seen in people with MS.

   Key point: Multiple sclerosis causes the conversion of the myelin sheath into sclerotic, or hard, patches that short-circuit the neurological transmissions that would normally pass through that point.

5. Describe saltatory conduction, in which a nerve impulse leaps from node to node, as being similar to flying cross-country with quick stops in between as compared to traveling the entire distance by car. Saltatory conduction is significantly faster than continuous conduction, and nerve impulses traveling on myelinated fibers are faster than those traveling on unmyelinated fibers.

   Key point: This visualization helps students understand the differences in the speed of transmission between gray matter and white matter.

6. Differentiate between afferent, efferent, and association neurons and describe the role of each. Point out that nerves, which are bundles of neurons, can carry sensory, motor, or both types of neurons at the same time, similar to a telephone wire that transmits messages both ways.

   Key point: Describe the direction in which the messages run as in relation to the CNS.

7. Distribute handouts of "brain maps" that show the most current, detailed outlines of the activities attributed to various parts of the brain.

   Key point: Students are fascinated to learn how much we have discovered through studying people with seizure disorders and other neurological conditions.

8. Discuss the effects of a stroke, or cerebrovascular accident, if the cranial bleed is located in Broca's area. Further elaborate on the various types of aphasia and their causes. Ask the students to predict the results of a bleed in either the gustatory or olfactory area.

   Key point: Students usually know that some people become aphasic following a stroke and others do not. This discussion helps them understand the processes involved.

9. Discuss epilepsy, including its past and present treatment strategies. Discuss the different types of seizures associated with epilepsy. Determine the difference between seizures related to injury and seizures as part of epilepsy.

   Key point: Students find brain dysfunction very interesting, and can often relate the information to either someone they know or TV programs they have watched.

10. Ask the students if they can guess whether they are predominantly left- or right-brained, and then list some of the characteristics associated with dominance of each on the board.

    Key point: "Artistic" or "analytic" are some of the adjectives frequently used to describe brain dominance. Explain that we all have the ability to use *both* sides of our brain, but that we typically display more characteristics of dominance by one side or the other. Note that a cerebrovascular accident (CVA) on the left side of the brain will affect the limbs on the right side of the body (and vice versa). Explain how the left side of the brain can compensate and "learn" some of the activities that were originally associated with the right side (and vice versa) after a brain injury or CVA. It is also important to explain how some brain functions may be permanently destroyed.

11. Emphasize that the hypothalamus is one of the key regulators of homeostasis and that it is particularly important in temperature control, water balance, metabolism, and hormone regulation. Also note that the medulla oblongata is important in maintaining homeostasis in that it regulates the vital activities of heart rate, blood pressure, and breathing.

    Key point: It is important to recognize the significance of these two regions of the brain in homeostasis, as they will be emphasized again in future chapters.

12. Describe the differences between Alzheimer's disease, Parkinson's disease, and Huntington's disease, and explain the reasons for their differences.

    Key point: These three conditions are well known and generate a lot of discussion in the classroom. Explain current research and treatment options.

13. Describe and discuss brain conditions that require psychiatric treatment such as depression, bipolar disorder, schizophrenia, multiple personality disorder, sociopathic behavior, or psychosis.

    Key point: By gaining knowledge of these conditions, students can better appreciate the complexity and individual variation within the nervous system.

14. Students have usually heard about "subdural hematomas" and the presentation of material on the meninges provides a good opportunity for discussion of this condition. This is also a good time to explain where an epidural anesthetic would be placed.

    Key point: These examples help students to visualize the layers of the meninges, along with their protective functions.

15. Tell the students of the mnemnonic device, *On Occasion, Our Trusty Truck Acts Funny— Very Good Vehicle Anyhow,* used for memorization of the 12 pairs of cranial nerves.

    Key point: This mnemnonic device requires a bit of explanation, but is still useful for memorizing the cranial nerves.

16. Ask the students to tell you all the things that they think would happen if they were faced with a sudden, stressful situation, and list their responses on the board. Relate their responses to the "fight-or-flight" mechanism of the sympathetic division of the autonomic nervous system, and then point out that the parasympathetic division is charged with the responsibility of bringing all of these physiological changes back to normal.

    Key point: In our fast-paced society, people are in sympathetic mode a good share of the time, and it is helpful for students to see the necessity of allowing the parasympathetic system to bring them back into homeostatic balance.

17. Discuss the relationship of spinal nerves to the vertebrae. Make sure to remind students that while a normal human has seven cervical vertebrae, he or she will have eight cervical nerves.

    Key point: Vertebrae are singular and the spinal nerves are in pairs. The first pair of cervical nerves arise superior to the first cervical vertebra.

18. Describe autism and all of its various types and treatments.

    Key point: Autism has been receiving a great deal of media attention and is widely misunderstood. A discussion of this topic, perhaps even using a guest speaker, can give further insight about this condition to the students.

19. List the conditions that have been treated (or are currently treated) by a partial lobotomy. Be sure to indicate the success rate for each.

    Key point: Students can associate the changes in brain function with removal of parts of brain regions.

20. Discuss the severity of a ruptured brain aneurysm, and why it is often fatal.

    Key point: This injury illustrates the brain's immense need for glucose and oxygen, and that deprivation of either can lead to brain death very quickly. As well, the students can appreciate how brain tissue is easily damaged if exposed directly to blood.

TRANSPARENCIES/MEDIA MANAGER INDEX

Indicates images that are on the Media Manager only.

ANSWERS TO END OF CHAPTER REVIEW QUESTIONS

Questions appear on pp. 277–279

Multiple Choice

1. b (p. 229)
2. a, b, c (pp. 245, 256)

3. d (p. 251)

4. d (pp. 232, 234)

5. c (p. 247)

6. 1-d; 2-h; 3-e; 4-g; 5-b; 6-f; 7-i; 8-a (pp. 245–246, 248)

7. a, c (p. 255; Table 7.2)

8. c (p. 256)

9. a, c (Figure 7.24; Table 7.1)

10. a, c (Table 7.2)

11. d (p. 231)

12. d (pp. 262, 267; Figure 7.28)

Short Answer Essay

13. Nervous system and endocrine system. (p. 229)

14. The structural classification includes all the nervous system organs. The major subdivisions are the central nervous system which includes the brain and spinal cord, and the peripheral nervous system which is mainly nerves. The functional classification divides the peripheral nervous system into afferent (sensory) and efferent (motor) branches. The motor division is further divided into the somatic and autonomic branches. (pp. 229–230)

15. The functional classification of neurons is based on the general direction of the impulse. Impulses traveling from sensory receptors to the CNS are afferent (sensory) neurons. Impulses traveling from the CNS to effector organs travel along efferent (motor) neurons. Neurons that are in the CNS and connect afferent and efferent pathways are called interneurons (or association neurons). (pp. 229–230)

16. Neurons are the "nervous cells"; they exhibit irritability and conductivity. The major functions of the glia are protection, support, myelination, and a nutritive/metabolic function relative to the neurons. Schwann cells are myelinating cells in the peripheral nervous system. (pp. 230–232)

17. A threshold stimulus causes a change in membrane permeability that allows Na^+ to enter the neuron through sodium gates. This causes local depolarization and generates the action potential, which is then self-propagating. This event is quickly followed by a second permeability change that restricts Na^+ entry but allows K^+ to leave the neuron, causing repolarization or resumption of the polarized state. One-way conduction occurs at synapses because axons (not dendrites) release the neurotransmitter. (pp. 232, 237–238)

18. Pain receptors; Pacinian corpuscles (deep pressure) and Meissner's corpuscles (light pressure); temperature receptors (e.g., Ruffini's corpuscles [heat]). The pain receptors are most numerous because pain indicates actual or possible tissue damage. (p. 235; Figure 7.7)

19. The minimum components of a reflex arc include a receptor, an afferent neuron, an integration center, an efferent neuron, and an effector. (p. 240; Figure 7.11)

20. Student drawings and responses can be checked by referring to Figure 7.13 and p. 243.

21. The pons also has important nuclei that participate in the control of respiratory rhythm. The medulla is vital because it contains the major respiratory centers, the vasomotor center (which controls blood vessel diameter, hence blood pressure), and the cardiac centers. Without breathing and heart activity, life stops. (p. 248)

22. The thalamus is a relay station for sensory impulses ascending to the cerebral cortex for interpretation; as impulses pass through the thalamus, one crudely senses that the incoming stimulus is pleasant or unpleasant. The hypothalamus is a major autonomic clearing center whose important functions include temperature regulation, water balance, and metabolic control; it also serves as an important center for emotions and drives (sex, rage, pleasure, satiety/appetite, thirst). (p. 246)

23. *Bone:* Enclosed by the skull. (p. 248) *Membranes:* The meningeal membranes—dura mater, arachnoid mater, and pia mater—enclose the brain within the skull and provide a passage for the circulation of CSF and its return to the blood. (pp. 249, 250) *Fluid:* Cerebrospinal fluid (CSF) cushions the brain from physical trauma. (p. 251) *Capillaries:* The capillaries of the brain are permeable only to glucose, a few amino acids, and respiratory gases. Hence, they protect the brain from possibly harmful substances in the blood. (p. 252)

24. Gray matter is neural tissue composed primarily of nerve cell bodies and unmyelinated fibers. White matter is composed primarily of myelinated fibers (p. 235). In the cerebral hemispheres, most of the gray matter is outermost (superficial), and the white matter is deep (pp. 243, 245); in the spinal cord, the white matter is outermost and the gray matter is internal or deep. (p. 256)

25. Major reflex center; pathway for ascending sensory impulses and descending motor impulses. (p. 255)

26. Twelve pairs. Purely sensory: Olfactory (I), optic (II), and vestibulocochlear (VIII). Activates the chewing muscles: trigeminal (V). Regulates heartbeat, etc.: Vagus (X). (p. 258; Table 7.1)

27. The head and neck region. (p. 258)

28. Thirty-one pairs. They arise from the dorsal (sensory) and ventral (motor) roots of the spinal cord. (p. 262)

29. *Dorsal rami:* Posterior body trunk. *Ventral rami:* Limbs and anterior, lateral body trunk. (p. 262)

30. *Cervical plexus:* Diaphragm, shoulder and neck muscles. *Brachial plexus:* Arm, forearm, wrist, and hand. *Lumbar plexus:* Lower abdomen, buttocks, anterior thigh, medial thigh, anteromedial leg. *Sacral plexus:* Lower posterior trunk, posterior thigh, leg, and foot. (Table 7.2)

31. The autonomic nervous system has a chain of two motor neurons (rather than one) extending from the CNS and is controlled involuntarily (rather than voluntarily). The ANS has different effector organs (cardiac muscle, smooth muscle, and glands), and it can release both acetylcholine (parasympathetic nervous system) and norepinephrine (sympathetic nervous system). This system has cell bodies of motor neurons inside and outside the CNS. Also, the two divisions of the ANS have antagonist actions to each other. (pp. 262, 266; Figure 7.27)

32. The parasympathetic division of the ANS is the "housekeeping system"; it acts to conserve body energy and to keep the body running at minimum levels of energy use during nonemergency periods. Its effect is seen primarily in the normal operation of the digestive system and the urinary system. The sympathetic division is the "fight-or-flight" system; it acts during periods of short-term stress to increase heart rate and blood pressure and to shunt blood glucose levels. Generally, sympathetic activity inhibits digestive system functioning. The parasympathetic system has the opposite effect. (pp. 268–270; Table 7.3)

33. Although both the sympathetic and presympathetic preganglionic fibers release acetylcholine, their postganglionic fibers (in close contact with the effector organs) release different neurotransmitters. The sympathetic fibers release norepinephrine and the parasympathetic fibers release acetylcholine. These different neurotransmitters produce opposing effects in the effector organs. (pp. 268–270)

34. Schwann cells produce myelin outside the CNS. They are specialized support cells that wrap tightly around an axon and enclose it. As a result, the neuron is insulated. (p. 232)

35. Both CVAs and TIAs result from restricted blood flow to brain tissue. CVAs result in permanent or long-lasting deficits, including paralysis, aphasias, and visual disturbances. In TIAs, the disturbances, though similar, are temporary because neurons do not die. (pp. 252, 254–255)

36. *Senility* is age-related mental deterioration (i.e., changes in intellect, memory, etc.). Permanent causes include factors that deprive neurons of adequate oxygen (such as arteriosclerosis) and degenerative structural changes (as in Alzheimer's disease). Reversible causes include drug effects, low blood pressure, poor nutrition, and hormone imbalances. (p. 273)

ANSWERS TO CRITICAL THINKING AND CLINICAL APPLICATION QUESTIONS

37. Alzheimer's disease. (p. 253)

38. Hypoglossal (XII). (Table 7.1)

39. The parasympathetic division is involved in the activation of the digestive viscera and with conserving body energy. Following a meal, this system promotes digestive activity and lowers the heart rate and the respiratory rate. The sympathetic division is only minimally active at this time. Therefore, the person will feel "very sleepy." If the person is overweight, he probably should not overexert himself. However, doing the dishes would not be hazardous to his health. (p. 270; Table 7.3)

40. Intracranial hemorrhage. (p. 252)

41. Sternocleidomastoid and trapezius muscles. (Table 7.1)

42. Cerebral palsy—it will not get worse. (p. 272)

43. Brachial plexus. (Table 7.2)

44. Schwann cells and oligodendrocytes deposit a fatty coat called myelin around axons. Like the rubber coat around household wires, myelin acts as an electrical insulator. (p. 232)

45. The reticular activating system was damaged. (p. 248)

46. The nervous system is formed during the first month of development so exposure to toxins at this time will cause great neural damage. (p. 272)

47. The femoral nerve, which originates at lumbar vertebrae one, two, three, and four (Table 7.2), experienced trauma by hockey stick. The femoral motor nerve innervates the rectus femoris muscle, which is the only one of the four quadriceps muscles that cause both hip joint flexion and knee joint extension. This nerve is also responsible for cutaneous sensation in that area. Clancy is not feeling any pain, which further indicates femoral nerve damage. (p. 214 in Chapter 6).

48. Accessory (IX) nerves. (Table 7.1)

CLASSROOM DEMONSTRATIONS AND STUDENT ACTIVITIES

Classroom Demonstrations

1. Film(s) or other media of choice.

2. Demonstrate a knee-jerk reflex. Ask for a student volunteer to come to the front of the class to assist you with the demonstration. Tap their knee with a reflex hammer and note the response. If the student is nervous and appears to be holding the knee still, distract them by asking them to look at one of their classmates off to the side, then tap their knee and note the difference in response.

3. Demonstrate a few other reflexes commonly used as diagnostic tools in medicine, such as Babinski's reflex, the biceps reflex, and Chaddock's reflex.

4. Use a dissectible human brain model to point out its various structural and functional areas.

5. Use a 3-D model of a motor neuron to point out structural characteristics of nerve cells.

6. Use a spinal cord model to illustrate the way in which the spinal nerves originate from the dorsal and ventral roots, and then split into rami.

7. Using the sciatic nerve of a frog, a stimulator, and an oscilloscope, demonstrate an action potential, or show a filmed version of this demonstration.

8. Invite a pharmacist to discuss the effects of selected drugs on the brain and nervous system. Include some of the more common street drugs, such as alcohol and cocaine, on the discussion list.

9. Demonstrate a TENS Unit, which reduces pain in a similar manner as "scratching an itch."

Student Activities

1. Have students clasp their hands together. Ask them whether they have the thumb of their left hand or their right hand on top, and whether this correlates with their understanding of which hemisphere of their brain is dominant.

2. Have students hold their index finger and thumb together on each hand, then touch the two hands together to form a small diamond between index fingers and thumbs. Have students focus on an object in the diamond with both eyes open. Close first one eye and then the other without moving your head or hands. Determine which eye is dominant based on the eye that is actually focused on the object in the diamond.

3. Provide full and cross-sectional drawings of the brain for students to color and label.

4. Have the students draw and label the ventricles of the brain.

5. Provide reflex hammers and the instructions for producing the patellar and Achilles stretch reflexes, and the plantar reflex. Have students work in pairs to produce and observe these reflexes.

6. Have students measure their heart and breathing rates at rest. Without giving any warning, blow a shrill whistle to produce a startle response in the members of the class. Have students retest their heart and breathing rates. Then, initiate a class discussion on the effects of the sympathetic division of the autonomic nervous system by asking students to indicate which of their body organs were affected by the sound and what the organ response was.

7. Have students practice conducting cranial nerve tests.

8. Ask students to bring in articles from magazines or from the Internet that discuss research about sex differences in the brain. Discuss the articles in class.

9. Ask students to bring in articles from magazines or from the Internet that discuss the role of neurotransmitters in depression and in brain disorders such as Parkinson's, or articles that cover the effect that common street drugs have upon them. Discuss the various articles.

10. Show a ten-minute clip of *Lorenzo's Oil* or *Regarding Henry* and engage the students in a class discussion.

11. Have students test their reaction times before and after exercise. Discuss results.

MULTIMEDIA

See page 182 for a listing of media distributors.

1. *Alzheimer's: The Tangled Mind* (FHS; 23 min., 1997, VHS, DVD). Discusses breakthroughs in treatments for this debilitating disease.

2. *The Brain* (FHS; 20 min., 1995, VHS, DVD). From *The New Living Body* series, this program uses combinations of CT, MRI, and advanced surgical techniques to explore what is known about how the brain works.

3. *Brain and Nervous System: Your Information Highway* (FHS; 31 min., 1998, VHS, DVD). From *The Human Body: Systems at Work*, this program explores the brain and nervous system using the analogy of computers and the Internet.

4. *Lorenzo's Oil* (136 min., 1992). A film that documents the real-life story of Lorenzo Odone, who has a rare myelin-degenerating terminal disease called adrenoleukodystrophy (ALD), and his parents (Augusto and Michaela) who collide with doctors, scientists, and support groups in their quest to develop an oil from the combination of two fats extracted from olive oil and rapeseed oil to prevent the body's production of very long chain fatty acids whose buildup leads to demyelination. See http://www.myelin.org; readily available at most national chain video distribution stores.

5. *Stress, Trauma, and the Brain* (FHS; 57 min., 1999, VHS, DVD). Three-part video program that highlights the fight-or-flight mechanism in modern living, the pioneer work in brain imaging, and an exploration of closed head injury, now known as "the silent epidemic."

6. *I Have Tourette's But Tourette's Doesn't Have Me* (HBO; 27 min., 2005, DVD). This documentary explores the lives of children suffering from Tourette's Syndrome. In the film, a wide variety of tics and the ways that the kids cope with being "different" are explored.

SOFTWARE

1. *The Animated Brain* (BV; Win/Mac). Emphasizes the relationships between brain structure and behavior.

2. *The Cranial Nerves* (ICON; Win/Mac). Offers realistic, 3-D illustrations and photographs to teach the various characteristics and properties of the twelve cranial nerves.

3. *The Graphic Brain* (BV; Windows). Assists in developing a functional approach to 3-D anatomy of the CNS.

4. *InterActive Physiology 9-System Suite* (ADAM, BC; Win/Mac). Interactive software that explores the physiology of the nervous system.

5. *Sylvius 2.0: Fundamentals of Human Neural Structure* (SIN; Win/Mac). Uses colorized graphics, animation, and cross-sectional diagrams to examine the anatomy of the brain.

6. *Synaptic Transmission in the CNS* (IM; Win). Details the process of synaptic transmission in the central nervous system.

Special Senses

CHAPTER SUMMARY

The special senses keep us informed as to what is going on in our external world. Sense receptors are found in large, complex sensory organs like the eye or in localized clusters of receptors like the taste buds. This chapter focuses on each of the sensory organs individually, but also seeks to show us that the way we experience the world is, in fact, a blending of the effects of various stimuli.

The eye is the first of the sense organs to be presented. External eye anatomy is described first, along with its accessory structures such as eyelids, eyelashes, eye muscles, and the lacrimal apparatus. Next, internal eye structures like the wall of the eyeball, retina, lens, and humors are explained in detail. The refractive properties of the eye are presented next, followed by a description of the visual pathways to the brain and an explanation of eye reflexes.

The ear and its role in hearing and balance are discussed next in the chapter. The anatomy of the ear begins with the outer ear structures, followed by the middle and inner ear. The mechanism of hearing is explained in detail, with emphasis on the role of the hair cells found in the organ of Corti. The mechanisms of equilibrium, the fifth sense, are then presented. Static and dynamic equilibrium are described and differentiated, followed by a discussion of some of the more common hearing and equilibrium deficits.

The chemical senses of taste and smell are presented in the final section. Chemoreceptors involved in both taste and smell respond to chemicals in solution. In the case of smell, olfactory receptors located in the roof of each nasal cavity are sensitive to a wide range of chemicals, whereas taste receptors located in the oral cavity are identified as five basic types: sweet, sour, bitter, umami, and salty. Because taste and smell are linked by their response to chemicals and enzymatic reactions in solution, students quickly understand the reason why food seems to have no taste when they have a cold, and why salty food tastes sweet when held in the mouth for 20–30 seconds. This and other examples of homeostatic imbalance related to the special senses are discussed at the end of the chapter.

SUGGESTED LECTURE OUTLINE

PART I: THE EYE AND VISION (pp. 281–294)

I. ANATOMY OF THE EYE (pp. 281–290)
   A. External and Accessory Structures
      1. Eyelids and Eyelashes
      2. Conjunctiva
      3. Extrinsic Eye Muscles
      4. Lacrimal Apparatus
   B. Internal Structures: The Eyeball
      1. Layers Forming the Wall of the Eyeball
         a. Fibrous Layer—Sclera and Cornea
         b. Vascular Layer—Choroid, Iris, and Pupil
         c. Sensory Layer—Retina
      2. Lens

TEACHING TIP

Point out that cones are sensitive to blue, green, and red wavelengths, not yellow, red, and blue, as students often expect. Discuss this in relation to traffic lights and the difficulty that a color blind person might have in differentiating between red and green.

II. PATHWAY OF LIGHT THROUGH THE EYE AND LIGHT REFRACTION (p. 290)
   A. Refraction
   B. Accommodation

III. VISUAL FIELDS AND VISUAL PATHWAYS TO THE BRAIN (pp. 290–291)

IV. EYE REFLEXES (pp. 291–294)
   A. Convergence
   B. Photopupillary
   C. Accommodation Pupillary

PART II: THE EAR: HEARING AND BALANCE (pp. 294–300)

I. ANATOMY OF THE EAR (pp. 294–296)
   A. External (Outer) Ear
      1. Pinna (Auricle)
      2. External Acoustic Meatus (Auditory Canal)
      3. Ceruminous Glands
      4. Tympanic Membrane (Eardrum)
   B. Middle Ear (Tympanic Cavity)
      1. Oval and Round Windows
      2. Pharyngotympanic (Auditory) Tube
      3. Ossicles
         a. Hammer (Malleus)
         b. Anvil (Incus)
         c. Stirrup (Stapes)
   C. Internal (Inner) Ear
      1. Bony (Osseous) Labyrinth
         a. Cochlea
         b. Vestibule
         c. Semicircular Canals

II. MECHANISMS OF EQUILIBRIUM (pp. 296–298)
   A. Static Equilibrium
   B. Dynamic Equilibrium

III. MECHANISMS OF HEARING (pp. 298–300)

IV. HEARING AND EQUILIBRIUM DEFICITS (p. 300)
   A. Deafness
      1. Conduction Deafness
      2. Sensorineural Deafness

PART III: CHEMICAL SENSES: TASTE AND SMELL (pp. 301–303)

I. OLFACTORY RECEPTORS AND THE SENSE OF SMELL (pp. 301–302)

II. TASTE BUDS AND THE SENSE OF TASTE (pp. 302–303)

MEDIA TIP

Sensation and Perception (FHS; 30 min., 2001). Illustrates how information about the world is gathered by sensory receptors, and is then transmitted to and interpreted by the brain.

PART IV: DEVELOPMENTAL ASPECTS OF THE SPECIAL SENSES (pp. 303–305)

    I. SIGHT
        A. Embryonic Development
           1. Strabismus
           2. Opthalmia Neonatorum
        B. Aging
           1. Presbyopia

    II. HEARING
        A. Otitis
        B. Presbycusis
        C. Otosclerosis

    III. CHEMICAL SENSES

KEY TERMS

accessory structures
accommodation
accommodation pupillary
  reflex
aqueous humor
auricle
basal cell
basilar membrane
bipolar cells
bony (osseous) labyrinth
cerumen (earwax)
ceruminous glands
chemoreceptors
choroid
ciliary body
ciliary zonule
circumvallate papillae
cochlea
cochlear duct
cochlear nerve
color blindness
commissure (canthus)
cones
conjunctiva
convergence
cornea
crista ampullaris
cupula
dynamic equilibrium
emmetropia
endolymph
external acoustic meatus
external (outer) ear

extrinsic (external) eye
  muscles
eyelashes
eyelids
facial nerve
fibrous layer
fovea centralis
fundus
fungiform papillae
ganglion cells
glossopharyngeal
glossopharyngeal nerve
gustatory cells
gustatory hairs
hair cells
hammer (malleus, anvil,
  incus)
hyperopia
internal ear
iris
lacrimal apparatus
lacrimal canaliculi
lacrimal glands
lacrimal sac
lateral commissure
  (canthus)
lysozyme
maculae
mechanoreceptors
medial commissure
  (canthus)
membranous labyrinth
middle ear (tympanic cavity)

myopia
nasolacrimal duct
neural layer
olfactory filaments
olfactory hairs
olfactory nerve
olfactory receptors
olfactory receptor cells
optic chiasma
optic disc (blind spot)
optic nerve
optic radiation
optic tracts
organ of Corti
ossicles
otolithic har membrane
otoliths
oval window
papillae
papillary reflex
perilymph
pharyngotympanic
  (auditory) tube
photopupillary reflex
photoreceptors
pigmented layer
pinna
presbyopia
presbycusis
pupil
refracted
refraction
retina

rods
round window
sclera
scleral venous sinus (canal
    of Schlemm)
semicircular canals
sensory layer
special senses
special sense receptors

spiral organ of Corti (hair
    cells)
static equilibrium
stirrup (stapes)
tarsal glands
taste buds
taste pore
tectorial membrane
tympanic membrane
    (eardrum)

vascular layer
vagus
vestibular apparatus
vestibular nerve
vestibule
visual acuity
vitreous body
vitreous humor

LECTURE HINTS

1. Use dissectible eye models during presentation of eye anatomy to help students visualize the structures of the eye as they are presented.

   Key point: It is important to emphasize the layering of the tunics and other structures of the eye prior to discussing the mechanisms involved in refraction.

2. Point out the location of the lacrimal gland in the upper, outer canthus of the eye. Students frequently think that tears come from the lacrimal canal itself and are generally surprised to find that they wash across the eye, then empty into the lacrimal canal at the lower, inner canthus.

   Key point: This is a good opportunity to discuss the protective properties of lysozymes in tears, as well as to talk about other benefits of tears, including lubrication and emotional release.

3. Discuss conjunctivitis, or pinkeye. Most students have seen the redness associated with this condition and it helps them visualize the location of this mucous membrane.

   Key point: The conjunctiva is a delicate mucous membrane that lines the eyelids and covers the anterior portion of the eyeball.

4. Point out that cones are sensitive to blue, green, and red wavelengths, not yellow, red, and blue, as students often expect. Discuss this in relation to traffic lights and the difficulty that a color blind person might have in differentiating between red and green.

   Key point: Colorblindness exhibits itself in a variety of ways, depending on the cones that are absent. Note that it is an X-linked characteristic of the 23rd chromosome, thus it occurs primarily in males. An XY male can manifest color blindness while receiving a defective X chromosome from his mother, whereas an XX female must receive a defective X from both her mother and father to manifest color blindness.

5. Explain why checking for pupils of equal diameter and documenting PERLA (Pupils Equal and Reactive to Light and Accommodation) are standard neurological signs.

   Key point: Pupils that are unequal in diameter or that fail to adjust their shape when a bright light is flashed in them can be indicative of such conditions as cerebral hemorrhage, which puts pressure on the optic nerve.

6. Students enjoy a detailed discussion of the principles of accommodation, particularly related to the conditions of myopia and hyperopia with which they are familiar. Point out that myopia means "near vision" (i.e., the person is able to see close-up), and hyperopia means "far vision" (i.e., the person is able to see distances). Also explain that age leads to a specific type of hyperopia called presbyopia, or old-age vision. The often-read novel, *Lord of the Flies*, describes a near-sighted boy who started fires with his glasses. However, a light-dispersing concave lens to correct myopia could never

start a fire, as only a convex (thick in the middle) lens to correct for hyperopia could concentrate light rays to start a fire.

Key point: An eyeball that is either too long or too short, or a lens that does not accommodate well, are homeostatic imbalances resulting in conditions outside the normal emmetropia.

7. Relate to students that because incoming light is refracted by a combination of both the cornea and the lens, laser eye surgery to correct myopia and hyperopia only needs to involve adjustment of the curvature of the outer cornea (not the lens).

    Key point: It is much easier to surgically reduce the curvature of the cornea to correct for myopia than to build up the curvature of the cornea to correct for hyperopia. Surgical correction for myopia has been done for a longer time and is thus more reliable than correction for hyperopia.

8. Discuss corneal and lens transplants with students and explain their high success rate.

    Key point: Because both of these structures are avascular, they are not as easily rejected by the body.

9. Explain that the eye and the ear are not only receptors for light and sound impulses, but are also energy transducers because they convert light and sound energy into the electrical energy of an action potential.

    Key point: It is important for students to understand that it is the electrical impulse that is interpreted by the brain, and if the visual and auditory interpretive areas of the brain are damaged, the person will neither see nor hear despite functioning sensory receptors.

10. Use dissectible ear models during the presentation of ear anatomy to help students visualize the structures of the ear as they are presented.

    Key point: It is helpful to students to visualize the structures of the ear that are important for hearing and those that are important for equilibrium.

11. Discuss how hearing aids work to correct hearing deficiencies. Explain to the students why all forms of deafness cannot be corrected in this fashion.

    Key point: Once students understand how hearing occurs, they can appreciate how a hearing aid helps with sound transmission.

12. Discuss the auditory (eustachian) tube and its normal role in pressure equalization. Students are quite familiar with the "pop" of their eardrum that precedes improved hearing when changing altitude in a car or a plane or scuba diving. Explain how chewing gum or yawning brings this about. Also explain the physiological and medical implications related to insertion of PE (Pressure Equalizing) tubes in children.

    Key point: Yawning or chewing gum forces air into the auditory tube, which balances the pressure between the outer and middle ear. In children, this tube is shorter and more horizontal, often leading to frequent middle ear infections (otitis media). Insertion of PE tubes helps drain the middle ear and keeps the pressure equal until the auditory tubes elongate and become more vertical as the child ages.

13. Discuss some of the more common conditions leading to vertigo (dizziness), such as Ménière's syndrome, otitis media, motion sickness, and diplopia.

    Key point: Students are amazed by the variety of conditions that can result from a homeostatic imbalance of the inner ear, and other structures important in balance and equilibrium.

14. Clearly differentiate between static equilibrium and dynamic equilibrium, as students frequently think of "balance" as a single mechanism.

Key point: Static equilibrium helps to keep our body informed of the position of our head in space (e.g., up or down), whereas dynamic equilibrium helps us to orient ourselves to the three planes of space in which our bodies move. They act together to keep us balanced and "on an even keel."

15. Ask students to describe a scent that triggers a specific memory for them, such as the smell of newly baked bread or a certain perfume. Note the connection between the olfactory senses and long-term memory. For example, students can learn anatomy from interactive dissection websites such as frogguts.com, but it may not reside in the long-term memory as well as actual "live" dissections because the wonderful smell of the specimen is absent.

Key point: The olfactory senses have a strong link to memory. This is an excellent example of how the brain interprets sensory input and even commits some of the messages to our memory banks.

16. Make reference to a "bitter pill," and point out that it is the taste buds' ability to detect alkaloids that accounts for this taste. Further explain that sour within the chemistry of cooking is a result of hydrogen ion detection (acidity), salty is metal detection, and sweet is, of course, sugar detection.

Key point: Correlating taste sensations with their chemical counterparts helps students to understand the way in which these various sensations can blend to make eating such an enjoyable experience.

17. *Umami* is a newly identified taste sensation that some Japanese researchers claim is separate from the commonly known four taste sensations of sweet, sour, salty, and bitter. Currently, there is disagreement in the scientific community as to whether umami should be given the same relative importance as the other four taste buds.

Key point: There is still controversy over the relative importance of this newly discovered taste bud.

TRANSPARENCIES/MEDIA MANAGER INDEX

ANSWERS TO END OF CHAPTER REVIEW QUESTIONS

Questions appear on pp. 307–308

Multiple Choice

1. d (p. 302)
2. b, c (p. 302; Figure 8.18)
3. b, d (p. 302)
4. c (Table 7.1 in Chapter 7)
5. b (p. 289)
6. a, c (p. 290; Figure 8.9)
7. a, b, c, d (pp. 291, 293)
8. a, c (pp. 295–298)
9. b (pp. 298, 300)
10. a, b, c (pp. 298, 300; Figure 8.16)

Short Answer Essay

11. *Lacrimal glands:* Saline solution and lysozyme. *Tarsal and ciliary glands:* Oil. *Conjunctiva:* Mucus. (p. 282)

12. The lacrimal secretions drain via the nasolacrimal duct into the nasal passages. (p. 282)

13. Internal structures: See Figure 8.4 (p. 285). Functions: *Lens:* Major focusing apparatus of the eye. *Retina:* Photoreceptive (light-sensitive) layer. *Choroid:* The nutritive (vascular) coat of the eye. *Ciliary body and ciliary zonule:* Smooth muscle structure that regulates the shape of the lens for focusing. *Iris:* Smooth muscle structure that controls the amount of light entering the eye. *Sclera:* Protective (fibrous) coat. *Cornea:* Transparent part of the sclera that allows light to enter the eye. *Pupil:* opening through which light passes. *Aqueous humor:* helps maintain intraocular pressure and provides nutrients to the lens and cornea. *Scleral venous sinus:* reabsorbs aqueous humor into the bloodstream. *Vitreous humor:* helps prevent the eyeball from collapsing inward. *Fovea centralis:* contains only cones and is the area with the greatest visual acuity. *Optic nerve:* transmits nerve impulses to the optic cortex. *Optic disc:* blind spot where optic nerve leaves eyeball. *Central artery and vein of the retina:* provides nutrients and removes waste products. (pp. 283–289)

14. Superior, inferior, lateral, and medial rectus muscles; and the superior and inferior oblique muscles. (Figure 8.3)

15. *Vitreous humor:* Posterior to lens; reinforces eyeball. *Aqueous humor:* Anterior to lens; reinforces eyeball and provides nutrients to the avascular lens and cornea. (p. 289)

16. The portion of the retina with no photoreceptors because it is the site at which the optic nerve leaves the eyeball. Light focused on this spot is not converted into vision or photoreception. (p. 286)

17. Iris. (pp. 283–284)

18. A small pit in the retinal layer that contains cones only is located lateral to the optic disk in each eye. Anything that must be viewed critically (discriminative vision) is focused on the fovea because it is the area of greatest visual acuity. (p. 286)

19. Cornea to aqueous humor, through pupil to aqueous humor to lens to vitreous humor to retina. The path of light goes through the ganglion cells first, then the bipolar cells before stimulating the rods and cones. (p. 290; Figure 8.4)

20. Photoreceptors (rods and cones) to bipolar cells to ganglion cells to optic nerve through the optic chiasma to optic tract to thalamus to visual cortex in the occipital lobe via the optic radiation. (pp. 284–285)

21. *Hyperopia:* Farsightedness. The individual has no problem with distance vision, which requires no accommodation; in near vision, however, the image is focused behind the retina because of a lazy lens or foreshortened eyeball. *Myopia:* Nearsightedness. The individual has no problem with near vision, but in distance vision, the image is focused anterior to the retina because of an overly strong lens, an elongated eyeball, or a cornea that is too curved. *Emmetropia:* Normal vision. The image is focused correctly on the retina in both near and far vision. (p. 292)

22. As one ages, the lens loses its elasticity, causing it to focus less acutely for close vision. Hyperopia. (p. 304)

23. When two (or more) different cone types are stimulated simultaneously the color perceived is intermediate (in wavelength or light) between them. Thus, stimulation of red and green cones produces the sensation of yellow; when all cones are simultaneously excited, we perceive white (all colors = white). (pp. 286, 288)

24. The ophthalmoscopic examination allows the examiner to determine the condition of the retina. Many blood vessel problems (e.g., high blood pressure, diabetes mellitus) can be detected early from such an examination; hence, it is extremely important in diagnosis. Degeneration of the optic nerve and retina can also be detected early. (p. 289)

25. Close vision involves both convergence and accommodation. Convergence requires the activation of the external eye muscles (primarily the medial recti) and the ciliary body within the eye. Distance vision requires none of these specific muscle actions because this position is when the eye is at rest. (pp. 290–291, 293)

26. *Outer ear:* The auricle (pinna) has no function in humans. The external acoustic meatus conducts sound vibrations from the external environment to the tympanic membrane (eardrum), which is involved in hearing only. *Middle ear:* The ossicles, which span the tympanic cavity, conduct vibrations received from the tympanic membrane to the oval window and fluids of the inner ear. The pharyngotympanic tube allows middle ear pressures to be equalized with those of the atmosphere. Involved in hearing only. *Inner ear:* Semicircular canals, vestibule, and cochlea are all part of the bony labyrinth. The semicircular canals and vestibule function in equilibrium maintenance, whereas the cochlea functions in hearing. (pp. 294–296; Figure 8.12)

27. Eardrum to ossicles (hammer to anvil to stapes) to oval window to perilymph in the bony cochlea to the membranous labyrinth to endolymph in cochlear duct to basilar membrane and organ of Corti. (pp. 298–300; Figure 8.16)

28. *Conductive deafness* arises from any interference with the conduction of vibrations from the outer to the inner ear due to ear wax accumulations, otitis media, fusion of the ossicles, or pressure imbalance between the middle and outer ear. (p. 300)

29. Inner ear vestibular apparatus (maculae in the vestibule and cristae ampullaris in the semicircular canals), eyes, proprioceptors of muscles and tendons. (pp. 296–298)

30. Gustatory cells. In the taste buds—primarily in papillae on the tongue, but also in the buccal mucosa and on the palate and pharynx mucosae. (pp. 302–303)

31. Sweet, sour, bitter, salty, and umami. (p. 302)

32. In the superiormost mucosa of the olfactory passageways. This is a poor site functionally because most air (which carries odors) passes inferior to this site. (p. 301)

33. Presbyopia (basically age-related farsightedness), presbycusis (sensineural deafness due to cumulative hearing insults), and dulled sense of taste and smell (these receptors are replaced more slowly). (pp. 304–305)

34. Of all the special senses, vision requires the most "learning" as babies can initially only focus on near objects. The eye must first enlarge, then external muscle coordination must develop, as must focusing ability and color vision. Depth perception develops relatively late, maturing just before school age. (p. 304)

ANSWERS TO CRITICAL THINKING AND CLINICAL APPLICATION QUESTIONS

35. His hearing receptors in the organ of Corti are being damaged (and are dying) by the excessively loud noise; sensineural deafness is occurring. (p. 300)

36. The children probably had conjunctivitis, caused by bacteria or viruses; it is highly contagious and could be easily transmitted between children at the day care center. (p. 282)

37. High intraocular pressure generally indicates that the patient has glaucoma. (p. 289)

38. The left optic tract carries all the visual information from the right half of the visual field. Thus, Lionel cannot see the right half of visual space. (p. 291)

39. The surgeon was trying to remove the tiny stapes from the oval window, to which it had rigidly fused, causing conduction deafness. (pp. 304–305) Such delicate surgery is difficult because the stapes is so tiny. Here, it proved impossible to remove this ossicle neatly enough to clear the oval window and restore hearing.

40. Myopia refers to nearsightedness. Parallel rays from objects far away are focused in front of her retina. She will need a concave corrective lens to diverge these rays so that they will converge on the retina. (p. 292)

41. Rods are very light sensitive photoreceptors used in dim light. Cones require intense light. Focusing hard on the star focuses light on the fovea centralis which only has cones, no rods. Perhaps the starlight is not strong enough to stimulate the cones. Vision at night relies heavily on rods. (pp. 284–286)

42. Static equilibrium receptors (maculae) report the position of the head with respect to gravitational pull changes when the body is standing still as in the elevator. Otoliths responding to changes in gravity sensation bent hair cells within the organ of Corti during elevator "drop" and continued on after the elevator stopped. (pp. 296–297)

43. Ms. Miniver's immune disorder reduced sensitivity within her taste bud receptors by the lack of salivary fluid available to mix with her ingested food. Gustatory cells are only able to respond to chemicals dissolved in saliva. Even the choicest cut of prime rib will not taste good to someone who has dry mouth. (p. 302)

CLASSROOM DEMONSTRATIONS AND STUDENT ACTIVITIES

Classroom Demonstrations

1. Film(s) or other media of choice.

2. Use 3-D models of the eye and ear to demonstrate the structural characteristics of these special sense organs.

3. Use models to show the six eye muscles and the movements controlled by each.

4. Dissect a cow's or sheep's eye so that students can observe the internal eye structures. Point out how fragile the retina is and draw attention to the fact that it is attached at a single point—the optic disk. Also, show the lens to the students and discuss how it would look with cataracts. Point out the tapedum lucidum and explain why it is not present in humans.

5. Spray cologne with a light citrus-based or "woodsy" scent into the air, and ask students to raise their hands when they first smell it. Then, go on to other matters, and approximately 5 minutes later, ask how many can still smell the cologne. Use this as a jumping-off point for your discussion on adaptation of the sensory apparatus.

Student Activities

1. To help explain that the fovea centralis is the area of sharpest vision, have the students all look at the same picture in their textbook. Ask them to notice any adjusting they do to bring the picture into sharper focus, such as moving the book or the position of their head. Point out that the fovea centralis exclusively contains cones.

2. Perform selected vision tests, including visual acuity using Snellen's chart and color deficiency using Ishihara's color plates.

3. Provide the students with a list of the refracting parts of the eye. Have them rearrange the list to correspond with the sequence through which light would travel as it moves from the outside to the interior of the eye, prior to stimulating the rods and cones.

4. Provide the students with a list of the vibrating parts of the ear. Have them rearrange the list to correspond with the sequence through which sound would travel as it moves from the outside to the interior of the ear, prior to stimulating the hair cells.

5. To examine the important connection between smell and taste in the taste and identification of foods, select one student to be the subject in the following experiment. The student closes his or her eyes and pinches the nostrils closed. Then he or she should attempt to distinguish mozzarella cheese from a hard-boiled egg white (cut into similar sized pieces) by taste alone, taking a sip of water between samplings. If the attempt is unsuccessful, the nostrils should be released and the test conducted again. Other foods also work well, such as apples and potatoes.

6. Have students wipe their tongues dry and place different food items on the dry surface. Measure the amount of time it takes to taste the substance depending on the region of the tongue that the food item is placed.

7. Display examples of optical illusions on the walls around the room and give students an opportunity to study and explain them.

8. Have your students answer the following question to demonstrate their understanding of how to select appropriate equipment and technology:

   Brandon has been wearing glasses since the third grade and is now 19 years old. He is being referred for possible Lasik, or laser eye surgery, which may provide near perfect vision for him. He is very excited about the prospect of throwing his glasses away! This is an example of recent advances in medical technology; what are some other examples?

   A. The Human Genome Project
   B. Tele-medicine
   C. Magnetic resonance imaging
   D. All of the above*

9. Have students examine several pairs of eyeglasses with respect to how thick or thin the corrective lenses are in the middle and estimate if the wearer is myopic or hyperopic, and how severe their correction is. Identify which lens correction would most effectively start a fire.

10. Show a ten-minute clip of *Wild Hearts Can't Be Broken* and engage the students in a class discussion.

MULTIMEDIA

See page 182 for a listing of media distributors.

1. *Cataracts and Vision Problems* (FHS; 18 min., 1994, VHS, DVD). Explains what cataracts are and how surgery works to improve vision, in most cases.

2. *The Senses* (FHS; 20 min., 1995, VHS, DVD). From *The New Living Body* series, this program demonstrates how the senses of sight and balance operate, as well as how they interact with each other.

3. *The Miracle Worker* (MGM; 106 min., 1962, DVD). The true story of deaf-blind Helen Keller and her teacher, Anne Sullivan, who taught her to communicate.

SOFTWARE

1. *Exploring Perception* (TW; Win/Mac). Explores such phenomena as apparent movement, pitch perception, sensory adaptation, and visual and auditory illusions.

The Endocrine System

CHAPTER SUMMARY

The endocrine system contains some of the most elegant and mysterious mechanisms of all the body systems. Considered to be the second great homeostatic system of the body (after the faster-acting nervous system), the endocrine system controls reproduction, growth and development, body defenses, metabolic processes, and blood chemistry. Through the use of hormones, the endocrine system maintains homeostatic balance within the body in a relatively leisurely and profound way. Hormones circulate in the blood until reaching the target organs upon which they are designed to act, where they bind with the awaiting cells and immediately begin to influence the internal machinery of those cells.

In this chapter, the mechanisms of hormone action are discussed first, differentiating between the actions of steroidal and nonsteroidal hormones. Next, the negative feedback mechanisms that control hormone release are presented. Hormonal, humoral, and neural stimuli are all explained through the use of selected examples. Endocrine glands are further described as ductless glands that release their hormones into blood or lymphatic fluid, in comparison to exocrine glands, which release their products directly into ducts on the epithelial surface.

In the final sections of this chapter, the major endocrine organs and their hormones' main actions and regulatory functions are presented. The hypothalamus, which also plays an important role in nervous system functioning, is noted for its major role in endocrine control based upon its relationship with the pituitary gland. The complexity of the pituitary gland, with its separate anterior and posterior lobes, is then described. The thyroid is presented next for its role in both metabolism and blood calcium levels, followed by a discussion of the counterbalancing action of the parathyroid glands in blood calcium regulation. The hormones of the adrenal glands, both cortical and medullar portions, are described in relation to their roles in long- and short-term stress-response. The islet cells of the pancreas and the hormones they produce are then discussed, along with the homeostatic imbalance of diabetes mellitus. The lesser-understood roles of the pineal and thymus hormones precede the section on the hormones of the ovaries and testes, and finally, the hormones produced by other tissues pocketed throughout the body, as well as the hormones produced by the placenta, are discussed. The major developmental aspects of the endocrine system, including its role in menopause, conclude the chapter.

SUGGESTED LECTURE OUTLINE

I. THE ENDOCRINE SYSTEM AND HORMONE FUNCTION—AN OVERVIEW (pp. 310–313)
    A. The Chemistry of Hormones (pp. 310–311)
        1. Amino Acid-Based Molecules
        2. Steroid-Based Hormones
        3. Prostaglandins
    B. Mechanisms of Hormone Action (p. 311)
        1. Direct Gene Activation
        2. Second-Messenger System

TEACHING TIP

Present numerous examples of homeostatic imbalance as related to the endocrine system. Use a series of opposites to help clarify the point, such as hypothyroidism vs. hyperthyroidism and gigantism vs. dwarfism.

C. Control of Hormone Release (pp. 311–313)
  1. Endocrine Gland Stimuli
     a. Hormonal Stimuli
     b. Humoral Stimuli
     c. Neural Stimuli

II. THE MAJOR ENDOCRINE ORGANS (pp. 313–332; Table 9.1)
  A. Pituitary Gland (pp. 314–319)
    1. Hormones of the Anterior Pituitary
       a. Growth Hormone (GH)
          i. Homeostatic Imbalances
             (1) Pitiutary Dwarfism
             (2) Gigantism
             (3) Acromegaly
       b. Prolactin (PRL)—Breast Milk Production
       c. Adrenocorticotropic Hormone (ACTH)
       d. Thyroid-Stimulating Hormone (TSH)
       e. Gonadotropic Hormones—Begin at Puberty
          i. Follicle-Stimulating Hormone (FSH)
          ii. Luteinizing Hormone (LH)
    2. Pituitary-Hypothalamus Relationship
    3. Hormones of the Posterior Pituitary
       a. Oxytocin
       b. Antidiuretic Hormone (ADH)
          i. Homeostatic Imbalances
             (1) Diabetes Insipidus
  B. Thyroid Gland (pp. 319–321)
    1. Thyroid Hormones
       a. Thyroxine (T_4)
       b. Triiodothyronine (T_3)
       c. Homeostatic Imbalances
          i. Goiters
          ii. Cretinism
          iii. Myxedema
          iv. Graves' disease
    2. Calcitonin—released in response to high blood calcium to enhance bone calcium deposition
  C. Parathyroid Glands (p. 321)
    1. Parathyroid Hormone (PTH)
       a. PTH Hyposecretion—Tetany
       b. PTH Hyposecretion—Bone Wasting and Fractures
  D. Adrenal Glands (pp. 322–326)
    1. Hormones of the Adrenal Cortex
       a. Mineralocorticoids—Aldosterone
       b. Glucocorticoids—Cortisone and Cortisol
       c. Sex Hormones—Androgens and Some Estrogens
       d. Homeostatic Imbalances
          i. Addison's Disease
          ii. Hyperaldosteronism

MEDIA TIP

Homeostasis (FHS; 20 min., 1995). From the *New Living Body* series, this program examines homeostasis from many aspects, including the role hormones play in the process.

iii. Cushing's Syndrome
iv. Masculinization
2. Hormones of the Adrenal Medulla
a. Epinephrine
b. Norepinephrine
E. Pancreatic Islets (pp. 326–328)
1. Insulin
2. Glucagon
3. Homeostatic Imbalance
a. Diabetes Mellitus
F. Pineal Gland (p. 329)
1. Melatonin
G. Thymus Gland (p. 329)
1. Thymosin
H. Gonads (pp. 329–332)
1. Hormones of the Ovaries
a. Estrogens
b. Progesterone
2. Hormones of the Testes
a. Androgens—Testosterone

III. OTHER HORMONE-PRODUCING TISSUES AND
ORGANS (p. 332; Table 9.2)
A. Placenta (p. 332)
1. Human Chorionic Gonadotropin (hCG)
2. Human Placental Lactogen (hPL)
3. Relaxin

IV. DEVELOPMENTAL ASPECTS OF THE ENDOCRINE
SYSTEM (pp. 332, 335)
A. Menopause (p. 332)
B. Aging (pp. 332, 335)

KEY TERMS

acrosome	dilation stage	fertilization
afterbirth	ductus deferens	fetus
alveolar glands	ectoderm	fimbriae
amnion	ejaculation	follicle cells
ampulla	ejaculatory duct	foreskin
areola	embryo	fundus
blastocyst	endoderm	gametes
body	endometrium	glans penis
broad ligament	epididymis	gonads
bulbourethral glands	erectile tissue	Graafian follicle
cervix	erection	greater vestibular glands
chorionic vesicle	estrogens	human chorionic
chorionic villi	expulsion stage	gonadotropin (hCG)
cleavage	external genitalia	hymen
clitoris	fallopian tubes	implantation
corpus luteum	false labor	inner cell mass

labia majora	ovum	seminiferous tubules
labia minora	parturition	shaft
labor	penis	sperm
lactating	perimetrium	spermatic cord
lactiferous ducts	perineum	spermatids
luteinizing hormone (LH)	placenta	spermatogenesis
mammary glands	placental stage	spermatogonia
meiosis	polar body	spermiogenesis
membranous urethra	pregnancy	spongy (penile) urethra
menarche	prepuce	suspensory ligaments
menopause	primary oocytes	testosterone
menstrual cycle	primary sex organs	trophoblast
mesoderm	primary spermatocyte	umbilical cord
mons pubis	progesterone	urethra
myometrium	prostate	uterine cycle
nipple	prostatic urethra	uterine tubes
oocyte	puberty	uterosacral ligament
oogenesis	relaxin	uterus
oogonia	reproductive system	vagina
ova	round ligament	vas deferens
ovarian cycle	scrotum	vesicular follicle
ovarian follicles	secondary oocyte	vestibule
ovarian ligaments	secondary sex characteristics	vulva
ovaries	semen	zygote
ovulation	seminal vesicles	

LECTURE HINTS

1. Describe the process of hormone attachment to its target organ as a lock-and-key mechanism, comparable to that discussed in previous chapters.

   Key point: In order for the cells of target organs to respond to a particular hormone, the hormone must attach to protein receptors on the target cell's surface (i.e., there must be a natural "fit"). For example, antidiuretic hormone (ADH or vasopressin) will have no effect on the liver heart, etc., but will only influence the kidneys since they have receptor sites for antidiuretic hormone.

2. Stress the anatomical and functional relationship between the nervous system and the endocrine system. Explain that although the nervous system is often considered the primary controller, with the neuron acting as the "star," the endocrine system is equally important though more subtle in its approach.

   Key point: The nervous and endocrine systems work closely together to coordinate and direct the key activities within the human body. Neither system could do the work alone, and although their mechanisms are different, their work in combination is unmatched for its sophistication and homeostatic importance.

3. Point out that the endocrine system represents the best in homeostasis and negative feedback. Use examples such as the counterbalancing effect between calcitonin of the thyroid gland and parathormone of the parathyroid glands in blood calcium regulation.

   Key point: This is an excellent chapter to focus on negative feedback and how homeostatic imbalances can cause disease, since the examples are unusually clear and understandable.

4. Discuss tropic hormones and explain the many instances in which hormones from one endocrine gland stimulate the production of hormones from another endocrine gland, which then act on other body organs and tissues.

   Key point: This is one of the most intriguing aspects of the endocrine system, and one which warrants particular attention because of its significance to overall body function.

5. Present numerous examples of homeostatic imbalance as related to the endocrine system. Use a series of opposites to help clarify the point, such as hypothyroidism vs. hyperthyroidism and gigantism vs. dwarfism.

   Key point: Students can readily understand that too much or too little of a certain hormone might have opposite and often life-threatening effects. These examples help them to visualize the results of these types of hormonal imbalances.

6. Discuss oxytocin and its significance in labor, delivery, and milk ejection. Explain that an "IV Pit" (intravenous synthetic oxytocin, called Pitocin) would be administered when women ready for childbirth cannot dilate sufficiently. Also, reiterate the *positive feedback mechanism* that oxytocin can induce.

   Key point: Pitocin is regularly used in IV form, not only to induce labor, but also to hasten labor and to help the uterus regain its postpartum shape after delivery. This provides an excellent starting point for discussion of the medical and ethical issues involved in its use.

7. Spend extra time outlining the connection between the hypothalamus and the anterior and posterior pituitary gland. This is an excellent opportunity to again show the intimate connection between the nervous and endocrine systems.

   Key point: Students have often heard the pituitary referred to as the "master gland." Emphasize that although the anterior pituitary produces numerous hormones, it releases those hormones in response to *releasing* or *inhibiting hormones* from the hypothalamus. Further point out that the posterior pituitary *does not* make its own hormones, but rather, it releases hormones made by the hypothalamus. Present the case that perhaps the hypothalamus can also be considered the "master gland."

8. The two disparate functions of the adrenal glands warrant extra attention. Discussion of the steroidal hormones produced by the adrenal cortex provides an excellent opportunity to examine steroid use from exogenous sources. Persons who abuse anabolic steroids for athletic or appearance purposes are aging body tissues such as the liver at a much faster rate. Males may never again be able to endogenously produce a high enough sperm count to produce children even years after they stop taking exogenous testosterone. Steroid therapy, with its benefits and inherent dangers, opens the floor for a stimulating discussion. Presentation of the hormones of the adrenal medulla provides another opportunity to review the "fight-or-flight" response previously discussed with the nervous system. Also point out that the two-layer cortex/medulla structure of the adrenal glands will be seen in other organs of the body as well, such as the kidneys.

   Key point: A discussion of the functions of the adrenal glands helps to again emphasize the fine-tuned integration between the nervous and endocrine systems, as well as the body's delicate balancing act in maintaining homeostasis.

9. Compare and contrast *diabetes mellitus* and *diabetes insipidus* based on the endocrine gland and hormones involved with each, their unique causes, time of onset, and their similar as well as dissimilar symptoms. Point out that polyuria (excessive urination) and polydipsia (excessive thirst) are common to both, but that glucosuria is exclusive to diabetes mellitus. Also explain the physiological mechanism of diabetic coma.

Key point: Students are usually familiar with the condition of "diabetes" but often do not realize that there are two distinct conditions involved, caused by homeostatic imbalance of two separate endocrine glands. Point out that there are many undiagnosed diabetics in American society who are cutting years off their longevity by not getting appropriate treatment.

10. If asked what comes to mind when someone mentions "hormones," students will usually say they think of estrogen, or "female hormones." This provides an excellent starting point for discussion of estrogen and testosterone and their roles in sexual development and reproduction. It also provides an opportunity to emphasize that the sex hormones represent only a few of the large number of important hormones in the body.

    Key point: Despite the fact that estrogen is one of the more recognized hormones, it is also one of the most misunderstood, and even maligned. A discussion of what estrogen can and cannot do is often helpful in expanding students' understanding of this hormone. Explain that menopause and andropause (male menopause) are basically puberty in reverse.

11. Discuss circadian rhythms and melatonin's role in this mechanism.

    Key point: Although poorly understood, the hormones of the pineal gland, of which melatonin is key, play a fascinating role in regulating our sleep patterns and day-night cycle. Rapid airplane travel across several time zones upsets normal circadian rhythmicity.

12. Discuss the importance of testosterone for gender determination in embryo development. Explain the effects that can occur when too little testosterone or estrogen is present during development and puberty.

    Key point: Emphasize to students the large influence hormones have not only before birth but also for development of secondary sex characteristics, gamete production, and sex cell maturation.

13. Explain the use of synthetic or animal hormones to treat conditions such as dwarfism (GH) or diabetes mellitus (insulin).

    Key point: Discuss with students the developments in medicine that provide hormone alternatives when endocrine glands do not function properly.

14. List and explain the use of hormones in agricultural food production for human consumption (e.g., bovine growth hormone).

    Key point: Students are often unaware of the other sources of hormones they could put into their bodies from the food they eat. Explain that not all effects are yet known from eating food that has come from animals exposed to excess hormones.

15. Discuss the link between some types of breast cancer and estrogen.

    Key point: Explain to students that cancer cells can grow in response to hormone levels in our bodies.

16. Describe hormone replacement therapy (HRT) for postmenopausal women including both risks and benefits.

    Key point: Many students are familiar with this therapy and can better understand its use once they know how the endocrine system works to maintain homeostasis.

TRANSPARENCIES/MEDIA MANAGER INDEX

Figure 9.1   Mechanisms of hormone action

Figure 9.2   Endocrine gland stimuli

Figure 9.3   Location of the major endocrine organs of the body

Indicates images that are on the Media Manager only.

ANSWERS TO END OF CHAPTER REVIEW QUESTIONS

Questions appear on pp. 337–338

Multiple Choice

1. d (Figure 9.3)
2. b (pp. 310–311)
3. a, c (p. 318)
4. c (p. 323)
5. a, b, c, d (pp. 314–315, 323, 326)
6. a, b, c, d (pp. 318, 320, 322–324)
7. a, b, c (pp. 320, 322–323)
8. b (p. 323)
9. b (p. 319)

Short Answer Essay

10. (a) Nervous system control is extremely rapid (milliseconds to seconds), whereas endocrine control takes minutes to seven days to bring about its effects. (b) Nervous system communication is via electro-chemical impulses, whereas the endocrine system uses blood-borne chemical "messengers" (hormones). (c) The nervous system

controls short-term processes, such as stimulation of muscle contraction and glandular secretion, whereas the endocrine system controls processes that go on for long periods of time (sometimes continuously), such as growth and maturation, metabolism, and the functioning of the reproductive system. (p. 310)

11. The mixed endocrine organs are the pancreas and gonads. The purely endocrine glands are the anterior pituitary, hypothalamus, thyroid, parathyroid, adrenal, thymus, and pineal gland. (pp. 313–314)

12. A hormone is an amino acid or steroid-based chemical substance produced by endocrine organs and liberated to the blood. Hormones activate target organs in specific ways by regulating the metabolic activities of other cells. (pp. 310–311)

13. *Hormonal stimulation:* Stimulation by TSH and ACTH of the thyroid and adrenal cortex (respectively) to release their hormones. *Humoral stimulation:* Stimulation by high glucose levels to release insulin; stimulation by high blood calcium levels to release calcitonin. *Nerve stimulation:* Stimulation by sympathetic nerve fibers of adrenal medulla to release epinephrine (adrenalin) to the blood. (pp. 311–312; Figure 9.2)

14. *Negative feedback,* the process by which the products of a chemical reaction "feedback" and inhibit their further synthesis, regulates the activity of all endocrine glands controlled by anterior-pituitary-tropic hormones, as well as those controlled by blood levels of nonhormonal substances. Most simply, when a hormone is at low levels in the blood, its synthesis is stimulated either by the release of an anterior-pituitary-tropic hormone (e.g., thyroxine production and release are stimulated by TSH) or by changing blood levels of certain substances (e.g., PTH production is stimulated by low blood calcium levels and insulin release is stimulated by high levels of blood glucose). As blood levels of the stimulated hormones increase, the stimulus substance is either turned off (in the case of tropic hormones) or ceases to exist (because hormonal action results in a "correction" of the blood levels of the trigger substances). Once there is no stimulus, the previously stimulated endocrine organ decreases its hormone output, and hormone levels drop once more. The cycle repeats again and again as hormone blood levels increase and decrease via negative feedback loops. (p. 311)

15. Cells that respond to a specific hormone are known as target cells. A hormone's target cells have plasma membrane receptors or internal receptors that are able to bind that particular hormone. Tissue cells from organs that are not target cells of a particular hormone lack those particular receptors and will not be affected by that particular circulating hormone. (p. 311)

16. *Anterior pituitary:* Protrudes from the inferior surface of the brain, encased in the sella turcica of the sphenoid bone. Produces: (a) GH, which causes overall body growth but particularly skeletal and muscular growth; a lack during childhood leads to pituitary dwarfism; over-secretion produces gigantism (children) or acromegaly (adult). (b) Prolactin (PRL), which stimulates lactation in females; an excess leads to inappropriate lactation. (c) Gonadotropic hormones FSH and LH, which stimulate the production of ova/estrogen/progesterone in females and sperm/testosterone in males; a lack results in sterility. (d) TSH, which stimulates the production of thyroxine by the thyroid gland; a lack results in hypothyroidism (cretinism in children, myxedema in adults); hypersecretion can result in hyperthyroidism and produce Graves' disease. (e) ACTH, which regulates the activity of the adrenal cortex; hypersecretion results in Cushing's syndrome; hyposecretion results (secondarily) in Addison's disease. The posterior pituitary releases two hormones made by the hypothalamus, ADH and oxytocin; a lack of ADH leads to diabetes insipidus. (pp. 314–316)

Pineal gland: Found at the superioposterior end of the third ventricle in the brain. The pineal gland releases melatonin, which is important for regulating sleep and wake cycles and inhibits precocious sexual development in humans. Early hypersecretion results in sexual maturity earlier than normal. (p. 329)

Thymus: Found in the anterior thorax, overlying the trachea and heart. Its hormone, thymosin, serves to "program" the T lymphocytes of the immune system for recognition of self from nonself. Athymic individuals lack the ability to mount an effective immune response. (p. 329)

Pancreas: Located in the abdomen, in the mesentery between the stomach and duodenum. Produces: (a) Insulin, basically a hypoglycemic hormone that promotes the uptake and metabolism of glucose by body cells; a lack of insulin leads to diabetes mellitus. (b) Glucagon, basically a hyperglycemic hormone that promotes the release of glucose by the liver when blood glucose levels are low; no documented hypersecretion or hyposecretion problems. (pp. 326–328)

Ovaries: Located in the abdominopelvic cavity, lateral to the uterus. Produce estrogen(s) and progesterone. Lack of these hormones leads to the inability to conceive or bear children and reduced development of secondary female characteristics. (p. 329)

Testes: Located in the scrotal sac, medial to the superior thighs. Produce testosterone, a lack of which leads to a reduction in sperm count and reduced development of secondary male characteristics. (p. 329)

(Note: Only those hypersecretion or hyposecretion effects considered problematic have been noted.)

17. The adrenal cortex produces glucocorticoids (e.g., cortisone, hydrocortisone), which are important in aiding the body to resist long-term stressors, such as bodily trauma and anxiety. Glucocorticoids mobilize blood sugar and decrease the severity of the inflammatory response. The adrenal medulla produces epinephrine, which, together with the sympathetic nervous system, aids the body to react quickly to short-term stressors by diverting blood to the heart, brain, and skeletal muscles and by increasing blood sugar, blood pressure, and heart rate. (pp. 323–326; Figure 9.12)

18. Releasing hormones of the hypothalamus (in addition to feedback inhibition). (p. 316)

19. A tumor. (p. 324)

20. Insulin: glucagon, glucocorticoids, and epinephrine. (pp. 323, 325–326) PTH: calcitonin. (p. 320)

21. ADH and aldosterone. ADH is produced by the hypothalamus and released by the posterior pituitary; causes the kidney tubules to increase their uptake and retention of water (from the kidney filtrate). Aldosterone, an adrenal cortical hormone, regulates sodium ion (and, secondarily, potassium ion) concentration in the blood. When sodium ion concentration is too low, aldosterone is released and causes the renal tubules to increase their reabsorption of sodium ions (and water follows by osmosis). (pp. 318–319, 322–323)

22. A goiter is an enlarged thyroid gland that results from a lack of iodine in the diet. The thyroid hormones thyroxine (T_4) and triiodothyronine (T_3) contain iodine, so when iodine is not present, functional hormones cannot be made. The anterior pituitary (via TSH) continues to stimulate the thyroid follicles to produce T_3 and T_4 when levels in the blood are low. This continued but ineffective stimulation leads to enlargement of the thyroid gland. (p. 319)

23. As their ovaries cease to function, aging women undergo menopause, experiencing such symptoms as hot flashes, and becoming susceptible to osteoporosis and arteriosclerosis. Both males and females tend to become increasingly hypothyroid with age; they also become more susceptible to adult-onset diabetes as pancreatic function declines. In addition, the decreasing amounts of antistress hormones lower resistance to infectious disease. (pp. 332, 335)

ANSWERS TO CRITICAL THINKING AND CLINICAL APPLICATION QUESTIONS

24. The dysfunction is hypersecretion of androgens, possibly from a tumor of the adrenal cortex. (p. 324)

25. The diagnosis is hyposecretion of growth hormone. The prescription is commercial pituitary growth hormone. The reason the girl might reach her growth potential is that the epiphyseal plates of her bones have not yet closed, allowing additional growth of the skeleton and body, in response to the hormone. (pp. 314–315, 317)

26. Pitocin and oxytocin stimulate contraction of the smooth muscle of the myometrium, thus strengthening the uterine contractions to expel the baby. (p. 318)

27. The catecholamines epinephrine and norepinephrine. The usual cause of hypersecretion is a tumor in the adrenal medulla. The catecholamines promote a rise in blood sugar (hyperglycemia), whereas thyroid hormones trigger glucose catabolism. (pp. 325–326)

28. Bloated face (sign of steroid excess), shriveled testes and infertility, liver damage, liver cancer, possible increase in risk for coronary heart disease, and psychiatric problems. (pp. 203–204 in Chapter 6)

29. Bertha may have Cushing's syndrome—hypersecretion of glucocorticoids from the middle region of the adrenal cortex. (p. 324)

30. Maryanne would have a high blood PTH level as her poor diet is low in calcium, which would trigger PTH release from the parathyroid glands to stimulate the release of calcium from the bones. (p. 321)

31. The doctor should look on the posterior (dorsal) surface of the thyroid gland. (p. 321)

CLASSROOM DEMONSTRATIONS AND STUDENT ACTIVITIES

Classroom Demonstrations

1. Film(s) or other media of choice.

2. Using a human torso model, indicate the body locations of the major endocrine organs.

3. Obtain photographs of individuals with endocrine disorders. For example, individuals with exophthalmos and/or goiter resulting from Graves' disease; with a distinctive moon face and buffalo hump, from Cushing's syndrome (as a result of adrenal hypersecretion); and gigantism, dwarfism, or acromegaly from growth hormone imbalances. Use these pictures to support the presentation of hyper- and hyposecretion disorders.

4. Obtain Pitocin in IV form, to show it during the discussion on the effects of oxytocin. Ask when an Ob/Gyn physician might consider a cesarean birth.

5. Have the students call out all of the responses they remember related to the "fight-or-flight" mechanism, contrasting it with the "rest and digest" mechanism, and write their responses on the board. Use this as a starting-point to explain the roles of epinephrine and norepinephrine.

6. Have an EMT, paramedic, or ER physician come to class to talk about the uses of epinephrine in emergency medicine, as well as their own adrenaline response to their job.

7. Have an EMT, paramedic, or ER physician come to class to talk about emergency treatment of patients with diabetes. Have them discuss treatment for hyperinsulinism as opposed to diabetic acidosis.

8. Have a guest speaker from the American Diabetes Association come to class to talk about the impact of diabetes on lives and the lifestyle changes involved in managing the disease. Include in the discussion the differences between insulin-dependent (IDDM) and non-insulin-dependent (NIDDM) diabetes mellitus.

9. Bring in a sample of an early pregnancy testing kit to use in conjunction with discussion of hCG (human chorionic gonadotropin) and its production by the developing placenta.

10. Show an ultrasound video (or three-dimensional ultrasound) of a developing fetus and explain why 10 centimeters' dilation is necessary for a vaginal birth.

11. Have a recovering drug addict come and speak to the class about the effects on the body (short- and long-term) of using drugs that contain epinephrine derivatives (e.g., methamphetamines).

Student Activities

1. Use a small fish to demonstrate the effects of hyperinsulinism, and to initiate a discussion of what measure should be taken with people exhibiting signs of hyperinsulinism. Prepare two beakers: Beaker A contains 200 mL water and 10 to 15 drops of commercial insulin; beaker B contains 200 mL of 10% glucose solution. Place a small fish (goldfish or sunfish) in beaker A. Have students observe the fish's actions as insulin diffuses into its bloodstream and note how long it takes for the fish to become comatose. When the fish is comatose, transfer it to beaker B and again have students observe and record its actions, noting how long it takes for the fish to recover. After completing the experiments, return the fish to the aquarium.

2. Have the students research the current applications and experimental uses of recombinant human growth hormone, and use their findings to promote a class discussion.

3. Have the students research the use of corticosteroids in such conditions as asthma, organ transplantation, and autoimmune disorders. Use this information to discuss the advantages and disadvantages of these drugs.

4. Attend an American Diabetes Association meeting (local chapter) with your students.

5. Have your students answer the following question to demonstrate their understanding of how to select appropriate equipment and technology:

   Ashley and Kim are becoming friends at summer camp. Ashley notices that Kim is wearing a medical alert necklace that reads, "DIABETIC." Ashley might expect that Kim has brought medication as well as which type of medical equipment with her to camp?

   A. Otoscope   B. Sphygmomanometer
   C. Leg brace   D. Glucometer*

MULTIMEDIA

See page 182 for a listing of media distributors.

1. *Diagnosing and Treating Diabetes* (FHS; 22 min., 1998, VHS, DVD). Explores the manifestation, diagnostic testing, treatment, and biochemistry of diabetes mellitus.

2. *Endocrine Control: Systems in Balance* (IM; 30 min., 1997, VHS). Discusses the endocrine system in relation to homeostasis.

3. *The Endocrine System* (UL, WNS; 17 min., 1998, VHS). Shows how eight glands of the endocrine system make and release hormones.

4. *Homeostasis* (FHS; 20 min., 1995, VHS, DVD). From the *New Living Body* series, this program examines homeostasis from many aspects, including the role hormones play in the process.

5. *Hormonally Yours* (FHS; 50 min., 2000, VHS, DVD). From the *Body Chemistry: Understanding Hormones* series, this program examines the role of hormones on gender and sexuality.

6. *Hormone Heaven?* (FHS; 50 min., 2000, VHS, DVD). From the *Body Chemistry: Understanding Hormones* series, this program strives to answer questions related to the role of hormones in maintaining youthful vigor.

7. *Hormone Hell* (FHS; 50 min., 1999, VHS, DVD). From the *Body Chemistry: Understanding Hormones* series, this program examines the ways in which hormones affect different stages of life.

8. *Hormone Imposters* (BF; 47 min., 1997, DVD). Examines the role of hormone-disrupting environmental toxins, such as plastics, in low sperm count, attention deficit disorder, etc.

9. *Hormones: Messengers* (FHS; 27 min., 1984, VHS, DVD). From the award-winning *Living Body* series, this exceptional program covers a number of body processes that are controlled and coordinated by hormones.

10. *The Sleep Famine: The Effects of Sleep Deprivation and Chronic Fatigue* (FHS; 54 min., 2000, VHS, DVD). Discusses the societal impact of fatigue and the implications of time-shifting the circadian clock.

SOFTWARE

1. *Nervous and Hormonal Systems* (ED; Win/Mac). Explores the interrelationships between the nervous and endocrine systems.

Blood

CHAPTER SUMMARY

Blood is the body's interior "river of life." It is blood's uniqueness as a "liquid tissue" that makes it so interesting to study. In the previous chapter, blood's role in transporting hormones around the body was explained—in this chapter, this key role of transport extends to nutrients, metabolic wastes, agents that combat injury and microbial infection, and, of course, oxygen.

Blood is composed of formed elements and plasma. The formed elements are erythrocytes, leukocytes, and platelets. The physical characteristics of blood, including color, pH, and temperature, are presented, followed by a description of the plasma composition. The next section provides a detailed analysis of each of the formed elements. The function of erythrocytes as carriers of oxygen is explained, highlighting the role of hemoglobin in this capacity. General characteristics of leukocytes are described and then differentiated into granulocytes and agranulocytes, with the role of the cell types each category presented. Platelets, also called thrombocytes for their clotting ability, are the last of the formed elements to be analyzed.

Hematopoiesis of the formed elements is presented in detail, including the role of erythropoietin, with the differentiation of hemocytoblasts into lymphoid and myeloid stem cells. The phases of hemostasis, or clot formation, are outlined next, followed by a summary of the homeostatic imbalances associated with hemostasis, which include undesirable clotting and bleeding disorders, such as thrombus formation or hemophilia.

The final section of the chapter usually piques the interest of students since it explains blood, blood type, and its impact on blood transfusions. The four ABO blood groups are presented first, along with a discussion of the phenomenon of agglutination, which elicits the symptoms of a transfusion reaction. Accompanying the presentation of Rh blood groups is an explanation of erythroblastosis fetalis, or hemolytic disease of the newborn, with which students are frequently familiar.

SUGGESTED LECTURE OUTLINE

I. COMPOSITION AND FUNCTIONS OF BLOOD (pp. 340–349)
   A. Components (p. 340)
   B. Physical Characteristics and Volume (p. 340)
   C. Plasma (pp. 340–342)
      1. Albumin
   D. Formed Elements (pp. 342–347; Table 10.2)
      1. Erythrocytes (Red Blood Cells)
         a. Hemoglobin (Hb)
         b. Anemia
         c. Sickle-Cell Anemia
         d Polycythemia
      2. Leukocytes (White Blood Cells)
         a. Leukocytosis

TEACHING TIP

Discuss Rh incompatibilities and erythroblastosis fetalis. Explain the treatment protocol associated with RhoGAM to prevent this occurrence in an Rh− woman pregnant with an Rh+ fetus.

MEDIA TIP

Blood—River of Life, Mirror of Health (HRM; 60 min., 1990). A thorough exploration of the way in which the blood reflects health issues.

KEY TERMS

ABO blood groups
agglutination
agranulocytes
albumin
ameboid motion
anemia
antibodies
antigen
basophils
blood
buffy coat
coagulation (blood clotting)

diapedesis
embolus
eosinophils
erythrocytes (red blood cells RBCs)
erythropoietin
fibrin
fibrinogen
formed elements
granulocytes
hematocrit
hematopoiesis

hemocytoblast
hemoglobin (Hb)
hemolysis
hemophilia
hemostasis
histamine
leukemia
leukocytes (white blood cells WBCs)
leukocytosis
leukopenia
lymphocytes

megakaryocytes
monocytes
neutrophils
PF3
physiologic jaundice
plasma
platelet plug formation

platelets
polycythemia
positive chemotaxis
prothrombin
prothrombin activator
Rh blood groups
serotonin

serum
thrombin
thrombocytopenia
thrombus
tissue factor (TF)
vascular spasms

LECTURE HINTS

1. Discuss hematocrit and hemoglobin lab tests and their significance in the diagnosis of the more common types of anemia.

   Key point: Hematocrit tests are used to diagnose those types of anemia caused by low numbers of RBCs, whereas hemoglobin tests are used to diagnose those types of anemia caused from deficient hemoglobin concentration in the blood.

2. A high hematocrit could also be due to dehydration, with the loss of blood plasma manifesting as an increase in the relative concentration of red blood cells even though an abnormal increase in the absolute number of red blood cells may not be present.

   Key point: A severely dehydrated person will not even bleed when skin is cut.

3. Explain sickle-cell anemia and its natural selection benefit in protecting against malaria. Briefly explain the difference between homozygous recessive sickle-cell anemia and heterozygous sickle-cell trait.

   Key point: Discussion of sickle-cell anemia provides an opportunity to show how the human body can and does adapt to environmental influences over time.

4. Most students realize that a deficiency of RBCs leads to anemia. Often, however, they do not realize that polycythemia can lead to elevated blood viscosity and hypertension.

   Key point: Pointing out the results of both deficient and excessive RBCs helps students understand the range of disorders resulting from homeostatic imbalance.

5. Students are quite interested in the hereditary condition of hemophilia and are particularly fascinated by its royal lineage. Make hemophilia an element of your discussion of coagulation events by noting which of the several possible clotting factors are frequently lacking in people with hemophilia.

   Key point: Hereditary bleeding disorders result from deficiency of any of the factors needed for clotting, but missing factor VIII and IX result in the two principal types of hemophilia.

6. Discuss the leukemias in relation to the cell type from which they originate, and differentiate between the acute and chronic forms of each.

   Key point: Students frequently have questions about leukemia when discussing leukocytes. Be prepared to answer general questions about the most common types.

7. Describe the process of bone marrow transplantation for treatment in leukemia patients.

   Key point: Point out to students that matches between donor and recipient are more precise for bone marrow transplants compared to blood transfusions. Explain the problems associated with rejection of the donor's bone marrow in patients that have leukemia and already have a suppressed immune system.

8. Explain the difference between the lab tests for prothrombin time (PT) and partial thromboplastin time (PTT) and their uses in determining the causes of unexplained bleeding.

Key point: Bleeding disorders and coagulation problems resulting from medication can cause imbalance at various stages in the coagulation process. Lab values out of the normal range for PT or PTT are each significant for specific conditions.

9. Explain to students that the liver is the source of most plasma proteins, including albumin and the clotting proteins.

    Key point: It makes sense homeostatically, then, that liver disease can lead to edema and bleeding disorders.

10. Although there are many blood groups, the ABO and Rh groups are clinically the most important. Other blood groups are often analyzed for purposes such as resolving inheritance disputes or in forensics.

    Key point: Explanation of the presence of antigens on the surfaces of red blood cells prepares the way for later discussion of the antigen-antibody response associated with immunity.

11. Outline the basics of ABO blood grouping. Include blood type, antigens present, antibodies present, and transfusion requirements (universal donor, universal recipient, etc.).

    Key point: Students enjoy learning about blood groupings, since their own blood type is often something with which they are familiar.

12. Discuss the different components of blood that can be donated. Indicate how often each type occurs.

    Key point: Many students donate blood and are often interested in not only the difference between types of donation, but also the conditions in which people could receive the blood that they have donated.

13. Discuss Rh incompatibilities and erythroblastosis fetalis. Explain the treatment protocol associated with RhoGAM to prevent this occurrence in an Rh– woman pregnant with an Rh+ fetus.

    Key point: Treatment protocols have made erythroblastosis fetalis far less common in this country than in decades past, but it continues to be of global significance as a health issue for women of child-bearing age.

14. Discuss how Greek and Latin researchers named blood and blood disorders along with other commonly used terms. Terms like "hypocrite" have a very precise meaning. *Hypo* means "underneath," such as a needle inserted under the skin. *Crit* means "a standard of measurement." Therefore, a hypocrite is someone who measures or judges others according to a certain standard but lives underneath (*hypo*) that standard himself.

    Key point: Greek and Latin researchers named blood and blood disorders along with other commonly used terms.

TRANSPARENCIES/MEDIA MANAGER INDEX

Indicates images that are on the Media Manager only.

ANSWERS TO END OF CHAPTER REVIEW QUESTIONS

Questions appear on pp. 358–359

Multiple Choice

1. a, b, d (pp. 343–344; Figure 10.5)
2. a, b, c, d (pp. 343–344)
3. d (p. 344; Table 10.1)
4. c (p. 344)
5. a, d (pp. 344–345)
6. a (p. 345; Table 10.2)
7. b, c (Table 10.2)
8. c (p. 351)
9. b, c, d (pp. 351, 353)
10. a, d (p. 354)
11. a (p. 350)
12. b (p. 342)

Short Answer Essay

13. Average blood volume of a healthy adult male is 5 to 6 liters. (p. 340)

14. Gases (oxygen, carbon dioxide, nitrogen). Foodstuffs (glucose, lipids, fatty acids, cholesterol, amino acids). Ions (calcium, iron, chloride and other salts). Hormones. Metabolic wastes (urea, uric acid, ammonia, creatinine). Antibodies. Clotting proteins. Other proteins, including various enzymes, albumin, and transport proteins. (pp. 340–342; Figure 10.1)

15. *Formed elements:* Blood cells (or living portion) found in blood. Erythrocytes are the most numerous; leukocytes and thrombocytes comprise the buffy coat. (Figure 10.1; Table 10.2)

16. *Anemia:* A decrease in the oxygen-carrying ability of the blood. Possible causes: A lack of dietary iron, hemorrhage, depression or destruction of the bone marrow, a lack of vitamin B_{12}, bacterial infections leading to blood lysis, genetic defects. (p. 343; Table 10.1)

17. *Granular WBCs:* Neutrophils—phagocytes; eosinophils—act during allergy and parasitic infections; basophils—release histamine and heparin during inflammatory reactions. *Agranular WBCs:* Monocytes—phagocytes; lymphocytes—part of the body's immune system; form antibodies and act directly against foreign substances that have managed to invade the body. (p. 345)

18. The myeloid stem cell produces erythrocytes, platelets, and all leukocytes except the lymphocytes. The lymphoid stem cell gives rise to lymphocytes only. (pp. 347–349; Figure 10.4)

19. The lymphocytes reside primarily in the lymphatic tissues. (p. 345; Table 10.2)

20. Hemostasis is initiated by a break in the blood vessel wall (or lining), initiating vascular spasms and causing platelets to cling to the damaged site. Once attached, the platelets release serotonin, which enhances vasoconstriction. Injured tissue cells release thromboplastin, which interacts with platelet phospholipids (PF_3), Ca^{2+} and plasma clotting factors to form prothrombin activator. Prothrombin activator converts prothrombin to thrombin. Thrombin, an enzyme, then converts soluble fibrinogen molecules into long fibrin threads, which form the basis of the clot. (pp. 349–350)

21. The liver is the source of fibrinogen and several other factors that are necessary for clotting. When the liver is damaged and dysfunctional, it becomes unable to synthesize the usual amounts of clotting factors. When this situation happens, abnormal and often severe bleeding episodes can occur. (p. 351)

22. Agglutinins are antibody molecules present in the plasma that agglutinate foreign RBCs (i.e., RBCs with different antigens present on their cell membranes). (p. 351)

23. A, B, AB, and O. (Table 10.3)

24. *Transfusion reaction:* The clumping and lysis of foreign (donor) RBCs by the host's agglutinins when a mismatched blood type is infused. This reaction occurs as the recipient's antibodies attack the antigens on the RBCs of the mismatched blood type, which causes agglutination and lysis. The clumping of RBCs may clog capillaries, and the released hemoglobin may block kidney tubules, eventually leading to renal shutdown. (pp. 351, 358)

25. The Rh– person does not have preformed antibodies against Rh+ blood when the first exposure occurs. However, if such a person once receives Rh+ blood, the Rh antigens on the RBC cell membranes are recognized as foreign, and anti-Rh antibodies are formed. On the second (and subsequent) transfusion of Rh+ blood, a typical antigen-antibody reaction occurs in which the mismatched donor's RBCs are agglutinated and lysed. (pp. 353–354)

26. High. The hematocrit, or packed cell volume, provides a good estimate of the relative volume of RBCs. RBCs are the site of hemoglobin in the blood, so if their number increases, one would also expect the total amount of hemoglobin in the blood to increase (barring certain problems with hemoglobin formation, such as iron deficiency). (pp. 342–343)

ANSWERS TO CRITICAL THINKING AND CLINICAL APPLICATION QUESTIONS

27. Erythropoietin. (p. 348)

28. Aplastic anemia; short-term: transfusion; long-term: bone marrow transplant; packed red cells. (pp. 343–344; Table 10.1)

29. Hemorrhagic anemia (and iron deficiency). (Table 10.1)

30. Polycythemia vera. (p. 344)

31. He has secondary polycythemia, which is the body's attempt to restore the homeostasis of blood oxygen levels in an environment above 4,500 feet of elevation where the barometric pressure is lower (the air is thinner) and less oxygen is available. The RBC

count will begin to decline as the body readapts to oxygen levels in "Boston air" because erythropoietin levels decline when excess oxygen is carried in the blood. (p. 344)

32. A crushed or torn artery sustains more tissue damage than a clearly severed one. Since the vascular spasm is proportional to the amount of tissue damage, a crushed or torn artery will lead to less blood loss. As well, the rougher surfaces on a crushed and torn artery will provide a better site for platelets to attach quickly. (pp. 349–350)

33. Fetal hemoglobin has a greater ability to pick up oxygen than hemoglobin, which is formed after birth. (p. 356)

CLASSROOM DEMONSTRATIONS AND STUDENT ACTIVITIES

Classroom Demonstrations

1. Film(s) or other media of choice.

2. Show models, transparencies, and slides of the various blood cells.

3. On the board, outline the constituents of blood, including plasma and all the formed elements, as well as the percentages of each that are normally found in healthy blood.

4. Show examples of stained leukocytes, explaining how Wright's and other stains are used to differentiate between the various granulocytes and agranulocytes.

5. Display equipment used to perform a hematocrit, sedimentation rate, and blood cell counts. Describe how these tests are conducted and what information they yield, then run a hematocrit so students can see the difference in the volume of plasma and formed elements.

6. Set up prepared slides or show transparencies of pathologies such as sickle-cell anemia, leukemia, erythroblastosis fetalis, and iron deficiency anemia. Ask students to discuss how these blood smears differ from blood smears from healthy individuals.

7. Invite a phlebotomist to talk to the class about the procedures and protocols they follow. Have the phlebotomist explain the different types of blood tubes used for blood collection. The phlebotomist could also explain the different tyeps of needles and the various sites used for drawing blood.

Student Activities

1. Use WARD's Simulated Blood Typing "Whodunit" Lab Activity. This is a fun, easy-to-use activity in which students become detectives and use blood typing techniques to solve a make-believe crime.

2. Show samples of stained WBCs and explain how Wright's and other stains are used to differentiate between granulocytes and agranulocytes and the cells found in each category.

3. Have students research diseases that are transmitted via blood. Discuss why many of these diseases are increasing in incidence and explain why careful handling of blood in the clinical agency is vitally important. Present information on standard precautions as recommended by the Centers for Disease Control and Prevention.

4. Collect data from the class about their own blood types. Blood typing is generally available for about $15 at any local hospital or clinic but the students could type their own blood using sterile lancets and blood test cards from Carolina Biological Supply Company. Compare these data to expected frequency.

MULTIMEDIA

See page 182 for a listing of media resources.

1. *Bad Blood* (FHS; 50 min., 1996, VHS, DVD). Explores the ancient fear associated with inherited conditions, including an examination of the royal link to hemophilia.

2. *Bleeding and Coagulation* (FHS; 31 min., 2000, VHS). Scrutinizes the body's mechanism of coagulation through the use of case studies.

3. *Blood* (FHS; 20 min., 1995, VHS, DVD). From the *New Living Body* series, this video explains blood and circulation through the story of a sickle-cell sufferer.

4. *Blood is Life* (FHS; 45 min., 1995, VHS, DVD). Award-winning video that provides a thorough introduction to human blood.

5. *Blood—River of Life, Mirror of Health* (HRM; 31 min., 1990, VHS). A thorough exploration of the way in which the blood reflects health issues.

6. *Diseases of the Blood: Issues and Answers* (FHS; 23 min., 1999, VHS, DVD). Explores breakthroughs in treatments for multiple myeloma and chronic lymphocytic leukemia.

7. *Mechanisms of Defense: Accident* (FHS; 28 min., 1989, VHS, DVD). From the award-winning *Living Body* series, this program follows the sequence of events of body reparation following an accident. Includes defensive reactions such as blood clotting.

8. *Sickle-Cell Anemia* (FHS; 30 min., 2001, VHS, DVD). Answers frequently asked questions about the causes of sickle-cell anemia and its treatment.

SOFTWARE

1. *InterActive Physiology 9-System Suite* (ADAM, BC; Win/Mac). Interactive software that explores the physiology of the cardiovascular system.

2. *Blood and the Circulatory System NEO/LAB* (LP; Win/Mac). Provides interactive exercises on blood typing, morphology, and genetics.

3. *Blood and Immunity* (CE, LP; Win/Mac). Teaches the components of blood, blood types, and the processes of blood. Includes information on HIV.

The Cardiovascular System

CHAPTER SUMMARY

The importance of the cardiovascular system cannot be overstated. This is one system that students frequently know something about, at least from a plumbing viewpoint, but they often don't completely understand the complexity of the system and the magnitude of its tasks. An essential component of presentation of the material is then to outline in detail the role of the cardiovascular system and its significance to all other body systems.

This chapter begins with the fundamental information about the heart by first discussing anatomy and then moving on to the more complex physiology. The section on anatomy covers the layers of the heart as well as its chambers, valves, and the vessels through which blood moves in and out of its various regions. A section on cardiac circulation explains the way the heart itself is supplied with oxygen-rich blood.

The structural and mechanical characteristics of the heart are followed by a discussion of its unique electrical intrinsic activity. The conduction system is outlined and relevant homeostatic imbalances are discussed. Concepts related to the electrical conduction system of the heart are always difficult to grasp, and key demonstrations and activities help solidify the students' understanding.

Following the section on the heart itself is the portion of the chapter dealing with the blood vessels. Arteries, veins, and capillaries are compared for their structural and physiological similarities as well as their differences. Names of the major vessels are given, as the route of blood is traced from its point of exit from the heart through the aorta to all parts of the body and back to the heart via the superior and inferior venae cavae. A look into the various mechanisms involved in blood pressure precedes a discussion of the special circulatory routes that supply the brain, liver, and developing fetus. Finally, the developmental aspects of circulation are considered.

SUGGESTED LECTURE OUTLINE

I. THE HEART (pp. 362–374)
    A. Anatomy of the Heart (pp. 362–368)
        1. Location and Size
        2. Coverings and Wall
        3. Chambers and Associated Great Vessels
            a. Atria
            b. Ventricles
            c. Superior and Inferior Venae Cavae
            d. Pulmonary Arteries
            e. Pulmonary Veins
            f. Aorta
        4. Valves
            a. Atrioventricular (AV) Valves
            b. Semilunar Valves
        5. Cardiac Circulation
        6. Homeostatic Imbalances

> **TEACHING TIP**
>
> Discuss the blood supply to the heart itself, pointing out that despite the fact that blood fills all the chambers of the heart, the heart feeds itself from the outside. Explain CAD (coronary artery disease) and its common sequelae, the bypass surgery known as a CABG (pronounced 'cabbage' and meaning coronary artery bypass graft).

a. Endocarditis
b. Angina Pectoris
c. Myocardial Infarction

B. Physiology of the Heart (pp. 368–374)

1. Intrinsic Conduction System of the Heart: Setting the Basic Rhythm
   a. Intrinsic Conduction System
   b. Homeostatic Imbalances
      i. Heart Block
      ii. Ischemia
      iii. Fibrillation
2. Cardiac Cycle and Heart Sounds
   a. Mid-to-Late Diastole
   b. Ventricular Systole
   c. Early Diastole
   d. Homeostatic Imbalances
      i. Murmurs
3. Cardiac Output (CO)
   a. Regulation of Stroke Volume (SV)
   b. Factors Modifying Basic Heart Rate (HR)
   c. Neural (ANS) Controls
   d. Physical Factors
   e. Homeostatic Imbalanaces
      i. Congestive Heart Failure (CHF)
      ii. Pulmonary Edema

II. BLOOD VESSELS (pp. 374–395)

A. Microscopic Anatomy of Blood Vessels (pp. 374–377)

1. Tunics
2. Structural Differences between Arteries, Veins, and Capillaries
3. Homeostatic Imbalanaces
   a. Varicose Veins
   b. Thrombophlebitis
   c. Pulmonary Embolism

B. Gross Anatomy of Blood Vessels (pp. 378–386)

1. Major Arteries of the Systemic Circulation (Figure 11.12)
   a. Arterial Branches of the Ascending Aorta
      i. Right and Left Coronary Arteries
   b. Arterial Branches of the Aortic Arch
      i. Brachiocephalic Trunk
      ii. Left Common Carotid Artery
      iii. Left Subclavian Artery
   c. Arterial Branches of the Thoracic Aorta
      i. Intercostal Arteries
      ii. Bronchial Arteries
      iii. Esophageal Arteries
      iv. Phrenic Arteries
   d. Arterial Branches of the Abdominal Aorta
      i. Celiac Trunk
      ii. Superior Mesenteric Artery

MEDIA TIP

The Human Cardiovascular System: The Heart (BC; 22 min., 1995). Provides an overview of the heart as the circulatory pump.

    iii. Renal Arteries

    iv. Gonadal Arteries

    v. Lumbar Arteries

    vi. Inferior Mesenteric Artery

    vii. Common Iliac Arteries

  2. Major Veins of the Systemic Circulation (Figure 11.13)

   a. Veins Draining into the Superior Vena Cava

    i. Radial and Ulnar Veins

    ii. Cephalic Vein

    iii. Basilic Vein

    iv. Subclavian Vein

    v. Vertebral Vein

    vi. Internal Jugular Vein

    vii. Brachiocephalic Vein

    viii. Azygos Vein

   b. Veins Draining into the Inferior Vena Cava

    i. Anterior and Posterior Tibial Veins and Fibular Vein

    ii. Great Saphenous Veins

    iii. Common Iliac Veins

    iv. Gonadal Veins

    v. Renal Veins

    vi. Hepatic Portal Vein

    vii. Hepatic veins

  3. Special Circulations (Figures 11.14–11.17)

   a. Arterial Supply of the Brain and the Circle of Willis

   b. Fetal Circulation

   c. Hepatic Portal Circulation

 C. Physiology of Circulation (pp. 387–395)

  1. Arterial Pulse

  2. Blood Pressure

   a. Blood Pressure Gradient

   b. Measuring Blood Pressure

   c. Effects of Various Factors on Blood Pressure

    i. Neural Factors: The Autonomic Nervous System

    ii. Renal Factors: The Kidneys

    iii. Temperature

    iv. Chemicals

    v. Diet

   d. Variations in Blood Pressure

  3. Capillary Exchange of Gases and Nutrients

  4. Fluid Movements at Capillary Beds

III. DEVELOPMENTAL ASPECTS OF THE CARDIOVASCULAR SYSTEM (pp. 395, 397)

 A. Embryonic Development

 B. Congenital Heart Defects

 C. Exercise

 D. Coronary Artery Disease

KEY TERMS

abdominal aorta
anterior cerebral artery
anterior interventricular
    artery
anterior tibial artery
anterior tibial vein
aorta
aortic arch
aortic semilunar valve
apex
arcuate artery
arteries
arterioles
ascending aorta
atria
atrioventricular (AV) bundle
    (bundle of His)
atrioventricular (AV) node
atrioventricular (AV) valves
auscultatory method
axillary artery
axillary vein
base
basilar artery
basilic vein
bicuspid (mitral) valve
blood pressure
brachial artery
brachial vein
brachiocephalic trunk
brachiocephalic veins
bradycardia
bundle branches
capillary beds
cardiac cycle
cardiac output (CO)
cardiac veins
cardiovascular system
celiac trunk
cephalic vein
cerebral arterial circle
chordae tendineae
circle of Willis
circulatory shock
circumflex artery
common carotid artery
common hepatic artery
common iliac arteries

common iliac vein
coronary arteries
coronary artery disease
coronary sinus
coronary sulcus (atrioventric-
    ular groove)
deep artery of the thigh
diastole
diastolic pressure
dorsal venous arch
dorsalis pedis artery
ductus arteriosus
ductus venosus
endocardium
epicardium
external carotid arteries
external iliac artery
external iliac vein
external jugular vein
femoral artery
femoral vein
fibrous pericardium
fibular vein
foramen ovale
gastric vein
gonadal arteries
great saphenous vein
heart rate (HR)
heart sounds
hepatic portal circulation
hepatic portal vein
hepatic veins
high blood pressure
hypertension
hypotension
inferior mesenteric artery
inferior mesenteric vein
inferior vena cava
interatrial septum
intercellular clefts
internal carotid arteries
internal iliac artery
internal iliac vein
internal jugular vein
interstitial fluid (tissue fluid)
interventricular septum
intrinsic conduction system
left gastric artery

ligamentum arteriosum
marginal arteries
median cubital vein
mediastinum
microcirculation
middle cerebral artery
myocardium
nodal system
pacemaker
parietal layer
pericardium
peripheral resistance
popliteal artery
popliteal vein
postcapillary venule
posterior interventricular
    artery
posterior tibial artery
posterior tibial vein
precapillary sphincter
pressure points
pulmonary arteries
pulmonary circulation
pulmonary semilunar valve
pulmonary trunk
pulmonary veins
pulse
Purkinje fibers
radial artery
radial vein
renal arteries
renal veins
right and left coronary
    arteries
semilunar valves
serous pericardium
sinoatrial (SA) node
splenic artery
splenic vein
stroke volume (SV)
subclavian artery
subclavian vein
superior mesenteric artery
superior mesenteric vein
superior vena cava
systemic circulation
systole
systolic pressure

tachycardia	ulnar artery	vasoconstriction
terminal arteriole	ulnar vein	veins
thoracic aorta	umbilical arteries	ventricles
tricuspid valve	umbilical vein	vertebral artery
tunica externa	valves	vertebral vein
tunica intima	vascular shunt	visceral layer
tunica media	vascular system	vital signs

LECTURE HINTS

1. Descriptively present the cardiovascular system as the great transportation system of the body, similar to a mail delivery system, that not only carries the oxygen and carbon dioxide people usually relate to it, but also delivers nutrients, removes toxic wastes, conveys heat, and transports the myriad of hormones that are essential to all regulatory functions.

   Key point: Drawing an analogy between the cardiovascular system and a mail delivery system helps students conceptualize the work of this intricate system.

2. Although the left side of the heart generates more pressure than the right side, approximately the same volume of blood is ejected from each side per beat. Ask students to think about what would happen if this were not the case. Follow up with a discussion on congestive heart failure.

   Key point: In CHF, blood pumped to the lungs by the right ventricle does not keep pace with blood pumped around the system by the left ventricle. Fluid builds up in the lungs, leading to the predominant symptom of CHF, which is breathing difficulty.

3. Students may recall that the average blood volume of a healthy adult male is 5–6 liters. All blood generally circulates completely through the body in about one minute while at rest.

   Key point: 5–6 liters/minute is the average resting cardiac output for an average healthy adult male.

4. Compare the body's self-regulating pacemaker, the SA node, to an artificial pacemaker in function and performance. Describe the 1,000,000 or more times each week that the heart's pacemaker fires and causes it to pump blood around the system and back again to the heart.

   Key point: Students are usually quite surprised to learn that humans have a built-in pacemaker that is actually much more efficient, longer lasting, and more versatile than an artificial one.

5. Stress that the only function of the valves of the heart is to ensure the one-way flow of blood. Explore with the students the consequences of incompetent or stenotic valves.

   Key point: This provides an opportunity to differentiate between the various types of murmurs and their etiology.

6. Discuss the chordae tendineae, or "heart strings." Explain their function as similar to the stays of an umbrella, designed to keep the heart valves from turning inside out under extreme pressure.

   Key point: The reference to something "tugging at their heart strings" gives students a concrete example of the way in which anatomy, particularly of the heart, has an established place in our language and literature.

7. Outline the remarkable engineering involved in the design of the blood vessels, which allows them to absorb the pressure emitted from the heart with each beat and to return blood back to the heart, usually on an uphill course against the constant pull of gravity.

   Key point: In differentiating between arteries, veins, and capillaries, emphasize that the structure of each type of vessel is related to the differing amounts of pressure they must each absorb from the heart, as well as their respective roles in blood transport.

8. A basic misconception students have is that arteries carry oxygenated blood and veins carry deoxygenated blood. While this is usually true, the heart is a notable exception. Remind students that arteries are defined as vessels that carry blood away from the heart and veins carry blood toward the heart.

   Key point: The pulmonary *arteries* carry deoxygenated blood from the right side of the heart to the lungs, and the pulmonary *veins* return oxygenated blood to the left side of the heart.

9. Veins are more superficial and are occluded when a phlebotomist applies a tourniquet that enables veins to rise as blood is still being pumped distally through arteries running underneath the tourniquet.

   Key point: Veins are low pressure vessels and need less strength, support, and elasticity than the arteries.

10. In discussing fetal circulation, point out that all fetuses have a "hole in their heart," and in fact two holes, which allow circulation to be routed around the non-inflated lungs. Explain the fact that if these "holes" don't close at or shortly after birth, then surgical closure is required, usually to correct a PDA (patent ductus arteriosus).

    Key point: Again, this is an example of a linguistic reference that has an actual anatomic basis, which students find fascinating.

11. Discuss the blood supply to the heart itself, pointing out that despite the fact that blood fills all the chambers of the heart, the heart cannot nourish itself from the inside. Explain coronary artery disease (CAD) and its common sequelae, the coronary artery bypass graft (known as CABG and pronounced "cabbage").

    Key point: It is important for students to recognize that the heart must be infiltrated with its own vascular supply in order to receive the oxygen and nutrients necessary for its survival. Any blockage in the vascular flow will lead to tissue damage, resulting in a myocardial infarction or "heart attack." Note the difference between open heart surgery (valve replacement, etc.) and open chest surgery (CABG).

12. Differentiate between atherosclerosis and arteriosclerosis, pointing out that "athero" means yellow, fatty plaque, and discuss the role of cholesterol in its development. Point out that there is no such thing as "good" and "bad" cholesterol, and that we actually need both types within our bodies for transportation purposes. Explain that it is simply a matter of ratio, or the proportion of low-density lipids to high.

    Key point: This is a good time to dispel the notion of good and bad cholesterol, and instead to help students understand that moderation is key to a healthy cardiovascular system. Point out that the lymphatic system dumps fats into the vena cavae immediately before blood returns to the heart.

13. Describe the various methods that can be used to treat atherosclerosis (e.g., stents, angioplasty).

    Key point: Students are generally familiar with the concept of blocked blood vessels, but are often unaware of treatments other than bypass surgery.

14. Discuss Olestra, the fat substitute, and its physiological effects on the body, including the blood vessels.

    Key point: Through advertising, students are usually quite familiar with nutritional substitutes, such as fat and sugar substitutes, but they often don't understand the mechanisms at play and the potential side effects from the use of these substitutes.

15. Discuss smoking and its cardiovascular implications, including arteriovascular insufficiency, ischemia, intermittent claudication with concomitant leg pain and cramps, thrombus formation, and impotence.

    Key point: The impact of smoking on the cardiovascular system is so significant that it is important to incorporate a discussion of the smoking-related disorders into the class presentation.

16. Present information on deep vein thrombi (DVTs) and their incidence related to bed rest and/or a sedentary lifestyle. Explain their connection to long distance travel, birth control pills, and genetics. Point out the irony that the treatment for DVTs includes bed rest along with anticoagulant medication.

    Key point: This discussion helps students gain perspective on potential serious homeostatic imbalances of the venous system and their causes.

17. Discuss the correlation of Group A streptococcal infections such as "strep throat" to rheumatic fever and rheumatic heart disease, which can lead to mitral valve damage.

    Key point: Students are usually familiar with the illness described as "strep throat," but often are unaware of its serious ramifications.

18. Explain the etiology and pathology associated with hypertension, along with methods of prevention and treatment options.

    Key point: Since hypertension is one of the major risk factors in coronary artery disease, stroke, congestive heart failure, and kidney failure, presentation of the causative factors and current thinking on prevention and treatment are important concepts for students to understand. Excessive salt in the diet retains more fluid within the vessels and thus increases blood pressure internally, as compared to external stressors that increase blood pressure externally.

19. Explain that the intrinsic electrical conduction can be picked by ECG electrodes placed anywhere on the external skin surface.

    Key point: Electrical activity goes from the body to the machine and heart paddles placed on an emergency patient are designed to stop the heart and hopefully enable normal autorhythmicity to take over. Explain that a rescuer would not want to give a patient just pulled out of a swimming pool several hundred joules of energy if the deck is not dry.

20. Differentiate between myocardial infarction, stroke, pulmonary embolism, and thrombi.

    Key point: Students often do not realize that these terms can all be related to one another since they refer to blockage of blood vessels in different parts of the body.

21. Explain the difference between an aneurysm and a ruptured aneurysm.

    Key point: The media often does not distinguish between these two terms, so students can get confused as to their effects and treatment.

22. Describe all of the different physical, chemical, and neurological factors that can modify heart rate.

    Key point: Explain to students that a wide variety of factors located all over the body can play a role in determining heart rate.

TRANSPARENCIES/MEDIA MANAGER INDEX

Indicates images that are on the Media Manager only.

ANSWERS TO END OF CHAPTER REVIEW QUESTIONS

Questions appear on pp. 399–401

Multiple Choice

1. d (Figure 11.3)
2. b (p. 372)
3. d (p. 368; Figure 11.6)

4. a, c (pp. 369–371)

5. c (p. 370)

6. a, c (p. 371)

7. b (p. 362)

8. a, c (p. 374; Figure 11.9)

9. d (p. 378; Figure 11.12)

10. a (Figure 11.12)

11. b (p. 383)

12. a, c, d (pp. 378, 380)

13. b (pp. 392–393)

14. a, b, c (p. 397)

15. c (pp. 372–373)

16. b (p. 362)

17. d (pp. 365–366; Figure 11.2d)

18. b (p. 366; Figure 11.2d)

19. b (pp. 363–364; Figure 11.2b)

SHORT ANSWER ESSAY

20. See Figure 11.2. (pp. 363–364)

21. Right atrium to right ventricle to pulmonary trunk to right and left pulmonary arteries to pulmonary capillaries of the lungs to right and left pulmonary veins to left atrium of the heart. Pulmonary circuit or pulmonary circulation. (p. 365; Figure 11.3)

22. The pericardial (serous) fluid acts as a lubricant to decrease friction as the heart beats. (p. 363)

23. *Systole:* Period of contraction of the heart (usually refers to ventricular contraction). *Diastole:* Period of relaxation of the heart musculature. *Stroke volume:* The amount of blood pumped out by a ventricle with each contraction. *Cardiac cycle:* The time for one complete heartbeat, from the beginning of one systole to the beginning of the next. (pp. 369, 372)

24. The heart has an intrinsic ability to beat (contract), which is different from all other muscles in the body. Whereas the nervous system may increase or decrease its rate, the heart continues to beat even if all nervous connections are cut. (p. 368)

25. SA node (pacemaker), AV node, AV bundle (bundle of His), bundle branches, Purkinje fibers. (p. 368)

26. Activity of the sympathetic nervous system (as during physical or emotional stress), excess or lack of certain vital ions, increased temperature, hormones (epinephrine, thyroxine), sudden drop in blood volume, age, gender, and exercise. (p. 368)

27. *Tunica intima:* A single layer of squamous epithelium; provides a smooth, friction-reducing lining for the vessel. *Tunica media:* A middle layer, consisting of smooth muscle and connective tissue (primarily elastic fibers). The elastic fibers provide for stretching and then passive recoil of vessels close to the heart, which are subjected to pressure fluctuations; the smooth muscle is activated by the sympathetic nervous system when vasoconstriction (and increases in blood pressure) is desired. *Tunica externa:* The

outermost layer, made of fibrous connective tissue; basically a protective and supporting layer. (pp. 374–376)

28. Capillary walls are essentially just the tunica intima (endothelium plus the basement membrane); thus, they are exceedingly thin. (p. 376)

29. Arteries are much closer to the pumping action of the heart and must be able to withstand the pressure fluctuations at such locations. Veins, on the distal side of the capillary beds of the tissues, are essentially low-pressure vessels that need less strength/support/elasticity than do arteries. (p. 376)

30. The presence of valves, the milking action of skeletal muscles against the veins as the muscles contract, the respiratory pump (pressure changes in the thorax during breathing). (p. 376)

31. Pulmonary arteries carry oxygen-poor blood and pulmonary veins carry oxygen-rich blood. Umbilical arteries carry oxygen-poor blood from the fetus and the umbilical vein carries the most oxygen-rich blood to the fetus. (pp. 365, 383–384)

32. Right wrist: Left ventricle to ascending aorta to aortic arch to brachiocephalic artery to subclavian artery to axillary artery to brachial artery to radial (or ulnar) artery to capillary network of wrist to radial (or ulnar) vein to brachial vein to axillary vein to subclavian vein to right brachiocephalic vein to superior vena cava to right atrium of the heart.

    Right foot: Left ventricle to ascending aorta to aortic arch to descending aorta to right common iliac artery to external iliac artery to femoral artery to popliteal artery to anterior tibial artery to dorsalis pedis artery to capillary network to anterior tibial vein to popliteal vein to femoral vein to external iliac vein to common iliac vein to inferior vena cava to right atrium of the heart. (Alternatively, the sequence between the capillary network and external iliac vein could be stated as: dorsal venous arch to great saphenous vein.) (Figures 11.12–11.13)

33. The hepatic portal circulation carries nutrient-rich blood from the digestive viscera to the liver for processing before the blood enters the systemic circulation. A portal circulation involves a capillary bed that is both fed and drained by veins; the usual circulation has a capillary bed that is fed by arteries and drained by veins. (pp. 385–386)

34. In a fetus, both liver and lungs are nonfunctional (the liver relatively so). The ductus venosus bypasses the liver. The ductus arteriosus and the foramen ovale bypass the lungs. The umbilical vein carries nutrient-rich and oxygen-rich blood to the fetus through the umbilical cord. (pp. 383–385)

35. *Pulse:* The alternate expansion and recoil of an artery that occur with each heartbeat. (p. 387)

36. Front of the ear: Temporal artery. Back of knee: Popliteal artery. (p. 387; Figure 11.18)

37. *Systolic pressure:* Pressure exerted by blood on the arterial walls during ventricular contraction. *Diastolic pressure:* Pressure exerted by blood on the arterial walls when the ventricles are relaxing (that is, during diastole). (p. 388)

38. Cardiac output is increased by increased venous return and increased heart rate. Peripheral resistance is increased by decreased diameter of the blood vessels and increased blood viscosity. (Figure 11.21)

39. Blood pressure is normally highest in the recumbent position and lowest immediately after standing up; however, the sympathetic nervous system quickly compensates in a healthy individual. Very often an individual can become hypotensive after remaining still in the sitting position for an extended period. (pp. 389–390)

40. Intercellular clefts allow limited passage of solutes and fluid. Fenestrated capillaries allow very free passage of small solutes and fluids. Capillaries lacking these modifications are relatively impermeable. (p. 394)

41. Veins that have become twisted and dilated because of incompetent valves. Inactivity (lack of skeletal milking activity against the veins), which allows the blood to pool in the lower extremities; increased pressure that restricts venous return (as in pregnancy and obesity). (p. 377, 397)

42. Blood flow in arteries is pulsatile because it is under a greater amount of pressure compared to veins. Arteries are located closer to the ventricles, so their walls must be capable of expanding and contracting under the changes in pressure when the ventricles contract. When blood reaches the veins, the pressure is very low, and so instead of veins having a pulsatile ability to maintain pressure, they instead have valves to prevent backflow. (pp. 387–388)

43. The greater the cross-sectional area in a blood vessel, the faster that blood can flow through that vessel. Smaller vessels, like capillaries, are only one cell thick in diameter, which slows down blood flow and allows nutrient and gas exchange to occur. (p. 374)

44. Arterioles are the blood vessels that are most important in regulating vascular resistance. These vessels can constrict as a result of activity from the sympathetic nervous system, which alters blood pressure. Atherosclerosis in these vessels also causes narrowing due to plaque deposits, which also affects blood pressure. (p. 388)

ANSWERS TO CRITICAL THINKING AND CLINICAL APPLICATION QUESTIONS

45. *Hypertension:* abnormally elevated or high blood pressure (generally described as systolic pressure consistently over 140 mm Hg and diastolic pressure consistently over 90 mm Hg in younger adults). (pp. 391, 394) *Arteriosclerosis:* "hardening of the arteries," the result of deposit of fatty-cholesterol substances and calcium salts onto the inner walls of the blood vessels. Arteriosclerosis can be a direct cause of hypertension because it decreases the elasticity of the arteries (thereby increasing peripheral resistance). (p. 393)

    Hypertension is often called the "silent killer" because it progresses initially (and often over a prolonged period) without obvious symptoms. Three lifestyle habits that might help prevent cardiovascular disease are regular exercise, a diet low in saturated fats and salt, and a decrease in stress. (Quitting smoking would also help.)

46. She has pulmonary edema. The right side of the heart is still sending blood to the lungs, but the left side of the heart, the systemic pump, is not pumping blood entering its chamber (from the pulmonary circuit) to the systemic circulation. As the pressure increases in the pulmonary vessels, they become leaky, and fluid enters the tissue spaces of the lungs. (p. 374)

47. Incompetence (not stenosis) of the pulmonary semilunar valve. Incompetent valves produce swishing sounds, and the pulmonary semilunar valve is heard at the superior left corner of the heart, as indicated in this question. (pp. 371–372)

48. The compensatory mechanisms of Mrs. Johnson include an increase in heart rate and an intense vasoconstriction, which allows blood in various blood reservoirs to be rapidly added to the major circulatory channels. (pp. 388–391; Figure 11.21)

49. The left atrium and the posterior portion of the left ventricle. (p. 367; Figure 11.2)

50. Chronically elevated due to increased blood volume. ADH promotes retention of water by the kidneys. (pp. 390–391; Figure 11.21)

51. Blood flow is increased to areas of need and decreased to areas of non-need due to constriction and dilation of arterioles as blood will flow down pathway of least resistance. Competition for blood flow between the GI tract, which needs more blood circulation for absorption, and the skeletal muscles, which simultaneously need more blood for exercise, will cause indigestion much more quickly than muscle cramping. (pp. 385, 389–390)

52. Standing erect for prolonged periods enables gravity to pool blood in lower extremities, particularly in the absence of muscle pump activity which increases venous return during movement. Reduction in venous return causes reductions in stroke volume, causing lightheadedness as blood flow to brain is reduced. Standing in a hot environment will also produce sweating, vasodilation, and a reduction of blood plasma, which further decreases stroke volume. (p. 376)

CLASSROOM DEMONSTRATIONS AND STUDENT ACTIVITIES

Classroom Demonstrations

1. Film(s) or other media of choice.

2. Show a video of a beating heart, ideally with heart sounds. Stress that while the right side of the heart is a pulmonary pump and the left side a systemic pump, both atria contract at the same time and both ventricles contract at the same time.

3. Use a dissectible heart model to show heart structure.

4. Use a dissectible human torso model to point out the major arteries and veins of the body.

5. Show the chordae tendineae, the "heart strings," on a dissected heart.

6. Show a chart of various types and grades of heart murmurs, explaining that some of them are considered nonpathological and are merely "functional" (related to low fluid volume, etc.).

7. Play a recording of normal and abnormal heart sounds to accompany your presentation of valve function and malfunction. (*Interpreting Heart Sounds* is available for loan from local chapters of the American Heart Association.)

8. Demonstrate the recording of an ECG.

9. Bring in a test tube or show pictures of blood in a test tube containing high fat content. Point out that at times the fat content is so high, you can actually see floating clumps of fat in the specimen.

10. Have a guest speaker from the American Heart Association talk to the class about the risk factors and leading causes of heart disease.

11. Bring in an old mechanical pacemaker and show its placement on the chest wall under the skin. Compare the heart's own pacemaker, the SA node, to the implanted mechanical device, explaining that artificial pacemakers keep a set pulse rate and are not regulated by increased or decreased activity.

12. Demonstrate the use of defibrillators, including AEDs, and explain their function in cardiac rescue. Also discuss CPR as it relates to heart function.

13. Show pictures of and describe "pitting" edema. Explain how fluid can fill the interstitial spaces to such a degree that an indentation will stay when the skin is pressed with the index finger.

14. Obtain synthetic bypass graft material and compare it in use and effectiveness to the preferred saphenous vein.

15. Describe the different symptoms of impending myocardial infarction (heart attack) in men and women. Provide statistics showing the increase in diagnosis of MI in women.

16. Show a video of a heart operation and the importance of a perfusionist, who assists the heart surgeon.

17. Have a phlebotomist speak to the class about locations to draw blood in children and in adults. Have the speaker explain the difficulties in drawing blood when the patient is obese or dehydrated, and the methods they use during those situations.

Student Activities

1. Demonstrate how apical and radial pulses are taken, and have students practice on each other.

2. Demonstrate the location of the radial, brachial, carotid, femoral, popliteal, and pedal pulses. Have students locate several of their own and compare their rate and rhythm. Discuss the clinical implications of weak or absent pulses in the extremities.

3. Demonstrate the auscultatory method of taking blood pressure and provide sphygmomanometers and stethoscopes for students to practice on each other.

4. Ask students to bring in a daily record of their blood pressure in the upright and supine positions for a specified period of time to chart and compare.

5. Provide simple drawings of a dissected heart and have the students follow the path of blood as it flows through the various chambers. Ask them to use red and blue pencils to differentiate between oxygenated and deoxygenated blood. Also ask them to label the chambers, valves, septa, and other distinguishing features.

6. Have students run in place or do jumping jacks for 3 minutes, then have them record their radial pulse (pointing out that a radial pulse is always thumb side). Have them continue to take their pulse every 30 seconds for 5 minutes, then graph the results. Point out that a steep decline in the first minute or so indicates rapid recovery by the heart.

7. Provide the students with a diagram of the major blood vessels for labeling.

8. Have students record their salt intake for one week. Provide them with a chart showing salt content in foods and also review the use of food labels. Have them graph their daily salt intake and compare it to the FDA limit. Discuss which foods, like milk products and pickles, are surprisingly high in salt content.

9. Encourage students to obtain CPR training and offer extra credit for documentation of certification during the semester.

10. Have students plan an investigation to learn more about heart rate and heart sounds. Have them select a problem, such as the relationship of age or weight, and determine its effect on heart rate and heart sounds. Have them formulate a testable hypothesis and list the steps for the investigation, including the selection of appropriate equipment and technology. They should implement the investigation, record the data in a chart, and draw conclusions from that data.

11. Have students plan an investigation to determine the effect of time of day on a selected vital sign. They should formulate a testable hypothesis and list the steps in the investigation to test this hypothesis, including the equipment and technology that would be used. With your approval, students should then implement their plan using their classmates as subjects. They should record the data and draw conclusions about the effect of time of day on the selected vital sign.

12. Have your students answer the following question to demonstrate their understanding of how to select appropriate equipment and technology:

    Mr. Wright is working in his garden. Suddenly he experiences tightness across his chest and knows this is not a good sign. He uses his cell phone to call 911, and rests until the ambulance arrives. The EMT will assess his condition and put electrodes across his chest to measure his heart action. What is the name of this medical equipment?

    A. Electrocardiograph*

    B. IV

    C. Thermometer

    D. Ophthalmoscope

13. Have a student perform an incremental stationary bicycle test and record heart rate and blood pressure from rest to exhaustion. Note how systolic blood pressure increases at higher exercise workloads and diastolic blood pressure remains nearly the same (important because diastole is when the heart is able to feed itself).

14. Where possible, bring students to a teaching hospital to observe open heart surgery and/or heart transplantation.

15. Have students dissect a cow's heart both sagittally and transversely to observe the differences in valves, chambers, wall thickness, and right/left sides.

MULTIMEDIA

See page 182 for a listing of media resources.

1. *A History of Artificial Heart Research* (FHS; 46 min., 1999, VHS, DVD). Details the frustration-filled history of development of an affordable, complication-free artificial heart.

2. *Circulatory System* (IM; 30 min., 2005, DVD). Examines the structure and functions of the circulatory system, using high-quality microscopic images.

3. *The Circulatory System: Two Hearts That Beat as One* (FHS; 28 min., 1984, VHS, DVD). From the award-winning *Living Body* series, this program outlines the structures of the heart and their functions.

4. *Coronary Heart Disease Revised* (PYR; 17 min., 2000, VHS). Three parts. Discusses the pathology behind coronary heart disease, as well as treatment options.

5. *Taking Charge of Your Heart* (FHS; 19 min., VHS, DVD). This program covers prevention and recovery from heart attacks and also identifies the common symptoms of an attack and reasons why people delay getting medical attention.

6. *Getting Your Heart in Shape* (FHS; 19 min., VHS, DVD). Emphasizes the importance of exercise and its effect on the cardiovascular system, and includes a discussion of sudden death in athletes.

7. *Hypertension: The Facts* (FHS; 29 min., 1998, VHS, DVD). Thoroughly examines all aspects of hypertension, including risk factors and treatment.

8. *Reducing the Risks of Cardiovascular Disease* (FHS; 27 min., 1998, VHS, DVD). Addresses the pathology and prevention of cardiovascular disease.

SOFTWARE

1. *Biology Explorers: Cardiovascular System* (NIMCO; Win/Mac). Explores the interactions between major organs and the cardiovascular system.

2. *Blood and the Circulatory System NEO/LAB* (LP; Win/Mac). Provides interactive exercises on blood typing, morphology, and genetics.

3. *Blood and Immunity* (LP; Win/Mac). Teaches the components of blood, blood types, and the processes of blood. Includes information on HIV.

4. *DynaPulse™200M* (WNS; Win). Acts as an excellent tool for studying cardiovascular function, including systole and diastole.

5. *InterActive Physiology 9-System Suite* (ADAM, BC; Win/Mac). Interactive software with a section on the cardiovascular system that explores the physiology of that system.

6. *Logal Explorer: Cardiovascular System* (WNS; Win/Mac). Explores the blood transport system including pressure and vessel elasticity.

7. *WARD's Physiology of the Circulatory System* (WNS; Win/Mac). Provides a complete review of the cardiovascular system.

The Lymphatic System and Body Defenses

CHAPTER SUMMARY

One of the least recognized of the body systems, the lymphatic system has been gaining ground in recognition and understanding over the past two decades, largely due to research into AIDS, cancer, and autoimmune disorders. It is very important in fighting disease and maintaining healthy homeostatic balance within nearly all body system. Although at first unfamiliar to students, this system quickly piques their interest as a lifesaving system that deserves their attention.

The two semi-independent parts of the lymphatic system are presented first, beginning with the lymphatic vessels and followed by the lymphoid tissues and organs. Next is a full description of body defenses, beginning with an explanation of the nonspecific defenses such as fever and the inflammatory response, which hinder the entry and spread of pathogens. Specific defenses then follow with special focus on the antigen-antibody response. Under immune system regulation, they destroy foreign cells. The cells of the immune system are also outlined and explained.

The next section of the chapter discusses the two types of immune response. Humoral (antibody-mediated) immunity is described first, highlighting the various roles of B cells and explaining the differences between active and passive types of humoral immunity. Cellular (cell-mediated) immunity is presented next, along with a description of the role T cells play in this type of immune response.

The final section of this chapter discusses homeostatic imbalances of the immune system. Organ transplantation and its associated risk of rejection are explained, along with allergies, immunodeficiencies, and autoimmune disorders. Finally, in discussing the developmental aspects of the lymphatic system, there is an explanation that our immune system begins to wane in later life, making us more susceptible to cancer, as well as autoimmune and immunodeficiency diseases.

SUGGESTED LECTURE OUTLINE

PART I: THE LYMPHATIC SYSTEM (pp. 403–408)

I. LYMPHATIC VESSELS (pp. 403–405)
- A. Lymph
- B. Lymph Capillaries
- C. Lymph Collecting Vessels
- D. Ducts

II. LYMPH NODES (pp. 405–407)
- A. White Blood Cells
- B. Node Structure

III. OTHER LYMPHOID ORGANS (pp. 407–408)
- A. Spleen
- B. Thymus gland
- C. Tonsils

TEACHING TIP

Outline the location and origin of lymph fluid, starting with blood plasma. Describe how it is called interstitial fluid once it is pushed out of the blood vessels, that it becomes lymph fluid when picked up by the lymph vessels, and finally, that it is again called blood plasma after it is cleansed and returned to the cardiovascular system.

D. Peyer's Patches
E. Mucosa-Associated Lymphatic Tissue (MALT)

MEDIA TIP

An *Inside Look: The Flu* (IM; 27 min., 2000). This exceptional video illustrates how cells of the immune system fight to protect the body against invasion by the influenza virus.

PART II: BODY DEFENSES (pp. 408–431)

I. INNATE BODY DEFENSES (pp. 409–415; Table 12.1)
   A. Surface Membrane Barriers (p. 409)
   B. Internal Defenses: Cells and Chemicals (pp. 409–415)
      1. Phagocytes
      2. Natural Killer Cells
      3. Inflammatory Response
      4. Antimicrobial Proteins
         a. Complement
         b. Interferon
      5. Fever

II. ADAPTIVE BODY DEFENSES: THE IMMUNE SYSTEM
    (pp. 415–431; Figure 12.19; Table 12.3)
   A. Antigens (Ag)
   B. Cells of the Adaptive Defense System: An Overview
      1. Lymphocytes
      2. Macrophages
   C. Humoral (Antibody-Mediated) Immune Response
      (pp. 418–425)
      1. Active and Passive Humoral Immunity
      2. Antibodies (Immunoglobulins, Igs)
         a. Basic Antibody Structure
         b. Antibody Classes
         c. Antibody Function
   D. Cellular (Cell-Mediated) Immune Response
      (pp. 425–427)
      1. Antigen Presentation
      2. Cytotoxic (Killer) T Cells
      3. Helper T Cells
      4. Regulatory T Cells
      5. Memory Cells
   E. Organ Transplants and Rejection (pp. 427, 429)
      1. Autografts
      2. Isografts
      3. Allografts
      4. Xenografts
   H. Disorders of Immunity (pp. 429–431)
      1. Autoimmune Diseases
      2. Allergies
      3. Immunodeficiencies

PART III: DEVELOPMENTAL ASPECTS OF THE LYMPHATIC SYSTEM AND BODY DEFENSES (pp. 431)

I. THE LYMPHATIC SYSTEM (p. 431)

II. THE IMMUNE SYSTEM (pp. 431, 435)

KEY TERMS

active immunity
adaptive defense system
afferent lymphatic vessels
agglutination
allografts
antibodies
antibody-mediated
  immunity
antigen (Ag)
antigen presentation
antigen-binding site
antimicrobial proteins
autografts
B lymphocytes (B cells)
cell-mediated immunity
cellular immunity
chemotaxis
clonal selection
clone
complement
complement fixation
contant (C) region
cortex
cytokines
cytotoxic (killer) T cells
diapedesis
edema
efferent lymphatic vessels
fever
follicles
germinal centers
hapten

helper T cells
hilium
histamine
humoral immunity
immune response
immune system
immunity
immunocompetent
immunoglobulins (Igs)
immunological memory
immunosuppressive therapy
incomplete antigen
inflammatory response
innate defense system
interferons
isografts
kinins
lymph
lymp capillaries
lymph nodes
lymphatic collecting vessels
lymphatic system
lymphatic vessels
lymphatics
lymphocytes
lymphoid organs
lysozyme
macrophages
medulla
membrane attack complexes
  (MAC)
memory cells

monoclonal antibodies
mucosa-associated
  lymphatic tissue (MALT)
natural killer (NK) cells
neutralization
non-specific defense system
nonself
passive immunity
pathogens
Peyer's patches
phagocytes
plasma cells
precipitation
primary humoral response
pyrogens
regulatory T cells
right lymphatic duct
secondary humoral
  responses
self tolerance
self-antigens
sinuses
specific defense system
spleen
T lymphocytes (T cells)
thoracic duct
thymus gland
tonsils
vaccines
variable (V) region
xenografts

LECTURE HINTS

1. Compare and contrast lymph vessels and blood vessels.

    Key point: Blood vessels form a closed loop or circuit whereas lymph vessels are an open, one-way system. Blood vessels have a pump (the heart) behind them helping to push fluids along, whereas lymph vessels are pumpless (and thus a pulse cannot be felt). Veins and lymph vessels are similar in that they are both thin walled and have one-way valves, and both rely on the milking action of the muscle pump system and pressure changes in the thorax to move fluids along.

2. Outline the location and origin of lymph fluid, starting with blood plasma. Describe how it is called interstitial fluid once it is pushed out of the blood vessels, that it becomes lymph fluid when picked up by the lymph vessels, and finally, that it is again called blood plasma upon its return to the cardiovascular system after cleansing.

    Key point: Point out that this is *all the same fluid*, but that it is called different things depending upon its location at any given time.

3. Reinforce that the right lymphatic duct drains one-fourth of the body (the upper right quadrant) and the thoracic duct drains the remaining three-fourths of the body.

   Key point: The asymmetry of this system is often confusing for students at first.

4. Describe edema as an excess of interstitial fluid and identify some of the common types, including pitting edema and anasarca (generalized edema). Explain that there are numerous causes resulting from homeostatic imbalance of many of the systems, including the renal, pulmonary, and cardiovascular systems.

   Key point: Approximately 24 liters of fluid per day are pushed out of the capillaries to bathe the cells, and if all 24 liters are not reabsorbed, the fluid left behind leads to edema.

5. Discuss post-mastectomy lymphedema and describe exercises and treatments that can help with interstitial fluid return. Also discuss the lymphedema of elephantiasis, usually caused by obstruction of the lymph vessel drainage by an infestation of filarial parasites (a condition most common in the tropics), and explain treatment options for this condition.

   Key point: This will help students visualize the results of poor or absent lymph return and the methods of treatment employed to correct this type of homeostatic imbalance.

6. Explain the various schools of thought related to tonsillectomy and adenoidectomy (T&A).

   Key point: Removal of the tonsils and adenoids following repeated upper respiratory infections is still practiced, although not to the degree it was in generations past. Increased awareness of the role of the lymph system in fighting disease has made it less desirable to remove lymph tissue during transient illnesses than in previous years.

7. List the numerous functions of the spleen, as well as the causes and consequences of splenomegaly. Explain the theories behind splenectomy.

   Key point: The spleen's numerous cleansing functions include control of encapsulated bacteria in the blood and destruction of old RBCs. Cirrhosis and heart failure can lead to spleen enlargement. In thrombocytopenia, the spleen eliminates platelets at a rate faster than they can be replaced, and one treatment option is removal of the spleen to prevent further platelet destruction.

8. List redness, heat, swelling, and pain as the four cardinal signs of the inflammatory response, and emphasize that fever and heat are not the same thing. Note that fever is NOT a symptom of this response. Also note that although inflammation is sometimes painful, students need to understand that the response is a beneficial, essential defense mechanism that paves the way for proper tissue repair. Finally, note that animals with higher body temperatures are generally more resistant to disease.

   Key point: Fever is a separate nonspecific defense mechanism. A fifth sign is occasionally listed as part of the inflammatory response, and that sign is decreased joint movement resulting from swelling.

9. Note that complement proteins represent a nonspecific defense, even though they may be activated as part of a specific response to an antigen. Also point out that complement fixation represents another example of positive feedback.

   Key point: The mechanism of complement fixation is often poorly understood by students and warrants extra time for discussion.

10. Use the acronym M.A.D.G.E. as a memory aid for students in learning the types of immunoglobulins. Emphasize that immunoglobulins are antibodies, and that the two words are synonymous.

    Key point: The word "immunoglobulin" is daunting to students until they realize it is just another term for antibody.

11. Discuss antihistamines and explain when and why they are taken, as well as the role of IgE in necessitating their use.

    Key point: Antihistamines are used to treat allergies, hives, and other hypersensitivity reactions brought about by IgE.

12. Explain the symptoms of anaphylactic shock and the necessary treatment for this life-threatening condition.

    Key point: Anaphylactic shock is a reaction between allergic antigens and IgE. It can only occur following previous exposure to the specific allergic antigen, and it results in bronchospasm, laryngeal edema, and circulatory collapse. Untreated, it can be fatal.

13. Discuss autoantibodies as the basis for autoimmune diseases such as rheumatoid arthritis, myasthenia gravis, and Graves' disease. Use the example of anti-sperm antibodies produced following vasectomy, and note that after 7 to 10 years, there is such an abundance of the antibodies circulating in the bloodstream that attempts at vasectomy reversal after that length of time are usually unsuccessful.

    Key point: Autoantibodies are produced by B cells in response to altered autoantigens, or "self-antigens," although the reasons for this reaction are still being researched.

14. Describe organ transplantation, including the types of organs that can be transplanted and what happens if the body rejects the transplant. Explain why corneal and lens transplants are so successful.

    Key point: Students are usually unaware of the large number of organs that can be transplanted, and may be more willing to become organ donors as a result.

15. Emphasize the importance of breastfeeding infants when possible.

    Key point: Stress the importance of antibody transferral from mother to infant to provide some immunological protection from infection.

16. Explain the use of an immunoglobin injection before traveling to remote areas.

    Key point: Discuss with students the benefits of an immune "boost" when they may be exposed to new antigens and medical help may not be immediately available.

TRANSPARENCIES/MEDIA MANAGER INDEX

Figure 12.1   Relationship of the lymphatic vessels to blood vessels
Figure 12.2   Distribution and special structural features of lymphatic capillaries
Figure 12.3   Distribution of lymphatic vessels and lymph nodes
Figure 12.4   Structure of a lymph node
Figure 12.5   Lymphoid organs
Figure 12.6   An overview of the body's defenses
Figure 12.7   Phagocytosis by a macrophage
Figure 12.8   Flowchart of inflammatory events
Figure 12.9   Phagocyte mobilization
Figure 12.10   Activation of complement, resulting in lysis of a target cell
Figure 12.11   Lymphocyte differentiation and activation
Figure 12.12   Clonal selection of a B cell stimulated by antigen binding
Figure 12.13   Primary and secondary humoral responses to an antigen

ANSWERS TO END OF CHAPTER REVIEW QUESTIONS

Questions appear on pp. 437–439

Multiple Choice

1. c (p. 404)
2. a (p. 406)
3. b (p. 406; Figure 12.4)
4. a, c (p. 408)
5. a, d (p. 431)
6. b, d (pp. 410–411; Figure 12.8)
7. c (p. 411)
8. a, c (pp. 413, 415)
9. b (p. 423; Table 12.2)
10. b, d (pp. 421–422)
11. d (p. 424)
12. a, b, c, d (pp. 429–430)
13. a (p. 432)

Short Answer Essay

14. Lymph nodes remove foreign material such as bacteria and tumor cells from lymph and produce lymphocytes. (p. 405)

15. *Blood* contains formed elements and plasma, which has water, salts, plasma proteins, and other dissolved substances such as nutrients, gases, wastes, and hormones. *Interstitial fluid* is derived from blood and contains similar components as plasma. *Lymph* is leaked fluid forced out of capillary beds due to hydrostatic and osmotic pressure; it is not reabsorbed into the bloodstream. (pp. 403–404)

16. The tonsils are particularly important in preventing bacterial and other foreign pathogens from entering the body via the pharynx. The spleen functions primarily as an RBC "graveyard," i.e., it destroys worn-out RBCs. It also produces lymphocytes and acts as a blood reservoir. (pp. 407–408)

17. Mucus provides a mechanical barrier for pathogens by trapping them. Mucosae are found on the outer surface of the eye and in the linings of all body cavities open to the exterior, that is, the digestive, respiratory, urinary, and reproductive tracts. (pp. 110–111)

    Lysozyme, an enzyme that destroys bacteria, is found in saliva and lacrimal fluid.

    Keratin, a protein in epithelial membranes, presents a physical barrier to microorganisms on the skin, as well as being resistant to most weak acids and bases and to bacterial enzymes and toxins.

    Acid pH of skin secretions inhibits bacterial growth. Vaginal secretions are also very acidic. Hydrochloric acid is secreted by the stomach mucosa and acts to kill pathogens.

    Ciliated mucosa of the upper respiratory tract sweep dust- and bacteria-laden mucus superiorly toward the mouth, preventing it from entering the lower respiratory passages. (see Table 4.1 in Chapter 4)

18. *Complement* is a group of 20 blood proteins that, when activated, causes lysis of the cell to which the antibodies are attached. Other roles of complement include opsonization, inflammatory actions such as stimulating mast cells and basophils to release histamine (which increases vascular permeability), and attracting neutrophils and other inflammatory cells to the affected area. (p. 413)

19. Interferons are secreted by virus-infected cells. They diffuse to nearby cells and bind to their membrane receptors, interfering with the ability of viruses to multiply within these cells. (pp. 413–414)

20. The *immune response* is the response of the body to foreign substances. (p. 415)

21. An *antigen* is a foreign substance (nonself) that is capable of activating an immune response and of interacting with the products (cells and antibodies of that response). An incomplete antigen is a small molecule that connects with our own proteins, unlike a complete antigen which does not. (p. 416)

22. *Humoral immunity* is that portion of the immune system that reflects the work of antibodies produced by B cells or their progeny plasma cells. *Cell-mediated immunity* reflects a cell-mounted attack against antigens that is mediated by T cells. (p. 416)

23. T cells, notably the helper T cells, regulate not only cell-mediated immunity but humoral immunity as well by interacting directly (or indirectly) with B cells. (pp. 416–417)

24. *Immunocompetence* is the capability of mounting an immune response against a particular antigen. The appearance of antigen-specific receptors on the surface of a B cell or T cell signals that it has developed immunocompetence. T cells are programmed in the thymus; B cells are most likely programmed in the bone marrow. (pp. 416–417)

25. Clonal selection involves the rapid cell division of the antigen-activated lymphocyte to produce a "family" or clone of identical cells, all bearing the same antigen-specific receptors. The macrophage is important in clonal selection because it "presents" the antigens to the immunocompetent cells. (pp. 418–419)

26. Members of a B cell clone include B memory cells, which are responsible for immunological "memory," and plasma cells, which are antibody-producing "factories." (pp. 418–419)

27. Helper T cells are the major regulatory cells; they activate the cytotoxic T cells and are the population disabled by HIV. Killer T cells interact directly with virus-infected (or foreign) cells to kill (lyse) them. Suppressor T cells cause the immune response to wind down when the enemy (antigen) has been destroyed or inactivated. (pp. 425–426, 432; Table 12.3)

28. The primary immune response occurs on the first meeting with the antigen; the secondary response is the second and subsequent meeting with the same antigen. The secondary response is faster because all the preparations (clonal selection and memory cells) have been made and immunological memory has been established. (pp. 418–419)

29. An antibody is basically Y-shaped. It consists of two heavy chains and two light chains, each with a constant region and a variable region. The constant regions determine antibody class and where and how the antibody acts in the body. The variable regions form the antigen-binding sites. (pp. 421–422)

30. The five classes of immunoglobulins are IgM, IgG, IgE, IgA, and IgD. IgD is attached to B cell membranes; IgG is most abundant in plasma and crosses placental barriers; IgE is involved in allergic responses; IgM is the first antibody released in the primary response and some are bound to B cell membranes. IgG and IgM bind complement. IgA is present in body secretions that bathe membranes, that is, in tears, saliva, and mucus. (pp. 422–423; Table 12.2)

31. Antibodies defend the body by fixing complement and by neutralizing, agglutinating, and precipitating antigens. (pp. 423–424)

32. Acute allergic responses occur and resolve within minutes and are mediated by IgE antibodies bound to mast cells. The mast cells release histamine upon antigen-antibody binding, and histamine causes blood vessels to become leaky. Typical symptoms are runny nose (or asthma), watery eyes, and hives. Delayed-reaction allergies are mediated by T cells and occur hours to days after exposure to the allergen. (pp. 430–431; Figure 12.20)

33. An autoimmune disease may result from a change in self-antigens, the appearance of self-antigens not previously recognized by the immune system, or the cross-reaction of antibodies produced against foreign antigens with self-antigens. (pp. 429–430)

34. Lack of memory B cells for a particular antigen would not enable the body to mount its normally stronger attack on a previously encountered pathogen, thus reducing the secondary humoral response. (p. 419)

ANSWERS TO CRITICAL THINKING AND CLINICAL APPLICATION QUESTIONS

35. The infant will develop artificially acquired active immunity. (p. 420)

36. IgA is found primarily in mucus and other secretions that bathe body surfaces. It plays an important role in preventing pathogens from entering the body. Lack of IgA would result in frequent major/minor infections of the sinuses or respiratory tract infections. (Table 12.2)

37. Actively acquired immunity to previous flu virus antigens will not protect against new proteins (antigens) on the viral coat. (pp. 418–420)

38. Lymph nodes and vessels help to return fluid to the circulatory system. Removal results in severe localized edema. She can expect chronic edema along the arm although some lymphatic drainage is eventually reestablished by regrowth of lymph vessels from veins. (pp. 403, 407)

39. Lymphocyte circulation through both blood and lymph is important because it greatly increases the chance of the lymphocytes coming into contact with antigens. (pp. 403–404)

CLASSROOM DEMONSTRATIONS AND STUDENT ACTIVITIES

Classroom Demonstrations

1. Film(s) or other media of choice.

2. Use the torso model to demonstrate the location of the lymph organs and tissues.

3. Invite a speaker from the local public health department to present the most current information on AIDS.

4. Form an AIDS panel with speakers from public health, local support groups, and AIDS sufferers.

5. Invite speakers to talk to the class on treatment options, current research, and issues related to living with multiple sclerosis, rheumatoid arthritis, myasthenia gravis, Graves' disease, type I diabetes mellitus, lupus, or any other immune-related disorder.

6. Invite a speaker from the local public health department to outline vaccine schedules as required or recommended by the government. Discuss current issues surrounding public resistance to vaccines, their benefits as well as potential side effects, and the debate about choice, especially with the recent discussion regarding autism.

7. Use video presentations and images to contrast the four major kinds of grafts: autografts, isografts, allografts, and xenografts. List the advantages and disadvantages of each.

Student Activities

1. Use WARD's Simulated Disease Transmission Lab Activity. This is a fun, eye-opening activity that helps students understand the speed and extensiveness with which diseases spread.

2. Ask students to research communicable diseases and present their findings on the top ten diseases in their local area compared to the national figures. Assist them in accessing information from the Centers for Disease Control and Prevention.

3. Provide diagrams of the lymph system for students to label.

4. Explain the process of testing for pitting edema by pressing a fingertip over a bony prominence for 5 seconds, then release. Have the students try this on themselves and note any evidence of edema or dehydration.

5. Have students draw a concept map or outline of the processes of defense secondary to injury.

6. Ask students to research physical and psychological stress and its impact on the immune system. Contrast the difference between eustress (good stress) and distress (bad stress).

7. Student assignment for class discussion: Look up articles in the newspaper or popular magazines that concern the social, medical, and economic problems surrounding AIDS. Emphasize the global implications of this disease.

8. Have students outline the four categories of immunity: naturally acquired active immunity, naturally acquired passive immunity, artificially acquired active immunity, and artificially acquired passive immunity. Be sure they include examples of each in their outline.

9. Have students research new developments on the HIV and HPV vaccines.

10. Provide microscope slides showing infected cells and the various immune responses to the infection.

11. Have students test their own blood type to view the agglutination reaction with antibodies to the A and B antigens on red blood cells.

MULTIMEDIA

See page 182 for a listing of media resources.

1. *AIDS: A Biological Perspective* (FHS; 30 min., 1995, VHS, DVD). Award-winning video that explores many of the difficult questions surrounding AIDS, including why a vaccine has been so difficult to find.

2. *Attacking Your Allergies* (FHS; 19 min., VHS, DVD). Examines allergies on a genetic and environmental level, with discussions on common allergens and medications, including immunotherapy.

3. *An Inside Look: The Flu* (IM; 27 min., 2000, VHS). This exceptional video illustrates how cells of the immune system fight to protect the body against invasion by the influenza virus.

4. *Living with Arthritis* (FHS; 28 min., VHS, DVD). This program covers treatment protocols, warning signs, and the impact of living without treatment, and includes medical commentary from the expert who created joint implants.

5. *Out of Control: AIDS in Black America* (FHS; 41 min., VHS, DVD). Investigative journalist Peter Jennings covers the rise in AIDS among the African American community and includes candid discussions with several black leaders.

6. *Defend and Repair* (NIMCO; 30 min., 1994, VHS). From the *Body Atlas* series, this video explores the world of the immune system in fighting invasion, as well as the body's mechanisms of repair.

7. *AIDS Education* (FHS; 1995, VHS, DVD). Two-part video series includes *Gone Tomorrow: AIDS Awareness* and *AIDS: A Biological Perspective.* This series explains the HIV virus, its behavior, and why it is so difficult to destroy.

8. *Human Immune System* (IM; 20 min., 2002, DVD). Explains how the immune system defends the body against foreign invaders.

9. *Immunizations* (FHS; 18 min., 1994). Explains the need for vaccinations against disease and identifies the recommended pediatric immunization schedule.

10. *Influenza* (FHS; 51 min., 2002, VHS, DVD). Examines the factors of transmission of the flu, including dangers to high-risk groups.

11. *Avoiding Infectious and Sexually Transmitted Diseases* (FHS; 1998, VHS, DVD). This two-part series includes *Human Sexuality: A Contemporary Guide* and *Total Health: Achieving Your Personal Best.* This program presents an overview of how to reduce the risk of infection, the body's natural defenses, symptoms of contraction, and available medical treatments.

12. *Vaccinations: Hidden Harm?* (FHS; 22 min., 1999, VHS, DVD). Examines the mixed messages that the public receives about vaccination.

13. *The Immune System at Work* (FHS; 17 min., 2003, VHS, DVD). An edition of *Science Screen Report* that explains the functions of the immune system, what happens when it fails, and the different roles of vaccines and penicillin.

SOFTWARE

1. *Blood and Immunity* (LP; Win/Mac). Teaches the components of blood, blood types, and the processes of blood. Includes information on HIV.

2. *Human Health* (FHS; Win/Mac). Looks at various health concerns, including heart disease, cancer, and autoimmune deficiencies, and lifestyle factors that contribute to them.

3. *InterActive Physiology 9-System Suite* (ADAM, BC; Win/Mac). Interactive software with a section on the immune system that explores the physiology of that system.

The Respiratory System

CHAPTER SUMMARY

The respiratory system is intimately connected to the cardiovascular system. Together, they work to supply all body cells with oxygen and dispose of metabolic end products such as carbon dioxide. Neither system can function alone, thus making them one of the most important homeostatic teams in the body.

In the first section of this chapter, the anatomy of the respiratory system is outlined. The nose, pharynx, larynx, trachea, bronchi, and bronchioles are discussed first. It is noted that in addition to being conducting zone structures that allow air to reach the lungs, these organs also purify, humidify, and warm incoming air. The lungs are presented next, including a review of their basic structure and position. The respiratory zone structures, comprised of the bronchioles, alveolar ducts, alveolar sacs, and alveoli within the lungs, are the actual sites of external respiratory gas exchange. An explanation of the role of the respiratory membrane in this exchange of gases through simple diffusion is provided.

The next section of this chapter presents respiratory physiology and the mechanics of ventilation. Pulmonary ventilation, inspiration, and expiration are all described. The ventilatory volumes are outlined, including tidal volume, inspiratory reserve volume, expiratory reserve volume, residual volume, and vital capacity. Differences between external respiration, which is the actual exchange of gases between the alveoli and the blood, and internal respiration, which is the exchange of gases between the systemic capillaries and the tissues, are explored. The factors involved in control of respiration are also described, including neural regulation, volition, emotional, and chemical factors.

The final section of this chapter explores respiratory disorders not previously presented in the chapter. Common respiratory conditions, such as COPD, cystic fibrosis, asthma, sinusitis, pleurisy, and many others, are discussed.

SUGGESTED LECTURE OUTLINE

I. FUNCTIONAL ANATOMY OF THE RESPIRATORY SYSTEM (pp. 441–448)
    A. The Nose (pp. 441–443)
        1. Structure
        2. Palate
        3. Paranasal Sinuses
    B. Pharynx (pp. 443–444)
        1. Regions
        2. Tonsils
    C. The Larynx (p. 444)
    D. Trachea (pp. 444–445)
    E. Main Bronchi (p. 445)
    F. Lungs (pp. 445–448)
        1. Structure
        2. Pleura
        3. Bronchioles

TEACHING TIP

Present an overview of several conditions categorized as chronic obstructive pulmonary diseases (COPD) such as asthma, emphysema, and chronic bronchitis. Point out that with emphysema, the respiratory center is sensitive to changes in oxygen instead of carbon dioxide. For this reason, it is wise not to administer high concentrations of oxygen to people with emphysema since doing so could result in forced apnea.

4. Alveoli
5. The Respiratory Membrane

II. RESPIRATORY PHYSIOLOGY (pp. 448–460)
   A. Mechanics of Breathing (pp. 449–452; Figure 13.7)
      1. Inspiration
      2. Expiration
      3. Intrapleural Pressure
      4. Nonrespiratory Air Movements
   B. Respiratory Volumes and Capacities (pp. 452–453; Figure 13.9))
   C. Respiratory Sounds (p. 453)
   D. External Respiration, Gas Transport, and Internal Respiration (pp. 453–456)
      1. External Respiration
      2. Gas Transport in the Blood
      3. Internal Respiration
   E. Control of Respiration (pp. 456–460)
      1. Neural Regulation: Setting the Basic Rhythm
      2. Nonneural Factors Influencing Respiratory Rate and Depth
         a. Physical Factors
         b. Volition (Conscious Control)
         c. Emotional Factors
         d. Chemical Factors

III. RESPIRATORY DISORDERS (pp. 460–461)
   A. Lung Cancer (pp. 458–459)
   B. Chronic Obstructive Pulmonary Disease (COPD) (pp. 460–461)
      1. Chronic Bronchitis
      2. Emphysema

IV. DEVELOPMENTAL ASPECTS OF THE RESPIRATORY SYSTEM (pp. 461–464)
   A. Surfactant (p. 461)
      1. Infant Respiratory Distress Syndrome (IRDS)
      2. Cystic Fibrosis
   B. Respiration Rate Changes (p. 464)
      1. Sudden Infant Death Syndrome (SIDS)
   C. Other Respiratory Problems (p. 464)
      1. Asthma
      2. Sleep Apnea

MEDIA TIP

U*nderstanding the Risks of Tobacco and Caffeine* (FHS; 29 min., 2001). From the new series, *Substance Abuse: Risks and Responsibilities*, this video addresses the major health risks associated with smoking tobacco and the excessive drinking of caffeinated beverages, with emphasis on lung cancer and other smoking-related conditions.

KEY TERMS

alveolar macrophages	bicarbonate ion	conducting zone structures
alveoli	breathing	dead space volume
apex	bronchial sounds	diaphragm
asthma	bronchioles	epiglottis
base	conchae	eupnea

expiration
expiratory reserve volume (ERV)
external intercostals
glottis
hard palate
hyaline cartilage
hyperpnea
hyperventilation
inspiration
inspiratory reserve volume (IRV)
intercostal nerves
intrapleural pressure
intrapulmonary volume
laryngopharynx
larynx
lingual tonsils
lungs
main (primary) bronchi

mediastinum
nares
nasal cavity
nasal septum
nasopharynx
nonrespiratory air movements
nose
nostrils
oropharynx
oxyhemoglobin
palate
palatine tonsils
paranasal sinuses
parietal pleura
pharyngeal tonsil
pharynx
phrenic nerves
pleural space
posterior nasal aperture

pulmonary pleura
residual volume
respiration
respiratory membrane (air-blood barrier)
respiratory system
respiratory zone
self-exciting inspiratory center
sleep apnea
soft palate
surfactant
thyroid cartilage
tidal volume (TV)
trachea
true vocal cords
vesicular breathing sounds
visceral pleura
vital capacity (VC)
vocal folds

LECTURE HINTS

1. Emphasize the interplay between the respiratory and cardiovascular systems.

   Key point: Of all the systems, these two are the most intimately connected. We separate them for study purposes, but they must really be considered a functional team.

2. Clearly pronounce *pharynx* (far′ inks) and *larynx* (lar′ inks) and have students repeat the correct pronunciation of these two terms. Reinforce that the pharynx (throat) is shared by air and food while the larynx (voice box) only has air passage.

   Key point: These are two of the most commonly mispronounced words in science. Students usually say *far′ niks* and *lar′ niks* and are surprised to learn that they have been mispronouncing these words all their lives. This is a good time to help them break a bad pronunciation habit.

3. Discuss tonsillitis and reiterate the discussion from the lymph chapter on the pros and cons of tonsillectomy and adenoidectomy (T&A).

   Key point: This is a common surgery that waxes and wanes in popularity, with more older students having had their tonsils removed than younger students. This is a good opportunity to explain the various lines of thinking involved in making a decision either for or against surgical removal of these organs.

4. Explain the function of the cough reflex to expel and prevent food from entering the lungs. Include a discussion of the Heimlich maneuver, which is used to dislodge an obstruction from the respiratory passages. Also correlate aspiration pneumonia to food or some other foreign object that has been inhaled into the respiratory passages and has not been successfully removed.

   Key point: This helps students understand the seriousness of aspiration and helps them develop a sense of the many natural and artificial mechanisms employed to prevent this occurrence.

5. Discuss the differences between tracheostomy and tracheotomy.

   Key point: Tracheostomy is the surgical opening into the trachea to provide a patent airway. Tracheotomy is the actual incision into the trachea to make the opening. Note that these two terms are often used as synonyms, even though medically they have distinct meanings.

6. Spend time differentiating between the visceral and parietal pleura. Note that the pain associated with pleurisy mimics that of the initial symptoms of a heart attack and results from these two membranes rubbing against each other like two pieces of sandpaper, rather than the usual gliding motion.

   Key point: The double layer of the pleura often confuses students, but they can usually visualize the friction that would result from two dry, rough surfaces rubbing together.

7. Emphasize the purely mechanical nature of inspiration and expiration. Explain that as the chest space expands, air will rush in to equalize the inner and outer pressures, and as the chest contracts, air will be pushed out again for the same reason. Point out that although the intercostal muscles are important at high levels of ventilation, it is the diaphragm that accomplishes most of the change in volume of the thorax during inspiration. Note that singers learn to control their diaphragm as they initiate sound from deep in their thorax.

   Key point: The body is continuously striving for balance and equilibrium, and the mechanisms of breathing are excellent representatives of this process.

8. Differentiate between atelectasis and pneumothorax. Explain that pneumothorax is just one of the many possible causes of atelectasis. Also note that atelectasis literally means "incomplete expansion" and pneumothorax means "air in the chest." Ask the students to then explain what hemothorax means. Describe the outcome of a sucking chest wound, such as might result from stabbing with a knife or piercing with a bullet or arrow.

   Key point: With a sucking chest wound, a puncture opening allows air to suck into the chest, collapsing the lung as it fills the chest cavity. In an emergency situation, collapse of the lung is stopped or prevented by applying an occlusive bandage over the opening. A credit card is the right size for this purpose.

9. Discuss the post-operative use of the incentive spirometer, which is the apparatus with the Ping-Pong ball in it. A post-operative patient is asked to inhale and suck the Ping-Pong ball to the top of the device, usually at least ten times per hour.

   Key point: This helps prevent pneumonia by keeping the lungs inflated while the patient is on bedrest. Historically, pneumonia was the leading cause of death in post-surgical patients, and this simple technique greatly reduces that risk.

10. Explain respiratory center failure and treatment options in such situations as cervical collapse of the spinal cord. Discuss ventilator dependency and the advent of phrenic pacing as an alternative in some cases. Students are usually familiar with Christopher Reeves, and a discussion of his injury helps them understand the respiratory ramifications.

    Key point: Spinal cord prolapse at the C-1 and C-2 levels results in respiratory failure, necessitating mechanical ventilation through a tracheostomy. C-3 or higher quadriplegics are relatively rare as traumatic injury this high in the spinal column necessarily requires artificial ventilation within about 5 minutes after the injury in order to stay alive. The rhyme, *C-3, -4, -5 helps you breathe to stay alive,* is easy to remember. In some cases, a phrenic pacing device similar to a cardiac pacemaker can be implanted into the chest wall to send electrical signals to the diaphragm, causing it to contract and move down. The passive processes of respiration proceed from there.

11. Students are usually familiar with hyperventilation and its link to anxiety. Explain the mechanism by which breathing into a paper bag acts to raise the CO_2 levels, thus

reversing the symptoms, but caution them that this can lead to hypoxemia, such as when children breathe excessively prior to contests to see who can hold their breath under water the longest in a swimming pool. Note that another, often preferred, method is to have the individual breathe through only one nostril with mouth closed until normal breathing is restored.

Key point: Hyperventilation results in lowered CO_2 levels, known as hypocapnia, such as when children breathe excessively prior to contests to see who can hold their breath under water the longest in a swimming pool. Immediate treatment is aimed at restoring the CO_2 levels, followed by determination of the underlying cause.

12. Present an overview of the chronic obstructive pulmonary diseases (COPD), and differentiate between asthma, emphysema, and chronic bronchitis. Point out that with emphysema, the respiratory center is sensitive to changes in oxygen instead of carbon dioxide. For this reason, it is wise not to administer high concentrations of oxygen to people with emphysema since doing so could result in forced apnea.

Key point: These conditions have many similarities as well as key differences. Emphasize the role of cigarette smoking in all of these conditions.

13. Explain the relationship of surfactant to lung expansion in infants. Discuss the results of incompletely developed lungs in premature infants, resulting in IRDS (infant respiratory distress syndrome).

Key point: Surfactant decreases surface tension, thus allowing alveoli to stay expanded and preventing lung collapse. Surfactant production is usually at a desirable level in a 32- to 36-week fetus. Infants born prior to this time often suffer from IRDS and must be maintained on a ventilator until adequate surfactant levels are achieved. Surfactant production can be stimulated by administration of a glucocorticoid one to two days prior to a preterm birth, and synthetic surfactant can be given to patients suffering from respiratory distress syndrome.

14. Explain the use of bronchodilators to treat asthma, and show how a severe asthma attack can be fatal.

Key point: Stress the importance of the muscles in the respiratory system for keeping the airway open.

15. Discuss the importance of prompt response when CPR is needed to keep oxygen moving throughout the body.

Key point: Re-emphasize the need of the brain for oxygen, and how quickly brain tissue dies when oxygen is absent.

16. Describe lung cancer, including its link with smoking, and also how tumors frequently appear in the lungs during metastasis.

Key point: Students are usually aware that smoking can lead to lung cancer, but often do not understand why many cancers metastasize to the lungs.

17. Explain the nonrespiratory movements of the respiratory system including coughing, yawning, hiccupping, and laughing.

Key point: Students are frequently interested in learning what causes these nonrespiratory movements.

TRANSPARENCIES/MEDIA MANAGER INDEX

Figure 13.1   The major respiratory organs shown in relation to surrounding structures

Figure 13.2   Basic anatomy of the upper respiratory tract, sagittal section

Indicates images that are on the Media Manager only.

ANSWERS TO END OF CHAPTER REVIEW QUESTIONS

Questions appear on pp. 466–467

Multiple Choice

1. d (pp. 441–447)
2. d (p. 451; Figure 13.7)
3. b (p. 451)
4. b (pp. 447, 451)
5. b, c (pp. 460–461)
6. c, d (p. 464)
7. b (p. 447)

Short Answer Essay

8. External respiration is the process of gas exchange that occurs between the blood of the pulmonary capillaries and the external environment (alveolar air). Internal respiration is the process of gas exchange that occurs between the blood of the systemic capillaries and the tissue cells. (pp. 448–449)

9. External nares to nasal cavities to nasopharynx to oropharynx to laryngopharynx to larynx to trachea to right or left primary bronchus to secondary (tertiary, etc.) bronchi to bronchioles (to alveolar ducts) to alveolus. (pp. 441–447)

10. The cartilaginous reinforcements keep the trachea patent during the pressure changes that occur during breathing. The incomplete rings of the posterior tracheal surface

make it flexible, allowing a food bolus traveling through the posterior esophagus to bulge anteriorly. (p. 444)

11. Primarily in the nasal cavities, but the warming and moistening process continues for the entire length of the respiratory passageways. (pp. 441–442)

12. Mucus serves to trap dust, bacteria, and other foreign debris that manage to enter the respiratory passageways. (pp. 441–445)

13. If either the middle ear or the sinuses are infected, the exudate will drain into the nasal passages and possibly lead to congestion, or "postnasal drip." Conversely, a nasopharyngeal infection can easily spread to the middle ear cavity or the sinuses because of the continuity of their mucosae, thus causing otitis media or sinusitis, respectively. (pp. 443–444)

14. Their walls are extremely thin (one layer of squamous epithelium plus a basement membrane) for easy gas exchange, and combined, they present an extremely large surface area. (p. 447)

15. *TV:* Tidal volume; the amount of air inspired or expired during a normal breath. *ERV:* Expiratory reserve volume; the amount of air that can be forcibly exhaled beyond a normal tidal expiration. *VC:* Vital capacity; total exchangeable air. (p. 452)

16. All nonrespiratory air movements are described in Table 13.1. (p. 452)

17. When the diaphragm contracts, it moves inferiorly, thereby increasing the intrathoracic volume in the superior-inferior dimension. The contraction of the external intercostal muscles elevates the rib cage, increasing the intrathoracic volume in the anterior-posterior and lateral dimensions. As the intrathoracic volume is increased, the intrapulmonary pressure decreases. (p. 457; Figure 13.7)

18. Oxygen is mainly transported bound to hemoglobin within RBCs. (p. 454–455)

19. Gases diffuse according to their concentration gradients, that is, from an area of their higher concentration to an area of their lower concentration. Venous blood is high in carbon dioxide and low in oxygen compared to alveolar air; thus, carbon dioxide tends to leave the pulmonary blood to enter the alveolar air, and oxygen tends to move from the alveoli into the pulmonary capillary blood. Arterial blood is high in oxygen and low in carbon dioxide; thus, the diffusion gradient in the tissues is opposite to that in the lungs. (p. 454–456; Figure 13.11)

20. Medulla (inspiratory and expiratory centers) and pons (apneustic and pneumotaxic centers). (p. 456)

21. Talking, coughing (and other types of nonrespiratory air movements), exercise, and increased body temperature. (p. 456)

22. Decreases in oxygen content of the blood and changes in carbon dioxide blood concentration (leading to increased or decreased blood pH). The latter factor is much more important in respiratory control. (pp. 457, 460)

23. *Hyperventilation* is rapid, deep breathing. During hyperventilation more carbon dioxide is expelled. Since this decreases the carbonic acid content of the blood, the blood pH increases (becomes more alkaline). To counteract this effect, the breathing rate must be decreased. (p. 460)

24. In emphysema, the individual has problems exhaling due to loss of elasticity of the lungs. Consequently, expiration becomes an active process, and the person is always tired. A barrel chest develops from air retention, but cyanosis is a late sign. In chronic bronchitis, inspiration is a problem because the respiratory passages are narrowed by the inflamed mucosa and excessive mucus. Infections are common because mucus pools in the lungs. Cyanosis occurs early in the disease. (p. 461)

ANSWERS TO CRITICAL THINKING
AND CLINICAL APPLICATION QUESTIONS

25. The boy most likely swallowed the bead and it entered the respiratory tract. It could probably be found in the right primary bronchus. (p. 445)

26. Voluntary control of breathing is limited by the body's need to obtain oxygen and get rid of carbon dioxide. When these processes are impaired, involuntary controls take over. (p. 456)

27. The larynx functions to provide an open airway to the trachea and lungs. Edematous swelling of the mucosa of the larynx would close the airway, blocking all air entering the trachea. Tracheotomy is a surgical incision into the trachea through the anterior neck. It allows air to reach the lungs when the larynx is blocked. (p. 444)

28. While swallowing, respiratory passages are blocked off so that food will be forced to enter the digestive tract. The soft palate rises to block the nasopharynx and the epiglottis folds over the opening into the larynx. If swallowing is uncoordinated, these openings could be blocked inappropriately and air flow prevented. (p. 443)

29. A drop in blood pH stimulates an increased rate and depth of breathing. Blowing off an increased amount of CO_2 helps to return the blood pH to the normal range (respiratory compensation). (pp. 457, 460)

30. *Pneumothorax* is a general term for air within the intrapleural space. *Atelectasis* is a condition of lung collapse whereby the lung is rendered useless for ventilation. His condition would be treated by closing the hole and drawing air out of the intrapleural space with chest tubes, which allows the lungs to reinflate and presumably resume normal function. (pp. 451–452)

CLASSROOM DEMONSTRATIONS AND STUDENT ACTIVITIES

Classroom Demonstrations

1. Film(s) or other media of choice.

2. Use the torso model to demonstrate the location of the respiratory organs.

3. Demonstrate the Heimlich maneuver as a technique for removing a foreign body, such as aspirated food, from the trachea or pharynx.

4. Invite a speaker from the American Lung Association to talk about the relationship between pulmonary diseases and smoking.

5. Demonstrate the cohesive effect that exists between the two pleural layers by putting a drop of water on a glass slide and then covering it with a second slide. Show that the slides easily move from side to side but are difficult to pull apart directly.

6. Use a skull to show the location of the sinuses.

7. Invite speakers to talk to the class on treatment options, current research, and issues related to living with cystic fibrosis, emphysema, or asthma.

8. Use a "model lung" consisting of a bell jar with balloon "lungs" and a rubber "diaphragm" to illustrate the fact that volume changes in the thorax lead to the flow of gases in and out of the lungs during breathing.

9. Show prepared slides or diagrams of healthy lung tissue and lung tissue from patients who died from emphysema or lung cancer.

10. Show preserved specimens of diseased lungs that exhibit signs of COPD, emphysema, cancer, or pulmonary embolism.

Student Activities

1. Prior to the beginning of lecture on the respiratory system, hand out a small straw, like those used as stir sticks, to each student. Ask them to breathe through the straw while you begin the lecture. After a few minutes, ask the students to describe the feelings they have from inadequate oxygen intake and relate those feelings to the way that a person with emphysema feels constantly.

2. Provide stethoscopes so that students can auscultate respiratory sounds over various regions of their classmate's thorax. Define some of the usual breath sounds (wheezing, rales, rhonchi) found with patients suffering from various respiratory conditions, such as asthma and chronic bronchitis.

3. Obtain several incentive spirometers so students can practice the technique of inhaling while moving the Ping-Pong ball up the cylinder. Explain that this is significantly more difficult following abdominal surgery or general anesthesia. Also have students measure their respiratory volumes, including tidal volume and vital capacity.

4. Provide straws, beakers of water, and pH paper. Have students use the straws to blow into the water in the beakers. Since exhaled air contains substantially more carbon dioxide than inhaled air, they will be adding carbon dioxide to the water, which will cause it to become acidic. Have them measure the pH of water at intervals to follow the change in pH.

5. Have the students practice different types of breathing, such as diaphragmatic, abdominal, and shallow breathing, and note the muscles and organs used in each method.

6. When discussing the importance of surfactant in aiding lung inflation, ask students to blow up balloons that are dry inside versus balloons that are wet inside. The surface tension of the water makes it difficult to inflate the balloon.

7. Assign students the task of researching the latest information on SIDS (sudden infant death syndrome) and come to class prepared to discuss their findings.

8. Assign students the task of researching cigarette smoking and its respiratory sequelae, including lung cancer and emphysema. Have them include the latest research on the effects of secondhand smoke in children.

9. Demonstrate two ways to blow up a balloon; blowing air into it and placing it within an airtight container before sucking out the air. The latter occurs within the intrapleural space surrounding the lungs.

10. Have students test their lung capacity before and after exercise using a spirometer, and discuss how they can calculate and measure their various respiratory volumes. Compare results between students of different ages and fitness levels.

MULTIMEDIA

See page 182 for a listing of media resources.

1. *Circulation, Respiration, and Breathing* (FHS; 20 min., 2001, VHS, DVD). This program explains the complementary functions of the circulatory and respiratory systems that work together to meet the body's energy needs.

2. *Breathing* (FHS; 20 min., 1995, VHS, DVD). From the award winning *The New Living Body* series, this video looks at the typical day in the life of a cystic fibrosis sufferer, and problems encountered by individuals with that hereditary disease.

3. *Respiration* (FHS; 14 min., 1996, VHS, DVD). From *The World of Living Organisms* series, this video describes external and internal respiration and explains how energy for bodily functions is produced.

4. *Respiratory System: Intake and Exhaust* (FHS; 25 min., 1998, VHS, DVD). From *The Human Body: Systems at Work* series, this program uses the analogy of an automobile's system of fuel intake and exhaust to explore the makeup and functions of the respiratory system.

5. *Understanding the Risks of Tobacco and Caffeine* (FHS; 29 min., 1998, VHS, DVD). From the new series, *Substance Abuse: Risks and Responsibilities*, this video addresses the major health risks associated with smoking tobacco and the excessive drinking of caffeinated beverages, with emphasis on lung cancer and other smoking-related conditions.

SOFTWARE

1. *InterActive Physiology 9-System Suite* (ADAM, BC; Win/Mac). Interactive software with a section on the respiratory system that explores the physiology of that system.

2. *Respiratory System* (WNS; Win/Mac). Simulates the mechanical and physiological workings of the human respiratory system.

The Digestive System and Body Metabolism

CHAPTER SUMMARY

The digestive system chapter is broken down into two distinct parts. Part I delves into the anatomy and physiology of the digestive system. This portion is the easier of the two parts for students to learn, since people have always been fascinated by the workings of their digestive system. Part II delves into the nutritional and metabolic aspects of digestion. Since these concepts are often difficult to visualize, this is often the area students find most confusing.

In outlining digestive system anatomy, the tubular structure of the alimentary canal, with openings at both ends (like a hose), is emphasized. The organs of this canal are the mouth, pharynx, esophagus, stomach, small intestine, and large intestine. Each of these components is described in detail, and examples of homeostatic imbalances are explained where pertinent. A discussion of the accessory digestive organs follows the information on the alimentary canal, including the salivary glands, teeth, tongue, pancreas, liver, and gallbladder. These accessory organs assist the process of digestion in a variety of ways, each of which is explained individually within the chapter. The overall general functions of the digestive system are presented next. They include ingestion, propulsion, mechanical digestion, chemical digestion, absorption, and defecation. Each of these activities is discussed in relation to the organs in which they occur.

In Part II, the basics of nutrition are presented. It is explained that once foods are digested and absorbed into the bloodstream, the next step involves utilization of the nutrients obtained. The major nutrients include carbohydrates, lipids, proteins, vitamins, and minerals. Metabolism is the mechanism by which these nutrients are used, and a detailed explanation of the two ongoing and interrelated metabolic processes, catabolism and anabolism, explains the process. Carbohydrate metabolism and production of ATP for energy is explored, along with fat metabolism and storage, as well as protein breakdown, which provides amino acids for new protein construction. The role of the liver in metabolism is also presented, as is cholesterol metabolism and transport.

The final section of this chapter explores the relationship between energy intake and energy output. Basal metabolic rate is compared with total metabolic rate. Processes involved in body temperature regulation are explained, and the most important developmental aspects are presented, along with some of the major homeostatic imbalances such as PKU and cleft palate.

SUGGESTED LECTURE OUTLINE

PART I: ANATOMY AND PHYSIOLOGY OF THE DIGESTIVE SYSTEM (pp. 469–493)

I. ANATOMY OF THE DIGESTIVE SYSTEM (pp. 469–481)
   A. Organs of the Alimentary Canal (GI Tract) (pp. 470–479; Figure 14.1)
      1. Mouth
      2. Pharynx

TEACHING TIP

Note that the villi, microvilli, and circular folds of the small intestine are key to major amounts of absorption, whereas the mucosa of the stomach lining produces large amounts of mucus that protects the stomach wall from digestion by its own juices. Emphasize the structural modifications in each area of the GI tract that lead to optimum digestion and absorption.

3. Esophagus
4. Stomach
5. Small Intestine
   a. Duodenum
   b. Jejunum
   c. Ileum
6. Large Intestine
   a. Cecum
   b. Appendix
   c. Colon
      i. Ascending
      ii. Transverse
      iiii. Descending
      iv. Sigmoid
   d. Rectum
   e. Anal Canal
   f. Anus
   B. Accessory Digestive Organs (pp. 479–481)
      1. Teeth
      2. Salivary Glands
      3. Pancreas
      4. Liver and Gallbladder

II. FUNCTIONS OF THE DIGESTIVE SYSTEM
    (pp. 481–493)
    A. Overview of Gastrointestinal Processes and Controls
       (pp. 481–485)
       1. Ingestion
       2. Propulsion
       3. Food Breakdown: Mechanical Digestion
       4. Food Breakdown: Chemical Digestion
       5. Absorption
       6. Defecation
    B. Activities Occurring in the Mouth, Pharynx, and
       Esophagus (p. 485)
       1. Food Ingestion and Breakdown
       2. Food Propulsion—Swallowing and Peristalsis
    C. Activities of the Stomach (pp. 485–488)
       1. Food Breakdown
       2. Food Propulsion
    D. Activities of the Small Intestine (pp. 489–492)
       1. Food Breakdown and Absorption
       2. Food Propulsion
    E. Activities of the Large Intestine (p. 492)
       1. Food Breakdown and Absorption
    F. Propulsion of the Residue and Defecation
       (pp. 492–493)

MEDIA TIP

The Human Digestive System (BC; 33 min., 1998). This video provides an excellent overview of the human digestive system.

PART II: NUTRITION AND METABOLISM (pp. 493–506)

I. NUTRITION (pp. 493–495)
   A. Dietary Sources of Major Nutrients (pp. 494–495)
      1. Carbohydrates
      2. Lipids
      3. Proteins
      4. Vitamins
      5. Minerals

II. METABOLISM (pp. 495–506)
   A. Carbohydrate, Fat, and Protein Metabolism in Body Cells (pp. 496–500)
      1. Carbohydrate Metabolism
      2. Fat Metabolism
      3. Protein Metabolism
   B. The Central Role of the Liver in Metabolism (pp. 500–502)
      1. General Metabolic Functions
         a. Glycogenesis
         b. Glycogenolysis
         c. Gluconeogenesis
      2. Cholesterol Metabolism and Transport
         a. Low-Density Lipoproteins (LDLs)
         b. High-Density Lipoproteins (HDLs)
   C. Body Energy Balance (pp. 502–506)
      1. Regulation of Food Intake
      2. Metabolic Rate and Body Heat Production
         a. Basal Metabolic Rate
         b. Total Metabolic Rate
      3. Body Temperature Regulation
         a. Heat-Promoting Mechanisms
         b. Heat Loss Mechanisms

PART III: DEVELOPMENTAL ASPECTS OF THE DIGESTIVE SYSTEM AND METABOLISM (pp. 506–507)

I. DEVELOPMENTAL ASPECTS OF THE DIGESTIVE SYSTEM AND METABOLISM (pp. 506–507)
   A. Digestive System Formation (pp. 506–507)
      1. Cleft Lip
      2. Cleft Palate
      3. Tracheoesophageal Fistula
      4. Cystic fibrosis
      5. Phenylketonuria (PKU)
   B. Childhood and Adolescence (p. 507)
      1. Gastroenteritis
      2. Appendicitis
      3. Gallbladder Problems
   C. Adulthood (p. 507)
   D. Aging (p. 507)

KEY TERMS

acidosis
alimentary canal
anabolism
anal canal
anus
appendicitis
appendix
ascending colon
ATP
baby teeth
basal metabolic rate (BMR)
bile
bile duct
blood sugar
bolus
brush border
brush border enzymes
buccal phase
canines
carbohydrates
cardioesophageal sphincter
catabolism
cecum
cellular respiration
cementum
cheeks
chief cells
cholecystokinin (CCK)
cholesterol
chyme
circular folds
coenzymes
colon
common hepatic duct
crown
cystic duct
deciduous teeth
defecation reflex
deglutition
dentin
descending colon
duodenum
electron transport chain
enamel
energy intake
energy output
enteroendocrine cells
esophagus
essential amino acids

evaporation
external anal sphincter
falciform ligament
gallbladder
gastric juice
gastrin
gastroenteritis
gastrointestinal (GI) tract
gingiva
gluconeogenesis
glucose
glycogen
glycogenesis
glycogenolysis
glycolysis
greater curvature
greater omentum
gum
hard palate
haustra
haustral contraction
high-density lipoproteins
    (HDLs)
hyperglycemia
hypoglycemia
ileocecal valve
ileum
incisors
internal involuntary sphinc-
    ter
jejunum
ketoacidosis
kilocalories (kcal)
Krebs cycle
lacteal
large intestine
laryngopharynx
lesser curvature
lesser omentum
lingual frenulum
lingual tonsil
lipids
lips (labia)
liver
low-density lipoproteins
    (LDLs)
lumen
major nutrients
mass movements

masticated
mesentery
metabolism
microvilli
milk teeth
minerals
minor nutrients
molars
mouth
mucosa
mumps
muscularis externa
myenteric nerve plexus
neck
neutral fats
oral cavity
oral cavity proper
oropharynx
palatine tonsils
pancreas
pancreatic ducts
pancreatic juice
parietal cells
parietal peritoneum
parotid glands
pepsin
pepsinogens
periodontal membrane
    (ligament)
peristalsis
permanent teeth
Peyer's patches
pharyngeal-esophageal phase
plicae circulares
polyps
premolars
proteins
pulp
pulp cavity
pyloric sphincter
pyloric valve
radiation
rectum
root
root canal
rugae
saliva
salivary amylase
salivary glands

secretin	sublingual glands	transverse colon
segmentation	submandibular glands	urea
serosa	submucosa	uvula
shivering	submucosal nerve plexus	vasoconstriction
sigmoid colon	swallowing	vestibule
small intestine	thyroxine	villi
soft palate	tongue	visceral peritoneum
stomach	total metabolic rate (TMR)	vitamins

LECTURE HINTS

1. The secretions made in various parts of the alimentary canal, the salivary glands, the liver, and the pancreas are derived from blood plasma, just as we saw with lymph fluid. Throughout the course of the classes on digestion, keep a running tab of the volume of plasma used to generate fluids for digestion.

   Key point: This will help students appreciate the role of the large intestine in reabsorbing water, and help them understand the life-threatening consequences of prolonged diarrhea, especially in children.

2. Note that the villi, microvilli, and circular folds of the small intestine are key to major amounts of absorption, whereas the mucosa of the stomach lining produces large amounts of mucus that protects the stomach wall from digestion by its own juices. Emphasize the structural modifications in each area of the GI tract that lead to optimum digestion and absorption.

   Key point: Each area of the GI tract is modified to perform specific digestive functions, such as absorption of nutrients, absorption of water, and breakdown of carbohydrates, proteins, or fats.

3. Emphasize that the rugae of the gastric mucosa allow the stomach to collapse in on itself or stretch to accommodate a large meal as the need arises.

   Key point: This is an example of another modification of the alimentary canal that assists in the digestive processes.

4. While discussing each section of the alimentary canal, emphasize which specific nutrients are being digested along the way and list the digestive enzymes involved in the digestion of each nutrient. At the end of the presentation, review the major areas of carbohydrate, protein, and lipid digestion and the enzymes involved in each.

   Key point: It is important for students to realize that breakdown of nutrients occurs along the entire alimentary canal, and that each region has its specialty.

5. Many instructors choose not to have the students learn the names and numbers of the teeth. This information is logical and is easily learned, and greatly enhances their understanding of dental health. Also, health care professionals routinely examine teeth when assessing homeostatic imbalances.

   Key point: Dental health is an important component of overall body health. Dental caries (decay) can lead to abscesses and even systemic infection. For that reason, focusing on teeth and learning their names and characteristics helps students to become smarter dental health consumers.

6. Explain the diet modifications that need to occur after gallbladder surgery. Discuss cholelithiasis (gallstones) and the current treatment options for this condition.

   Key point: Gallstones arise when bile is stored too long or becomes excessively concentrated. Treatment options include surgical removal and lithotripsy.

7. Explain the various types and causes of jaundice.

    Key point: Jaundice can be pathologic, as with hepatitis, nonpathologic, as with jaundice of newborns, or obstructive, as with cholelithiasis. Understanding this condition as a sign rather than a disease helps students visualize the physiological processes involved.

8. Discuss cirrhosis and its causes.

    Key point: Students often consider cirrhosis a direct manifestation of alcoholism and are surprised to learn that it has numerous causes, including chronic hepatitis, malnutrition, and heredity. Alcoholism is also associated with dehydration.

9. In discussing peristalsis, point out that astronauts are able to swallow in any position, and that although gravity helps move things through the alimentary canal, the process continues even in the absence of gravity.

    Key point: Peristalsis occurs in many regions of the alimentary canal and is a major factor in the movement of chyme through the system.

10. Explain the digestive implications of cleft lip and palate in the sucking reflex.

    Key point: Although this condition is readily treated in the United States, it continues to be of major significance in third world countries where it often goes untreated, with serious nutritional implications.

11. Spend extra time on the production of ATP through the various processes, including the Krebs cycle, glycolysis, and the electron transport chain.

    Key point: These are complex processes that require extra effort in presentation, but it is important for students to grasp the correlation between the metabolic processes of catabolism and anabolism.

12. Reinforce the concepts learned in the cardiovascular chapter about the benefits and dangers of cholesterol. Remind the students that the HDLs and LDLs are neither "good" nor "bad."

    Key point: Both HDLs and LDLs are necessary components of steroid hormones and vitamin D. It is their relative ratio in the blood that is the determining factor in whether they have harmful side effects.

13. Discuss the importance of maintaining low pH in the stomach and then explain how other parts of the digestive tract neutralize the acidic pH that leaves this region. Include a discussion of heartburn and ulcers.

    Key point: Revisiting the pH concept at this point allows the instructor to re-emphasize the proper functioning of enzymes and proteins in different parts of the body.

14. Explain how gastric bypass and lapband surgery can be used to treat obesity. Discuss the nutritional and physiological implications of these surgeries.

    Key point: With obesity being so much more prevalent, students are curious to learn about the effects of these procedures.

15. Describe the various types of cancer associated with the digestive system, including their prognoses and treatment options.

    Key point: While some research into certain cancers (e.g., colon cancer) has made large strides in terms of treatment, others such as pancreatic or esophageal cancers still have very poor prognoses.

16. Describe and discuss irritable bowel syndrome (IBS), Crohn's disease, and acid reflux disease.

    Key point: Students are usually familiar with these conditions and can relate personal experiences to treatment options.

17. Discuss how the alimentary canal is actually the "exterior" of the body and that food does not actually enter the body cells prior to absorption.

   Key point: Indicate the close relationship between the digestive and lymphatic systems to make sure no foreign materials can enter the cells of the body.

TRANSPARENCIES/MEDIA MANAGER INDEX

Indicates images that are on the Media Manager only.

ANSWERS TO END OF CHAPTER REVIEW QUESTIONS

Questions appear on pp. 514–516

Multiple Choice

1. a, c, d (pp. 469–471)
2. b (p. 481)
3. c (pp. 472, 482)
4. 1-e; 2-h; 3-c; 4-b; 5-g; 6-a; 7-f; 8-d (pp. 472–481)
5. d (pp. 472–475)
6. d (Figure 1.8 in Chapter 1)
7. c, d (Table 14.1)
8. d (p. 490)
9. d (p. 492)
10. a (p. 480; see also Chapter 9)
11. b (if blood glucose levels remain high), d (p. 483)
12. b (p. 480; Figure 14.10)
13. c (p. 496)

Short Answer Essay

14. See Figure 14.1 (p. 470).
15. See Figure 14.1 (p. 470). The arrows should point as follows: from salivary glands into the oral cavity; from the liver and pancreas into the small intestine.
16. Mucosa, submucosa, muscularis, externa, serosa. (p. 472; Figure 14.3)
17. *Mesentery:* The peritoneal extension that suspends the alimentary tube organs in the abdominal cavity and provides for entry and exit of nerves and blood vessels to those organs. *Peritoneum:* The double layer of serous membrane that lines the abdominal cavity walls (parietal peritoneum) and covers the exterior of the abdominal cavity organs (visceral peritoneum). (p. 472)
18. *Small intestine:* Duodenum, jejunum, ileum. (p. 461; Figure 14.6) *Large intestine:* Appendix, cecum, ascending colon, transverse colon, descending colon, sigmoid colon, rectum, anal canal. (p. 476)
19. The normal number of permanent teeth is 32; there are 20 deciduous teeth. Enamel covers the tooth crown; dentin makes up the bulk of the tooth. *Pulp:* Connective tissue invested with blood vessels and nerve endings; located within the central pulp cavity of a tooth. (p. 480; Figure 14.10)
20. Parotid, submandibular, and sublingual. (p. 480)
21. The bread would begin to taste sweet as the starch is digested to its glucose building blocks. (Figure 14.13)
22. *Mouth:* The teeth break or tear the food into smaller fragments. *Stomach:* The third obliquely oriented muscle layer in the muscularis externa allows the stomach to physically churn or pummel the contained foodstuffs. (pp. 473, 479)
23. The protein-digesting enzymes of the stomach (mainly pepsin) are activated and function best at a low pH. The mucus secreted by the stomach glands protects the stomach from self-digestion. (pp. 473–475)

24. *Emulsify:* To physically break apart larger particles into smaller ones; to spread thin. (p. 481)

25. Gastrin, a hormone produced by the stomach cells, stimulates the stomach glands to produce increased amounts of enzymes, mucus, and hydrochloric acid. (p. 485)

26. The buccal phase, which takes place in the mouth and is voluntary, consists of the chewing of food and the forcing of the food bolus into the pharynx by the tongue. The involuntary phase, which follows the buccal phase, involves the closure of all nondigestive pathways to the entry of food and the conducting of the food to the stomach by peristaltic waves of the pharyngeal and esophageal walls. (p. 485)

27. Segmental movements are local, rhythmic constrictions of the intestine, which primarily serve to mix the food with digestive juices. Peristaltic movements involve alternate waves of contraction and relaxation of the intestinal walls, by which the food is propelled along the tract. (p. 482)

28. During ingestion, the sandwich is taken into the mouth. Digestion occurs both mechanically (during chewing of the sandwich and stomach churning) and chemically (in the mouth, stomach, and small intestine). The nutrients are absorbed primarily through the wall of the small intestine. Any indigestible material is eliminated through defecation. The end-products of protein digestion are amino acids; of fat digestion, glycerol or monoglycerides and fatty acids; of carbohydrates, simple sugars (monosaccharides). (pp. 481–483)

29. Water, some vitamins (K and B), and some ions. (p. 492)

30. Feces, the final product delivered to the rectum, is primarily indigestible food residue and bacteria. (p. 492)

31. *Defecation reflex:* A cord-mediated reflex that causes the walls of the sigmoid colon and rectum to contract and the anal sphincters to relax when feces enters the rectum. *Constipation:* A situation in which the stool is hard (usually from excessive dehydration) and difficult to pass. *Diarrhea:* A passage of watery stool; generally results from an irritation of the bowel that causes the contents to be propelled along too rapidly for adequate water reabsorption. (pp. 492–493)

32. *Metabolism:* The sum total of all chemical reactions that occur in the body. *Anabolism:* A metabolic process in which more complex structures or molecules are constructed from simpler ones. *Catabolism:* A metabolic process in which more complex substances are broken down into simpler substances. (p. 495)

33. *Gluconeogenesis:* The formation of glucose from noncarbohydrate sources, that is, from fats or proteins. *Glycogenolysis:* The breakdown of glycogen to its glucose building blocks. *Glycogenesis:* The formation of glycogen from glucose. (p. 500)

34. Proteins are the most important food group for the building of cell structures. (pp. 498, 500)

35. When excess fats are oxidized, acidosis is likely. Starvation and diabetes mellitus. (p. 498)

36. Oxidation of 1 g of carbohydrate produces 4 kcal; 1 g of protein produces 4 kcal; 1 g of fat yields 9 kcal. You would have consumed 290 kcal (80 kcal from protein, 120 kcal from carbohydrate, and 90 kcal from fat). (p. 502

37. The balance is lost as heat (some of which warms the body tissues and blood). (p. 504)

38. Heat is lost from the body by radiation from the skin surface or by evaporation of perspiration from the skin surface. Body heat is retained by withdrawal of blood from the skin capillaries (thus preventing radiation); body heat is generated at an increased rate by the initiation of shivering. (p. 504)

39. *Fever:* controlled hyperthermia or a body temperature that is controlled at higher-than-usual levels. Fever is the body's protective response to some type of malfunction, trauma, or infection in the body. (p. 506)

40. *Middle-aged adults:* Ulcers, gallstones, inflammatory disease of the gallbladder. *Adolescents:* Appendicitis. *Elderly individuals:* Peridontal disease, malabsorption, stomach/colon cancer. (p. 507)

ANSWERS TO CRITICAL THINKING AND CLINICAL APPLICATION QUESTIONS

41. John was suffering from heat exhaustion due to an excessive loss of body fluids (indicated by his wringing wet T-shirt) and his low blood pressure and cool clammy skin. To help his recovery, he should be given fluid and electrolyte therapy and be cooled down. (p. 506)

42. Harry's symptoms indicate a fever caused by his bacterial pneumonia. The white blood cells battling the pneumonia release pyrogens that act directly on the hypothalamus, causing its neurons to release prostaglandins. The prostaglandins reset the hypothalamic thermostat to a higher temperature, causing the body to initiate heat-promoting mechanisms. Vasoconstriction reduces heat loss from the body surface, promotes cooling of the skin, and shivering. (p. 506)

43. Histamine is one of the chemical stimuli for HCl secretion; thus, an antihistamine drug will inhibit HCl secretion; perforation, peritonitis, and massive hemorrhage. She was told not to take aspirin because it can cause stomach bleeding. (pp. 488–489)

44. Leakage of HCl and pepsin from a perforating gastric ulcer will literally erode and digest away other tissues with which these chemicals come into contact. The pancreas is immediately adjacent to the stomach, and therefore is susceptible to damage. (pp. 487–489)

45. Rickets, a childhood disease in which bones lack calcium salts. Weight-bearing bones, such as the bones of the legs and pelvis, may bend, deform, or break. Milk is a source of vitamin D, that acts as a cofactor to enhance calcium absorption in the small intestine. (p. 142)

46. Tracheoesophageal fistula. This condition can be corrected surgically. (p. 506)

47. Acidosis or ketosis. Glucose supplies are low and fats are oxidized (incompletely) to provide ATP. (p. 498)

48. *Hypothermia* is an extremely low body temperature due to prolonged exposure to cold. Uncorrected hypothermia can lead to dangerous reductions in respiratory rate, blood pressure, and heart rate, any of which can cause death in the elderly. (p. 504)

49. Diarrhea, or watery stools, results from any condition that rushes food through the large intestine so quickly that it cannot reabsorb sufficient water. Prolonged diarrhea may result in dehydration and electrolyte imbalances. (p. 493)

50. Bacteria in the large intestine manufacture vitamin K. The antibiotics that Ginny was taking also inhibited normal bacterial growth in her large intestine. As a result, no vitamin K was produced, which led to vitamin K deficiency. (p. 492)

CLASSROOM DEMONSTRATIONS AND STUDENT ACTIVITIES

Classroom Demonstrations

1. Film(s) or other media of choice.

2. Use a torso model to demonstrate the location of the digestive organs.

3. Use a human skull or jaw model to introduce the different tooth shapes, names, and numbers.

4. Rennin will turn casein (milk protein) into a curd in an infant's stomach; the liquid that is left is called whey. Adding some rennin, available from biological supply companies, to milk will quickly demonstrate this point. Ask students why they think this might be beneficial in infants.

5. The digestive function of the liver is to produce bile. With the students' assistance, compile a list of the liver's other functions as studied so far, then introduce new functions related to metabolism.

6. Demonstrate the emulsifying action of bile. First mix oil and water together and allow the layers to separate. Then add bile salts and shake vigorously. Point out that the layer of oil has been dispersed into hundreds of tiny fatty spheres by the action of the bile salts.

7. Borrow a specimen jar containing gallstones from a local GI surgeon to enhance your presentation of why gallstones form and why they are painful.

8. Demonstrate the molecular models of carbohydrate, fat, and protein molecules, and show the breaking of their bonds during digestion by enzymes.

9. Invite a guest speaker from the local dental hygienist's organization to come to class and present information on the benefits of good oral health and why flossing daily, in addition to regular brushing with fluoride, is important.

10. Invite a guest speaker from the local endoscopy clinic to speak to the class on the importance of colonoscopy and hemoccult testing, particularly in people over the age of 50.

11. Obtain a used diaper from the local hospital nursery to show students meconium stool, and use this as a starting point for discussion of the composition of this first feces. Explain how it differs from later stools.

12. Bring in guest speakers to compare and contrast different diet options (low carb, low fat, etc.) for losing and maintaining weight.

13. Show prepared slides of fecal material that have normal bacterial flora from different regions of the digestive tract.

STUDENT ACTIVITIES

1. Bring bread to class and have the students each chew a piece. Ask them how it tastes when it has been chewed for a long period of time before it is swallowed (it should taste sweet) due to the presence of salivary amylase.

2. Ask students to research various types of diets and come to class prepared to present their findings for class discussion.

3. Have the students research ulcers, diverticuli, intestinal polyps, and hemorrhoids. Discuss the signs and symptoms of each, focusing on the presence or absence of blood in the stools.

4. Bring in several hemoccult slides. Ask for volunteers willing to test their feces and bring the slides back to the class for analysis. Discuss the significance of hidden or occult blood as compared to frank blood.

5. Have students calculate their total caloric intake over a 24-hour period by using a simple caloric guide (obtainable in most drugstores). Then have them analyze their diet with an eye to what improvements could be made to their eating habits.

6. When discussing the swallowing mechanism, have students place their hands on their larynx so that they can feel it rise when they swallow. Provide small cups of water as needed.

7. Have the students obtain a small sample of their own blood from a finger stick and have them analyze it for glucose content. Discuss the expected levels of glucose before and after a meal in normal individuals versus diabetic individuals.

8. Show a 10-minute clip of *Lorenzo's Oil* or *Supersize Me* and engage the students in a class discussion.

9. Show the film *Supersize Me* and assign your students a paper covering the issues and debates raised by this movie. For example, they could discuss whether they felt that the movie was an unbiased presentation of the obesity/fast food issue or propaganda against big-money corporations. Why? Another possible topic for a paper is a discussion on who should bear the burden of responsibility for obesity and its health effects and costs. Why or why not? The students could also discuss the likelihood of eating a more healthful diet and the reasoning for it. Additional topics covering issues raised by this movie can be found on the Internet.

MULTIMEDIA

See page 182 for a listing of media resources.

1. *An End to Ulcers: A Journey of Discovery* (FHS; 57 min., 1998, VHS, DVD). This program outlines the history of diagnosis and treatment of ulcers and the extraordinary discovery that *H. pylori* are the true cause of most peptic ulcers.

2. *Breakdown* (FHS; 28 min., 1984, VHS, DVD). From the award-winning *The Living Body* series, this video investigates the digestive consequences of eating a meal, following the food through the entire alimentary canal.

3. *Managing Cholesterol* (FHS; 28 min., 2005, VHS, DVD). Illustrates the effects of LDL and HDL cholesterol on the heart and circulatory system, and includes three varied case studies and expert commentary.

4. *The Anatomy of Digestion* (FHS; 50 min., 2005, VHS, DVD). Gunther von Hagens takes the viewer step-by-step through each process of the digestive system and explains such concepts as burps, heartburn, and ulcers.

5. *Food and Digestion* (FHS; 27 min., 2004, VHS, DVD). This program features graphics and simple experiments to illustrate how the body absorbs nutrients from different types of food and differentiates between mechanical and chemical digestion.

6. *Digestion: Eating to Live* (FHS; 28 min., 1984, VHS, DVD). From the award-winning *The Living Body* series, this video looks at appetite and hunger, and shows the actions of the salivary glands, the swallowing reflex, and the stomach churning.

7. *Digestion and Fluid Balance* (WNS; 30 min., 1997, VHS). This video examines the digestive and excretory systems, and shows their roles in removing nutrients from food and eliminating waste products.

8. *The Digestive System* (IM; 24 min., 1997, DVD). This video demonstrates how the digestive system breaks food down into usable form and distributes it to the circulatory system.

9. *Digestive System: Your Personal Power Plant* (FHS; 25 min., 1998, VHS, DVD). From *The Human Body: Systems at Work* series, this program examines the processes by which the digestive system acts as a power plant for the body by turning food into energy.

10. *Exploring Vegetarianism: A Healthy Alternative* (FHS; 19 min., 1999, VHS, DVD). This program answers many of the questions often asked about vegetarianism and its place in healthy nutrition.

11. *Fad Diets: The Weight Loss Merry-Go-Round* (FHS; 16 min., 1998, VHS, DVD). This programs looks at the dangers and frustrations of fad diets while showing how healthy eating habits can lead to ideal weight for life.

12. *Lorenzo's Oil* (136 min., 1992, DVD). A film that documents the real-life story of Lorenzo Odone, who has a rare myelin-degenerating terminal disease called adrenoleukodystrophy (ALD), and his parents (Augusto and Michaela) who collide with doctors, scientists, and support groups in their quest to develop an oil from the combination of two fats extracted from olive oil and rapeseed oil to prevent the body's production of very long chain fatty acids whose buildup leads to demyelination. See http://www.myelin.org. This film is readily available at most national chain video distribution stores.

13. *What's New about Vitamins and Phytonutrients* (FHS; 20 min., 2005, VHS, DVD). Explains the importance of plant-based nutrients in wellness and the prevention of cancer and heart disease, along with a discussion on the consequences of heavy vitamin supplement use.

14. *Supersize Me* (100 min., 2004, DVD). Documents filmmaker Morgan Spurlock's investigation of the American obesity epidemic by interviewing experts and laypersons nationwide on the perils of excessive fast-food consumption and by anatomically, physiologically, and psychologically documenting his personal deteriorating health while going on a "McDonald's Only" eating binge for 30 consecutive days. This documentary won the award for Best Director at the prestigious Sundance Film Festival in January 2004 by investigating differing opinions as to corporate vs. consumer responsibility for the rising obesity level in American youth and adults, nutritional education, school lunch programs, and how and why Americans are literally eating themselves to death. This film is available at most national chain video distribution stores.

15. *When Food is the Enemy: Eating Disorders* (FHS; 25 min., 2001, VHS, DVD). This program examines the emotional issues that lie behind eating disorders, as well as their consequences and methods of treatment.

SOFTWARE

1. *The Human Digestive System* (NIMCO; Win/Mac). Accesses endoscopic pictures and lab experiments to show the human digestive system at work.

The Urinary System

CHAPTER SUMMARY

The kidneys, as described by Marieb, "are perfect examples of homeostatic organs" that perform a wide variety of functions. They filter fluid from the bloodstream and process the filtrate. They excrete nitrogenous wastes and excess ions, rid the body of drugs and toxins, and retain needed ions and nutrients. They manufacture urine and regulate the volume and chemical makeup of blood. They balance water and salts, as well as acids and bases. They also convert vitamin D to its active form and produce hormones that function to regulate blood pressure and stimulate RBC production. This chapter outlines each of these functions and explains the homeostatic link between them.

The first section of this chapter discusses the chief organs of the urinary system, the kidneys. Each kidney has a structure similar to its neighbors, the adrenal glands, in that they have an outer cortex and an inner medulla. Blood supply to the kidneys is extensive, since one-quarter of the total blood supply of the body goes through them each minute. The structural and functional units of the kidneys are the nephrons, consisting of the glomerulus and the renal tubule. Glomeruli act as filters to perform the passive process of filtration, reabsorption and secretion are performed by the renal tubules, and urine formation is a result of all three of these processes. Urine has distinct characteristics, and it is explained that many diseases manifest themselves in abnormal urine composition, thus emphasizing the value of routine urinalysis.

The next section of the chapter outlines the structure and function of the other organs of the urinary system (e.g., the ureters, urinary bladder, and urethra). Micturition is explained as the act of emptying the bladder, also known as voiding, or urination. The kidney's role in fluid and electrolyte balance is explored next, and the link between water and salt is explained. The role of the kidneys in maintaining acid-base balance is also presented. Of the many mechanisms for regulating blood pH, the renal mechanisms are described as slower but more potent than other mechanisms, thus enhancing their importance. Finally, several examples of homeostatic imbalance of the urinary system are explored, including polycystic kidney, hypospadias, and glomerulonephritis.

SUGGESTED LECTURE OUTLINE

I. KIDNEYS (pp. 518–528)
    A. Location and Structure (pp. 518–521)
        1. Blood Supply
           a. Renal Arteries
           b. Renal Veins
    B. Nephrons and Urine Formation (pp. 521–528)
        1. Nephrons
        2. Urine Formation (Figure 15.5)
           a. Glomerular Filtration
           b. Tubular Reabsorption
           c. Tubular Secretion
        3. Characteristics of Urine

TEACHING TIP

When discussing filtration and tubular reabsorption, an analogy to cleaning closets can be made. One effective way to clean out a closet is to remove everything (filtration), and then put back into the closet only what you want to keep (reabsorption). The rest is thrown away.

II. URETERS, URINARY BLADDER, AND URETHRA
(pp. 528–531)
A. Ureters (p. 528)
B. Urinary Bladder (pp. 528–529)
C. Urethra (pp. 529–530)
D. Micturition (pp. 530–531)

III. FLUID, ELECTROLYTE, AND ACID-BASE BALANCE
(pp. 531–537)
A. Maintaining Water and Electrolyte Balance of Blood
(pp. 531–535)
1. Body Fluids and Fluid Compartments
a. Intracellular Fluid
b. Extracellular Fluid
2. The Link Between Water and Salt
3. Regulation of Water Intake and Output
a. Thirst
b. Antidiuretic Hormone (ADH)
c. Aldosterone
d. Renin-Angiotensin Mechanism
B. Maintaining Acid-Base Balance of Blood
(pp. 535–537)
1. Blood Buffers
2. Respiratory System Controls
3. Renal Mechanisms

IV. DEVELOPMENTAL ASPECTS OF THE URINARY SYSTEM
(pp. 538, 540)
A. Fetal Kidneys
1. Polycystic Kidneys
2. Hypospadias
B. Infections and Inflammatory Conditions
1. Glomerulonephritis
C. Aging

KEY TERMS

acid-base balance
acidosis
afferent arteriole
aldosterone
alkalosis
antidiuretic hormone (ADH)
arcuate arteries
arcuate veins
bicarbonate buffer system
Bowman's capsule
calyces
collecting duct
cortical nephrons

cortical radiate arteries
cortical radiate veins
creatinine
distal convoluted tubule (DCT)
efferent arteriole
electrolyte balance
external urethral sphincter
extracellular fluid (ECF)
frequency
glomerular capsule
glomerular filtration
glomerulus

interlobar arteries
interlobar veins
internal urethral sphincter
intracellular fluid (ICF)
juxtamedullary nephrons
kidneys
loop of Henle
medullary pyramids
micturition
nephrons
nitrogenous waste products
nocturia
osmoreceptors

peritubular capillaries	renal pyramids	tubular secretion
physiological acidosis	renal tubule	urea
podocytes	renal vein	ureters
proximal convoluted tube (PCT)	renin	urethra
	renin-angiotensin mechanism	urgency
renal artery	segmental arteries	uric acid
renal columns	specific gravity	urinary bladder
renal cortex	thirst mechanism	urinary system
renal medulla	trigone	urine
renal pelvis	tubular reabsorption	voiding

LECTURE HINTS

1. To clear up a common misconception about the location of the kidneys, accurately describe their location in the superior lumbar region.

   Key point: Kidneys are retroperitoneal, meaning *behind* the peritoneum and *outside* the peritoneal cavity. Students are usually surprised to learn that the kidneys are not in the same cavity as most of the other abdominal organs.

2. Explain that the kidneys are held in place in the upper lumbar area by the fat surrounding them. Any condition leading to extreme weight loss can lead to nephroptosis, or drooping of the kidneys, which can then lead to kinked ureters and hydronephrosis.

   Key point: Anorexia nervosa is one of the many conditions leading to nephroptosis. This mental illness, with its physical manifestation, is an interesting topic to use in explaining the process of nephroptosis and its sequelae.

3. Spend time explaining the gross anatomy of an individual kidney, then follow it with a presentation of the anatomy of a single nephron. Once both have been described, point out the regions in the kidney where the various structures of the nephron are located. For example, the loops of Henle drop into the renal medulla, whereas the glomerular capsule is in the cortex. Once students have this combined picture in mind, ask them to visualize a *million* or more nephrons in *each* kidney.

   Key point: It is important for students to conceptualize the arrangement and sheer number of nephrons working in each kidney. This helps explain why a person can lose or donate one kidney, and still have a functioning urinary system that meets their needs. This is one of the many remarkable back-up systems in the human body.

4. Draw a complete nephron on the board, then clearly show the location of the two distinct capillary beds associated with each nephron. From there, outline movement of the filtrate through the nephron from its filtration into the capsule, through the proximal convoluted tubule, loop of Henle, and distal convoluted tubule. Emphasize the locations of tubular reabsorption and secretion. Clearly note the materials, such as water, ions, and wastes, being reabsorbed or secreted.

   Key point: This will help students conceptualize the process of urine formation.

5. When discussing filtration and tubular reabsorption, an analogy to cleaning closets can be made. One effective way to clean out a closet is to remove everything (filtration), and then put back into the closet only what you want to keep (reabsorption). The rest is thrown away.

   Key point: This analogy helps students visualize the process more clearly.

6. Explain to students that the kidneys are not only the primary organs for elimination of wastes, they also control the plasma concentration of other important substances, such as water and electrolytes. This control is usually under the influence of hormones, including the two antidiuretics.

   Key point: This is a good opportunity to show the interplay between the endocrine system and the urinary system.

7. First itemize the normal constituents of urine, then make a second list of abnormal constituents and the possible causes for their presence in the urine.

   Key point: There are numerous medical conditions that lead to abnormal constituents in the urine. Give some examples, such as urinary tract infections and diabetes mellitus, and explain the pathophysiology behind their presence. Physicians refused to acknowledge that the blue "water" excreted by King George in the movie *The Madness of King George* could help diagnose his condition.

8. Although students realize that kidneys are excretory organs, they forget about the other functions of the kidneys. Remind them that the kidneys regulate the rate of red blood cell production, are important in activation of vitamin D, and have a significant impact on blood pressure and pH. Discuss the numerous homeostatic imbalances a person on dialysis must face.

   Key point: This is an opportunity to look at the "big picture," rather than simply focusing on the primary function of an organ.

9. Discuss the reasons why urinary tract infections are more common in females than males, and differentiate between ascending urinary tract infections and descending urinary tract infections.

   Key point: Females typically suffer from more UTIs due to their shorter urethra, although males with prostatic hypertrophy also have a high incidence of UTI. Explain that ascending UTIs are much more common than descending UTIs because of the likelihood of pathogens entering through the urethral meatus.

10. Explain that bladder control and prevention of incontinence in children are usually related to physiological maturity that occurs around age 2 and are *not* related to intelligence.

    Key point: People often take great pride in getting their children "potty trained," but it is important to remember that sphincter control is a *physiological* process, not an *intellectual* process. If parents start trying to train their child before they are physically ready, they are going to frustrate both themselves and the child with their unreasonable expectations. They may, in fact, end up "training" themselves rather than their child.

11. Discuss some of the reasons for and potential consequences of intermittent and indwelling catheterization.

    Key point: Catheterization is performed in order to obtain sterile urine specimens, to precisely monitor urine output, to remove urine from the bladder of an individual with a spinal cord injury, and numerous other reasons. Urinary tract infection from contamination by pathogens is always a concern with catheterization.

12. Explain the connection between water and salt in maintaining blood volume and in blood pressure changes.

    Key point: Wherever salt goes, water follows. Sodium ion is the electrolyte most responsible for the osmotic flow of water. A person who heavily salts food will end up retaining a good deal of water, potentially leading to edema, circulatory overload, and high blood pressure. Conversely, a person with low sodium intake may become dehydrated and experience low blood pressure.

13. Discuss the formation and removal of kidney stones. Explain why passage of kidney stones is extremely painful.

    Key point: Compare the formation of kidney stones with gallstones, and explain their influences on maintaining homeostasis.

TRANSPARENCIES/MEDIA MANAGER INDEX

Figure 15.1	Organs of the urinary system
Figure 15.2	Internal anatomy of the kidney
Figure 15.3	Structure of the nephron
Figure 15.4	The kidney depicted schematically as a single large, uncoiled nephron
Figure 15.5	Sites of filtration, reabsorption, and secretion in a nephron
Figure 15.6	Basic structure of the female urinary bladder and urethra
Figure 15.7	Position and shape of a distended and an empty urinary bladder in an adult man
Figure 15.8	The major fluid compartments of the body
Figure 15.9	The continuous mixing of body fluids
Figure 15.10	Water intake and output
Figure 15.11	Flowchart of mechanisms regulating sodium and water balance help maintain blood pressure homeostasis
Figure 15.12	Dissociation of strong and weak acids
Table 15.1	Abnormal Urinary Constituents
A Closer Look	Renal Failure and the Artificial Kidney*
Systems in Sync	Homeostatic Relationships Between the Urinary System and Other Body Systems

Indicates images that are on the Media Manager only.

ANSWERS TO END OF CHAPTER REVIEW QUESTIONS

Questions appear on pp. 541–543

Multiple Choice

1. d (p. 521)
2. d (p. 521)
3. c (p. 528)
4. b, c, d (pp. 533–534)
5. a, b, c, d (p. 524)
6. d (p. 531)
7. c (p. 531)
8. c (pp. 536–537)

Short Answer Essay

9. *Kidneys:* Formation of urine, regulation of acid-base balance, electrolyte balance, and water balance of the blood. *Ureters:* Conduct urine from the kidneys to the bladder.

Bladder: Temporary storage of urine. *Urethra:* Conduct urine from the bladder to the body exterior. (pp. 518, 528–529)

10. The kidneys are retroperitoneal in the superiodorsal lumbar region of the body. (p. 518; Figure 15.1)

11. See Figure 15.2 (p. 520).

12. It remains in the blood. (p. 524)

13. Glomerulus to glomerular (Bowman's) capsule to proximal convoluted tubule, through loop of Henle and distal convoluted tubule to the collecting duct (which leaves the cortex of the kidney and traverses the renal columns and medullary region to empty into a calyx, which in turn empties into the kidney pelvis) to ureter to bladder to urethra. (pp. 521, 523)

14. The glomerulus is the "filter"; blood fluids and substances smaller than proteins pass out of the blood at the glomerulus into the renal tubules. (p. 523)

15. The kidney controls water balance, ion levels, and the acid-base balance of the blood. (p. 518)

16. Filtrate is equivalent to blood plasma without the plasma proteins. Urine is "processed filtrate," that is, filtrate from which useful substances (amino acids, glucose, needed ions, and water) have been reabsorbed into the blood. (p. 524)

17. Aldosterone causes the kidney tubule cells to reabsorb more sodium ions (and to secrete potassium ions). As the sodium ions are reabsorbed, water follows by osmosis. Thus, aldosterone causes the removal of sodium ions (and water, secondarily) from the filtrate. (pp. 533, 535)

18. Antidiuretic hormone (ADH). Diabetes insipidus, a condition in which huge volumes of water are lost from the body into the urine, resulting in severe dehydration. (pp. 532–533)

19. Sodium balance, ECF, and blood pressure are all regulated by aldosterone. Aldosterone regulates sodium content of the ECF, which is important for osmotic water flows. Falling sodium levels in the ECF trigger aldosterone to be released, which retains sodium in the kidneys. When the solute content of the filtrate changes, blood pressure also changes. (pp. 533–535)

20. Chemical buffer systems resist changes in pH by either providing an ion that can bind excess hydrogen ions in the presence of a strong acid, or release hydrogen ions in the presence of a strong base. (pp. 535–536)

21. The respiratory system can play an important role in acid-base balance in the body. When too much carbon dioxide is present in the body (which lowers the blood pH by producing carbonic acid), respiratory rate and depth will increase to restore blood pH. These increases remove excess carbon dioxide. As well, when pH rises, respiratory rate and depth will decrease, which allows carbon dioxide to accumulate until blood pH is restored. (p. 537)

22. The presence of abnormal substances in the urine is diagnostic of a pathology and may indicate a problem before other symptoms are present. (pp. 525, 527)

23. The internal urethral sphincter is a thickened area of the bladder-urethra junction. It is formed by the smooth muscle of this junction and it is involuntary. It keeps the urethra closed when urine is not being passed. By contrast, the external urethral sphincter is made from skeletal muscle and it is voluntarily controlled. When stored urine has been forced past the internal sphincter into the upper part of the urethra, we feel the urge to void. The external urethral sphincter can then be voluntarily relaxed to allow voiding, or we can choose to keep it closed and postpone bladder emptying temporarily. (pp. 529–530)

24. *Micturition:* Voiding, or emptying of the bladder (so that urine is flushed from the body).

    Micturition reflex: When approximately 200 mL of urine have collected in the bladder, stretch receptors in its wall are activated. Impulses, transmitted to the spinal cord and then back to the bladder (a reflex arc), cause the bladder to contract, and urine is forced past the internal sphincter. It is then that one feels the urge to void. If the time is inconvenient, voiding can be prevented by voluntary closure of the external sphincter and, within a few seconds, bladder contractions cease. After 200 to 300 mL more urine have collected in the bladder, the reflex is initiated once again. (p. 530)

25. Prolonged stasis of urine in the bladder can result in calculi and encourages infectious disease of the bladder. (p. 528)

26. *Incontinence:* Inability to voluntarily control the external urethral sphincter. (p. 530)

27. It is more common in females because the urethra is short and lies close to the posterior anal body orifice. Improper toilet hygiene, that is, wiping back to front, carries colonic bacteria to the urethra, thereby promoting infection of the normally sterile urinary passages. (pp. 529–530)

28. Infections. (See *Homeostatic Imbalance* sections throughout chapter)

29. The efficiency of the kidneys (particularly in relation to their ability to form concentrated urine) declines as arteriosclerosis plagues the kidney circulation and as the renal tubules begin to deteriorate. A loss of bladder size and tone leads to increasing episodes of urgency, frequency, and incontinence. In males, prostatic hypertrophy may lead to urinary retention accompanied by calculi and frequent cystitis. (pp. 538, 540)

ANSWERS TO CRITICAL THINKING AND CLINICAL APPLICATION QUESTIONS

30. Renal calculi (kidney stones). Predisposing conditions are frequent bacterial infections of the urinary tract, urinary retention, and alkaline urine. The woman's pain comes in waves because the stone is probably passing through the ureter. Pain occurs when the ureter walls close in on the sharp calculi as they are being eased through the ureter by peristalsis. (p. 528)

31. Acute glomerulonephritis due to a reaction to streptococcus bacteria. (p. 538)

32. Urinary tract infection (urethritis and cystitis), probably by *E. coli*. (pp. 529–530)

33. Pituitary; hyposecretion of ADH; diabetes insipidus. (p. 533)

34. Parathyroid hormone (PTH), released from the parathyroid gland, enhances the reabsorption of calcium by kidney tubules, and decreases the retention of phosphates. Hypersecretion of PTH would cause elevated blood calcium (hypercalcemia). (See "A Closer Look"—Chapter 10)

35. RBC production declines with total kidney failure due to reduced levels of erythropoietin. Recombinant erythropoietin has been developed and helps these patients. When perfected, artificial blood substitutes will help. (pp. 526–527; see also "A Closer Look"—Chapter 10)

36. A high salt diet would cause the kidneys to work harder as water will always move into and out of the filtrate. (Note: Some might disagree with this when massive amounts of water are ingested.) (pp. 531–532)

37. A specific gravity of 1.001 indicates a very dilute urine. Diuretic drugs that increase urine output or chronic renal failure following surgery in older persons are always suspect. Brain surgery might have injured the hypothalamus or posterior pituitary,

leading to diabetes insipidus, whereby the loss of very large amounts of very dilute urine can cause severe dehydration and electrolyte imbalances. (pp. 525, 527, 533)

CLASSROOM DEMONSTRATIONS AND STUDENT ACTIVITIES

Classroom Demonstrations

1. Film(s) or other media of choice.

2. Use a dissectible human torso model or a model of the urinary system to demonstrate the location of the organs of this system.

3. Use a model of a longitudinally sectioned kidney to identify its major anatomical regions: cortex, medulla, pelvis, and associated blood supply. If the nephron is shown as a part of the model, also demonstrate the anatomic regions of the nephron and describe their specific functions in filtrate formation or processing.

4. Visit a kidney dialysis center or have a guest speaker from the center come to present information on the process of dialysis.

5. Invite speakers to talk to the class on treatment options, transplantation protocols, current research, and issues related to living with kidney failure. Discuss why kidney donation is becoming more commonplace, and the danger of continuing to play dangerous competitive sports with only one kidney.

6. Display a hydrometer and other materials used to perform a urinalysis, and discuss the importance of urinalysis in both routine physicals and pathological diagnoses.

Student Activities

1. Use WARD'S Simulating Urinalysis Lab Activity. This activity allows students to perform a urinalysis and to microscopically examine casts and a range of other urinary tract phenomenon.

2. Ask students to research the thirst mechanism and be prepared to discuss it in class. Ingestion of pop, coffee, and tea instead of water has caused the American public to be chronically dehydrated. Discuss the impact of this dehydration on overall health, and how a yellow concentrated urine indicates more water consumption is needed and a clear and colorless urine indicates more water consumption is not necessary.

3. Provide diagrams of the urinary system for students to label.

4. Reiterate the process of testing for edema in light of information now known about the urinary system. Have the students check themselves and note any evidence of edema.

5. Request that the students talk with a nurse at a local hospital to find out why I&O (fluid intake and output) records are so carefully maintained on ill patients. Use this information as the basis for class discussion.

6. Have the students record their salt intake for the period of one week. Remind them to include both added salt and salt found in foods and liquids they ingest. At the end of the week, ask them to find their average daily intake of salt and compare it to the U.S. recommended daily allowance (RDA). Discuss the foods or beverages with the highest salt content.

7. Ask the students to research uses of urine in cultural or religious practices. Students are usually unaware of the fact that freshly voided urine is sterile and has historically been used in many ways, including washing soldiers' wounds in times of war and drinking by people of some cultures as a religious practice.

8. Discuss that the thirst mechanism is not well developed in humans and humans often remain dehydrated for days after extreme fluid loss through sweat, even when liberal amounts of water are available. Most animals will drink back precisely enough fluid to regain lost water weight following physical exertion in a hot and humid environment.

9. Explain that the hypothalamus is the body's temperature control center in addition to regulating both thirst and appetite. Persons have actually gained weight after starting a swimming program as they feel like they are starving when body temperature and sweat loss have minimal changes after swimming as compared to running or cycling.

10. Show a 10-minute clip of *The Madness of King George* and engage the students in a class discussion.

MULTIMEDIA

See page 182 for a listing of media resources.

1. *Caring for People with Renal Impairment* (FHS; 28 min., 1996, VHS, DVD). This program discusses end-stage renal disease and its management, including hemodialysis and transplant.

2. *The Kidney* (FHS; 15 min., 1996, VHS, DVD). From *The World of Living Organisms* series, this program discusses the structure and function of the kidneys and describes how they help maintain homeostasis.

3. *The Madness of King George* (110 min., 1994, DVD). Relates how the eccentric behavior of King George III progresses into madness as England loses the colonies in the American Revolution. King George's arrogant royal physicians refuse to acknowledge that his chronically blue-colored urine might be diagnostic of his deteriorating physical and mental condition. This film is available at most national chain video stores.

4. *The Urinary Tract: Water!* (FHS; 28 min., 1989, VHS, DVD). From the award-winning *The Living Body* series, this video shows the crucial part water plays in the body's functioning and how it keeps it in balance.

5. *Whose Kidney is it Anyway?* (FHS; 52 min., 1996, VHS, DVD). This video shows the dilemma surrounding a father who has already donated a kidney to one of his sons and wishes to donate the other kidney to his second son and go on dialysis himself. Should doctors let him go ahead?

6. *The Kidney* (FHS; 14 min., 1996, VHS, DVD). This program explains the structure and function of kidneys and how they maintain homeostasis.

SOFTWARE

1. *InterActive Physiology 9-System Suite* (ADAM, BC; Win/Mac). Interactive software with sections on the urinary system and fluids and electrolytes that explore the physiology of that system and its effect on fluid and electrolyte balance.

2. *Fluids and Electrolytes* (NIMCO; Win/Mac). Teaches more than 200 fundamental principles in the field of fluids and electrolytes.

3. *Kidney Functions* (NIMCO; Win/Mac). Explores the numerous functions of the kidneys.

The Reproductive System

CHAPTER SUMMARY

Of all the body systems, the reproductive system is usually the most interesting to students. They frequently start with a good, although general, base of information and are eager to build on what they already know. For this reason, it is often one of the most fun of the body systems to cover.

In this chapter, the male anatomy and reproductive functions are presented first. The testes and their accessory ducts are each described, followed by an explanation of the accessory glands and their secretions. The secretions from the seminal vesicles and prostate gland combine with sperm to form semen, and the secretions from the bulbourethral glands cleanse the urethra of acid and serve as a lubricant during sexual intercourse. The role of the scrotum in temperature regulation is explained, as is the function of the penis in sperm delivery. Following the anatomy of the male reproductive system is an overview of the process of spermatogenesis, or sperm production. Testosterone production is explained and the secondary sex characteristics that this hormone stimulates are outlined.

The next section of this chapter covers the female anatomy and reproductive functions. The ovaries and their accessory ducts are each described, followed by an explanation of the role of the uterus and vagina, as well as a description of the external female genitalia. Oogenesis, or egg production, and the ovarian cycles are presented next. The role of hormones in regulating the cyclic changes that occur monthly in the ovary are explained, followed by a breakdown of the menstrual cycle into its three stages: menses, the proliferative stage, and the secretory stage. The biological role of the mammary glands to produce milk completes this overview of female reproduction.

The final section of this chapter provides a survey of pregnancy and embryonic development. The obvious joint role of the male and female reproductive systems is to produce offspring. Beginning with fertilization, the process proceeds through embryonic and fetal development, culminating in childbirth. The anatomical and physiological changes that occur to the mother during pregnancy are discussed, and finally, the process of childbirth and the three stages of labor are presented. In the section on developmental aspects, some of the more intriguing homeostatic imbalances are discussed, including pseudohermaphroditism and the chromosomal abnormalities of X0 females and Y0 males.

SUGGESTED LECTURE OUTLINE

I. ANATOMY OF THE MALE REPRODUCTIVE SYSTEM (pp. 546–549; Figure 16.2)
   A. Testes (p. 546)
      1. Seminiferous Tubules
   B. Duct System (pp. 546–548)
      1. Epididymis
      2. Ductus Deferens
      3. Urethra
   C. Accessory Glands and Semen (pp. 548–549)
      1. Seminal Vesicles

TEACHING TIP

Outline spermatogenesis and oogenesis together to help students understand their similarities as well as differences.

171

       2. Prostate Gland
       3. Bulbourethral Glands
       4. Semen
   D. External Genitalia (p. 549)
       1. Scrotum
       2. Penis

II. MALE REPRODUCTIVE FUNCTIONS (pp. 550–553)
   A. Spermatogenesis (pp. 550–552)
   B. Testosterone Production (pp. 552–553)

III. ANATOMY OF THE FEMALE REPRODUCTIVE SYSTEM (pp. 552–557; Figure 16.8)
   A. Ovaries (pp. 553–554)
       1. Follicles
       2. Corpus Luteum
   B. Duct System (pp. 554–556)
       1. Uterine (Fallopian) Tubes
       2. Uterus
       3. Vagina
   C. External Genitalia (pp. 556–557)
       1. Labia Majora and Minora
       2. Clitoris

IV. FEMALE REPRODUCTIVE FUNCTIONS AND CYCLES (pp. 557–561)
   A. Oogenesis and the Ovarian Cycle (pp. 557–559)
   B. Uterine (Menstrual) Cycle (pp. 559–561)
       1. Days 1–5: Menstrual Phase
       2. Days 6–14: Proliferative Phase
       3. Days 15–28: Secretory Phase
   C. Hormone Production by the Ovaries (p. 561)
       1. Estrogens
       2. Progesterone

V. MAMMARY GLANDS (pp. 561–563)
   A. Lactation
   B. Mammography

VI. SURVEY OF PREGNANCY AND EMBRYONIC DEVELOPMENT (pp. 563–571)
   A. Accomplishing Fertilization (pp. 563–564)
       1. Zygote
   B. Events of Embryonic and Fetal Development (pp. 565–566)
       1. Cleavage
       2. Embryo
       3. Blastocyst
       4. Trophoblast
       5. Germ Layers
       6. Placenta
       7. Fetus

MEDIA TIP

Gender Biology: Men and Women Really Are Different (FHS; 22 min., 2001). This program explores the emerging field of gender-based biology and gender implications in medical treatments.

   C. Effects of Pregnancy on the Mother (pp. 566–569)
       1. Anatomical Changes
       2. Physiological Changes
           a. Gastrointestinal System
           b. Urinary System
           c. Respiratory System
           d. Cardiovascular System
   D. Childbirth (pp. 569–571)
       1. Initiation of Labor
       2. Stages of Labor
           a. Stage 1: Dilation Stage
           b. Stage 2: Expulsion Stage
           c. Stage 3: Placental Stage

VII. DEVELOPMENTAL ASPECTS OF THE REPRODUCTIVE
      SYSTEM (pp. 572–578)
   A. Chromosomes
   B. Puberty
   C. Menarche
   D. Contraception (*A Closer Look*)
   E. Menopause

KEY TERMS

accessory reproductive
   organs
acrosome
afterbirth
alveolar glands
amnion
ampulla
areola
blastocyst
body
broad ligament
bulbourethral glands
cervix
chorionic vesicle
chorionic villi
cleavage
clitoris
corpus luteum
dilation stage
ductus deferens
ectoderm
ejaculation
ejaculatory duct
embryo
endoderm
endometrium

epididymis
erectile tissue
erection
estrogens
expulsion stage
external genitalia
fallopian tubes
false labor
fertilization
fetus
fimbriae
follicle cells
foreskin
fundus
gametes
glans penis
gonads
Graafian follicle
greater vestibular glands
human chorionic
   gonadotropin (hCG)
hymen
implantation
inner cell mass
labia majora
labia minora

labor
lactating
lactiferous ducts
luteinizing hormone (LH)
mammary glands
meiosis
membranous urethra
menarche
menopause
menstrual cycle
mesoderm
mons pubis
myometrium
nipple
oocyte
oogenesis
oogonia
ova
ovarian cycle
ovarian follicles
ovarian ligaments
ovaries
ovulation
ovum
parturition
penis

perimetrium
perineum
placenta
placental stage
polar body
pregnancy
prepuce
primary oocytes
primary sex organs
primary spermatocyte
progesterone
prostate
prostatic urethra
puberty
relaxin
reproductive system

round ligament
scrotum
secondary oocyte
secondary sex
    characteristics
semen
seminal vesicles
seminiferous tubules
shaft
sperm
spermatic cord
spermatids
spermatogenesis
spermatogonia
spermiogenesis
spongy (penile) urethra

suspensory ligaments
testosterone
trophoblast
umbilical cord
urethra
uterine cycle
uterine tubes
uterosacral ligament
uterus
vagina
vas deferens
vesicular follicle
vestibule
vulva
zygote

LECTURE HINTS

1. Remind students that the male reproductive system shares structures with the urinary system, whereas the female reproductive system does not. Point out that this difference is evident even during embryonic development.

   Key point: This point may seem obvious, but it is surprising to learn how many people actually don't realize this key concept.

2. Point out that development of the testes within the abdominal cavity is similar to development of the ovaries, but that the testes descend into the scrotum for temperature control of sperm, usually prior to birth. Cryptorchidism, or undescended testes, is a condition that can lead to sterility unless surgically corrected. Explain why hot tubs could be considered a form of male birth control.

   Key point: The asymmetry of this system is often confusing for students at first.

3. Discuss the conditions of hypospadias and epispadias and their consequences.

   Key point: Hypospadias is the opening of the urethra on the undersurface of the penis, whereas epispadias is the opening of the urethra on the dorsal surface. Depending on severity, both conditions can decrease male fertility by causing inadequate deposition of sperm, and both are usually corrected surgically.

4. Clearly itemize the components of semen.

   Key point: Students frequently think semen and sperm are synonymous and are surprised to learn that semen is a combination of several secretions.

5. Discuss prostatic cancer and benign prostatic hypertrophy (BPH), and differentiate between their signs, symptoms, and treatment options.

   Key point: BPH is common in men over 50 and results in urinary urgency, frequency, bladder infection, and other urinary difficulties. The hypertrophied prostatic tissue that is strangling the urethra is often removed surgically, or newer treatments, including drugs and radiation, can be used to shrink the enlarged tissue. Prostatic cancer is the third most common cancer in males, and incidences of this cancer are on the rise. Early detection is important and PSA (prostate-specific antigen) is becoming a common screening tool.

6. Outline spermatogenesis and oogenesis together to help students understand their similarities as well as differences.

    Key point: This is a good opportunity to emphasize the differences between mitosis and meiosis.

7. Itemize the secondary sex characteristics of both males and females. Remind students of the role of hormones in sexual development, and discuss the effects of homeostatic imbalances of these hormones.

    Key point: This becomes a good point of discussion since there is increasing scientific concern over the exposure of both males and females to synthetic estrogens from plastics and pesticides.

8. Note that the layers of the uterus follow a pattern of layering we have seen with other organs and tissues. Also point out that the cervix refers to the "neck" of the uterus, to differentiate it from cervical vertebrae found in the actual neck region.

    Key point: The endometrium, myometrium, and perimetrium follow a pattern seen with such organs as the heart and nerves. Recognizing this pattern helps students better visualize the layers. Recognizing root word meanings, such as "cervix," helps explain why it can be used in reference to entirely different regions.

9. Discuss the incidences of cervical, uterine, ovarian, and breast cancer in women, as well as screening tools and treatment options.

    Key point: An annual Pap smear is the screening tool of choice for early detection of cervical cancer. Breast cancer is the leading cause of death in American women and screening includes monthly self-examination and annual mammography for certain age groups. Early detection of uterine or ovarian cancer is still unsatisfactory.

10. Outline the process of fertilization and follow the path of the fertilized egg from conception to implantation. Discuss ectopic pregnancy and placenta previa.

    Key point: Students are usually quite interested in the fertilization process and have often heard of complications that can arise. Explaining that fertilization generally takes place in the fallopian tubes helps explain the incidence of ectopic pregnancy, and implantation close to the cervical opening explains the seriousness of placenta previa.

11. Review the stages of the menstrual cycle (and note the correct spelling of menstruation, since many people are unaware of the "u").

    Key point: Both males and females are frequently unsure of the menstrual stages but are often too embarrassed to admit that they don't know about such a common, normal part of female life.

12. Explain how birth control pills work to prevent pregnancy.

    Key point: Describe how these synthetic hormones "trick" the body into thinking it is pregnant, thereby stopping ovulation and preventing pregnancy.

13. Clearly differentiate between the terms *prostate* and *prostrate*, and between *perineum* and *peritoneum*.

    Key point: These terms are often used incorrectly by students and laypersons in general.

14. Explain some of the genetic conditions associated with chromosomal abnormalities, such as Down and Turner's syndrome. Remind the students of previous discussions about x-linked disorders such as hemophilia and choroideremia.

    Key point: This is an excellent opportunity to give a brief overview of some of the more prominent or intriguing hereditary conditions.

15. Describe eclampsia, or toxemia of pregnancy, and discuss early detection and treatment.

    Key point: Eclampsia, the most serious complication of pregnancy, is a severe hypertensive disorder characterized by convulsions and coma, which can lead to death. Early detection is critical, and the primary means of early detection is through urine testing for proteinuria, an excellent early sign of increasing blood pressure. Treatment involves bedrest and seizure management.

16. Discuss the different types of birth control methods. Explain the efficacy and side effects of each.

    Key point: Students may be aware of only one or two methods, and may not understand how they actually prevent contraception.

17. Explain the term *miscarriage* and contrast it with abortion. Describe the potential causes of miscarriage, including exposure to various household chemicals and toxins.

    Key point: Many students do not realize that they could have actually "miscarried" a pregnancy and not have known it if it did not implant in the uterus. Many students are also unaware of the impacts of exposure to many common chemicals during pregnancy.

TRANSPARENCIES/MEDIA MANAGER INDEX

A Closer Look Contraception: Preventing Pregnancy

Focus on Careers Doula*

Systems in Sync Homeostatic Relationships Between the Reproductive System and Other Body Systems

Indicates images that are on the Media Manager only.

ANSWERS TO END OF CHAPTER REVIEW QUESTIONS

Questions appear on pp. 580–582

Multiple Choice

1. d (p. 548)
2. a (pp. 556–557)
3. d (p. 556)
4. d (pp. 552, 559–561)
5. b (p. 557)
6. b, c, d (p. 554)
7. d (p. 551)
8. a (pp. 555–556)
9. c (pp. 557–559)
10. b (pp. 553–554)
11. d (p. 565)
12. a, d (p. 570)
13. a, d (Table 16.1)

Short Answer Essay

14. The testes are the male gonads. They form sperm and testosterone. (p. 546)
15. To provide a liquid medium for carrying sperm out of the male body and into the female reproductive tract. Prostate gland, seminal vesicles, and bulbourethral glands. (pp. 548–549)
16. Erection. (p. 549)
17. *Ejaculation:* Propulsion of sperm (in seminal fluid) out of the male's body. (p. 548)
18. Internal body temperature is too high for the production of viable human sperm. The lower temperature that is required is provided for by the testes being housed in the scrotum, a divided skin sac that hangs outside the body cavity, posterior to the penis. (p. 549)
19. Hypertrophy of the prostate gland, which surrounds the urethra, constricts the urethral passageway, thus inhibiting the passage of semen. (pp. 548–549; Figure 16.2)
20. Spermatogenesis begins during puberty under the influence of FSH from the anterior pituitary. LH (another anterior pituitary hormone) causes the testes to produce testosterone at that time. Testosterone is also necessary for normal sperm production. (pp. 550, 552)

21. Increased hair growth all over the body and particularly on the face, axillary and pubic regions; deepening of the voice; enlargement of the skeletal muscles; thickening of the bones. (p. 552)

22. Testosterone is still produced and secondary sex characteristics and sex drive are retained after a vasectomy. Sperm are still produced but cannot reach the body surface after this relatively minor procedure. (p. 548)

23. The ovary. It produces eggs (actually oocytes) and the female sex hormones estrogen and progesterone. (pp. 553–554)

24. The term *urogenital system* is more applicable to males because their urinary and reproductive systems share some of the same pathways. (p. 548)

25. *Uterine (Fallopian) tubes:* The usual site of fertilization; conduct the oocyte (or embryo) to the uterus. *Uterus:* The site of implantation of the embryo. *Vagina:* The birth canal and the chamber through which menstrual flow leaves the body. (pp. 554–556)

26. The distal ends of the uterine tubes have fingerlike extensions called fimbriae, which wave and create fluid currents to draw the ovulated body into the uterine tube. (p. 554–555)

27. *Follicle:* An immature egg (oocyte) surrounded by one or more layers of smaller cells called follicle cells. *Ovulation:* Ejection of an oocyte (surrounded by a capsule of follicle cells) from the ovary. (p. 553)

28. The human oocyte becomes an ovum only if sperm penetration occurs, at which time the secondary oocyte completes the second meiotic division to produce the ovum nucleus and a polar body, which is ejected. (pp. 553, 557–558)

29. Both growing and mature (Graafian) ovarian follicles form estrogen. The second hormone produced by the ovary is progesterone. (p. 561)

30. See pp. 559–561 of the text. It provides the uterine environment needed for implantation.

31. *Menopause:* The period during which a woman's ovarian function (thus, reproductive ability) gradually declines and finally ends. (p. 576)

32. *Fertilization:* Fusion of the sperm and egg nuclei to form the nucleus of the fertilized egg, or zygote. It normally occurs in the uterine tube of the female. Implantation involves the erosion of the uterine mucosa by the embryo, and then the covering over of the embedded embryo by mucosa regrowth. (pp. 563–565)

33. During pregnancy the woman's respiratory and urinary systems must function "for two." Respiration becomes increasingly difficult as the uterus enlarges and presses the abdominal organs superiorly against the diaphragm. Cardiac output and blood pressure also increase to meet the increased circulatory demands. Changes in the woman's weight distribution and center of gravity make walking more difficult and lead to muscle strain. Urinary frequency sometimes occurs as the uterus presses on the bladder. (pp. 566–568)

34. Estrogens reach their highest levels in the mother's blood, which leads to weak uterine contractions. Certain cells of the fetus begin to produce oxytocin, along with the mother's hypothalamus. Prostaglandins released by the placenta also stimulate more frequent and powerful uterine contractions. (pp. 569–570)

35. During stage 2 (expulsion stage). (p. 570)

36. The indifferent stage occurs up until eight weeks of embryonic development. During this time, the reproductive structures of the male and female embryos cannot be differentiated. (p. 571)

37. The major events of puberty in males include enlargement of testes and scrotum; appearance of pubic, axillary, and facial hair; penis growth; and the presence of mature sperm in semen. In females, the major events of puberty include breast development and menarche. (p. 573)

38. Except for prostatic hypertrophy, aging males seem to have few age-associated reproductive system problems. Reproductive capacity in females ends during menopause. Problems associated with the relative lack of female hormones after menopause include high blood pressure, bone loss, and predisposition to vaginal infections. (pp. 576, 578)

ANSWERS TO CRITICAL THINKING AND CLINICAL APPLICATION QUESTIONS

39. The woman is in the second, or expulsion, stage of labor. Since this stage typically takes 50 minutes for the first birth and 20 minutes in subsequent births, she probably would not have time to get to the hospital. (p. 570)

40. It is possible for an oocyte to be ovulated from a right ovary into the peritoneal cavity, and then move through the fluid of the peritoneal cavity all the way to the infundibulum of the left uterine tube. Several cases have been documented of women like Lucy bearing children. (pp. 554–555)

41. The mucus produced by these glands cleans the urethra of urine residues. (p. 549)

42. Her only options are coitus interruptus, or withdrawal of the penis just before ejaculation, or rhythm or fertility awareness methods, based on recognizing the period of ovulation or fertility and avoiding intercourse during those intervals. (pp. 574–576)

43. Ibuprofen is a prostaglandin inhibitor; such drugs can inhibit labor in the early stages. (p. 570)

44. Castration would prevent the development of secondary sex characteristics, which includes deepening of the voice due to enlargement of the larynx. (p. 552)

45. Polar bodies have essentially no cytoplasm so they deteriorate and die quickly. (p. 559)

CLASSROOM DEMONSTRATIONS AND STUDENT ACTIVITIES

Classroom Demonstrations

1. Film(s) or other media of choice.

2. Use a dissectible human torso model to demonstrate the location of the reproductive organs.

3. If available, use a "pregnant" torso model to illustrate the most desirable positioning of the placenta and the vertex presentation of a fetus along with the placement of fetuses during a multiple pregnancy.

4. Use models showing the process of meiosis in spermatogenesis and oogenesis.

5. Use embryonic-fetal development models to show the stage of cleavage, the blastula, etc.

6. If available, show preserved specimens of human embryos or fetuses in various stages of development to illustrate the later changes that occur during gestation.

7. Invite a speaker from the local public health department to present the most current information on STDs.

8. Invite a nurse from the local hospital labor and delivery department to talk about childbirth from their perspective.

9. Form a panel of women who have gone through pregnancy and childbirth and ask them to discuss their experiences with the class.

10. Invite a midwife or doula to speak to the class on their role in the delivery process.

11. Invite a genetic counselor to speak to the class on the role of genetic counseling in family planning.

Student Activities

1. Have students find and bring in articles that deal with the effects of maternal drug use or alcoholism on the fetus. Use this information as a starting point for class discussion, including a discussion of fetal alcohol syndrome.

2. Ask students to research sexually transmitted diseases and present their findings on the top five STDs in their local area compared to the national figures.

3. Provide diagrams of the reproductive system for students to label.

4. Display various types of contraceptive techniques as an adjunct to a discussion of birth control.

5. Have students participate in breast or prostatic cancer awareness activities, AIDS walks, or other activities relevant to the study of the reproductive system.

6. Have students research and report on advances in assisted fertilization as a starting point for class discussion.

7. Ask students to come to class prepared to talk about natural childbirth, home birthing, episiotomy, cesarean section, circumcision, and other topics related to childbirth.

MULTIMEDIA

See page 182 for a listing of media resources.

1. *1 + 1: A Natural History of Sexuality* (FHS; 53 min., 2001, VHS, DVD). This program examines four billion years of history to find an answer to the question of why sex has evolved into the primary mode of procreation.

2. *Birth: Eight Women's Stories* (FHS; 70 min., 1993, VHS). Gold medal winner, this video follows eight women giving birth in a variety of circumstances, including natural birth at home and induced vaginal delivery.

3. *Boy or Girl? When Doctors Choose a Child's Sex* (FHS; 15 min., 1999, VHS, DVD). This video examines medical and ethical implications associated with sex assignment in cases of ambiguous genitalia.

4. *BPH: Aging and the Enlarged Prostate* (FHS; 23 min., 2001, VHS, DVD). This program examines the symptoms, medications, surgical interventions, and future treatment options for this common medical condition.

5. *Gender Biology: Men and Women Really Are Different* (FHS; 22 min., 2001, VHS, DVD). This program explores the emerging field of gender-based biology and gender implications in medical treatments.

6. *A Human Life Emerges* (FHS; 33 min., 1995, VHS, DVD). Part of a two-part series, this program presents a close-up view of reproduction from fertilization through gestation and culminating in birth.

7. *The Human Female Reproductive System* (UL; 29 min., 1997, VHS). This video describes the structures, functions, and hormones of the female reproductive system and examines selected homeostatic imbalances of the system.

8. *The Human Male Reproductive System* (UL; 29 min., 1997, VHS). This video describes the structures, functions, and hormones of the male reproductive system and examines selected homeostatic imbalances of the system.

9. *A Question of Genes: Inherited Risks* (FHS; 106 min., 1997, VHS, DVD). This program explores medical and ethical questions raised by genetic testing and future uses of genetic research.

10. *Reproduction* (FHS; 14 min., 1996, VHS, DVD). From *The World of Living Organisms* series, this program surveys various aspects of reproductive life, including contraception, STDs, and fertility.

11. *Reproduction: Designer Babies* (FHS; 20 min., 1995, VHS, DVD). From *The New Living Body* series, this program examines some of the issues raised by the potential uses and misuses of genetic technology.

SOFTWARE

1. *Genetics* (FHS; Win/Mac). Investigates the basic principles of heredity, the history of genetics, clinical aspects of gene-related disorders, and ethical issues.

2. *Meiosis* (QUE; Win/Mac). Explains the process of meiosis.

MULTIMEDIA RESOURCE DISTRIBUTORS

The following media resource distributors are referenced under Multimedia in the Instructor Guide. **Please Note:** *Distribution company names and web addresses change frequently.*

ACBP Annenberg/CPB Project
The Corporation for Public
Broadcasting
P.O. Box 2345
S. Burlington, VT 05407-2345
1-800-LEARNER
www.learner.org

ADAM A.D.A.M. Software, Inc.
1800 RiverEdge Parkway, Suite
100
Atlanta, GA 30328
770-980-0888
http://education.adam.com

AIMS AIMS Media
9710 Desoto Avenue
Chatsworth, CA 91311-4409
800-367-2467/818-773-4300
www.aimsmultimedia.com

AMB Ambrose Video
145 West 45th Street, Suite 1115
New York, NY 10036
800-526-4663/212-768-7373
www.ambrosevideo.com

BBC2 BBC-Two
PO Box 1922
Glasgow, G2 3WT
08700 100 222
www.bbc.co.uk/bbctwo

BC Benjamin Cummings
1301 Sansome Street
San Francisco, CA 94111-2525
800-950-2665/415-402-2500
www.aw-bc.com

BF Bullfrog Films
P.O. Box 149
Oley, PA 19547
800-543-FROG (3674)/610-370-
1978
www.bullfrogfilms.com

BV BrainViews, Ltd.
3175 Bird Drive
Ravenna, Ohio 44266
www.brainviews.com

CBS Carolina Biological Supply
Company
2700 York Road
Burlington, NC 27215
800-334-5551
www.carolina.com

CE CyberEd, Inc.
P.O. Box 3480
Chico, CA 95927-3480
888-318-0700/530-899-1212
www.cybered.net

CM Concept Media
PO Box 19542
Irvine, CA 92623-9542
800-233-7078
www.conceptmedia.com

ED Edumatch, Inc.
86 West Street
Waltham, MA 02451-1110
800-637-0047
www.edumatch.com

FHS Films for the Humanities and
Sciences
P.O. Box 2053
Princeton, NJ 08453
800-257-5126/609-419-8000
www.films.com

HRM HRM Video
41 Kensico Drive
Mount Kisco, NY 10549
800-431-2050
www.hrmvideo.com

ICON Icon Learning Systems
295 North Street
Teterboro, NJ 07608
800-631-1181
www.netterart.com

IM Insight Media
2162 Broadway
New York, NY 10024
800-233-9100/212-721-6316
www.insight-media.com

KV	Kinetic Video 255 Delaware Avenue Buffalo, NY 14202 800-466-7631/716-856-7838 www.kineticvideo.com
LP	Laser Professor 351 Lakeside Lane, Suite 308 Houston, TX 77058 800-550-0335/281-333-5550 www.laserprofessor.com
MF	Miller-Fenwick, Inc. 2125 Greenspring Drive Timonium, MD 21093 800-432-8433 www.milner-fenwick.com
NIMCO	NIMCO, Inc. P.O. Box 9 102 Highway 81 N Calhoun, KY 42327-0009 800-962-6662 www.nimcoinc.com
PYR	Pyramid Media P.O. Box 1048/WEB Santa Monica, CA 90406 877-730-2022/202-429-5755 www.pyramidmedia.com
QUE	Queue, Inc. 1450 Barnum Avenue, Suite 207 Bridgeport, CT 06610 800-232-2224/800-775-2729 www.queueinc.com
SIN	Sinauer Associates, Inc., Publishers 23 Plumtree Road P.O. Box 407 Sunderland, MA 01375-0407 413-549-4300/413-549-1118 www.sinauer.com
TW	Thomson Learning PO Box 6904 Florence, KY 41022-6904 800-354-9706/800-487-8488 www.wadsworth.com
UL	United Learning 1560 Sherman Avenue, Suite 100 Evanston, IL 60201 800-323-9084 www.unitedlearning.com
WNS	WARD's Natural Science 5100 West Henrietta Road Rochester, NY 14692-9012 800-962-2660/585-359-2502 www.wardsci.com

Additional Media Resources

Anatomical Chart Company
4711 Golf Road
Suite 650
Skokie, IL 60076
847-679-4700/847-679-9155
www.anatomical.com

Biodisc, Inc.
6963 Easton Court
Sarasota, FL 34238-2610
800-453-3009/800-921-3009
www.biodisc.com

Communication Skills, Inc.
49 Richmondville Avenue
Westport, CT 06880
800-824-2398/203-226-8820
www.communicationskills.com

Connecticut Valley Biological Supply
82 Valley Road
PO Box 326
Southampton, MA 01073
800-628-7748/800-355-6813
www.ctvalleybio.com

Denoyer Geppert Company
PO Box 1727
Skokie, IL 60076-8727
800-621-1014/866-531-1221
www.denoyer.com

Educational Activities, Inc.
P.O. Box 87
Baldwin, NY 11510
800-645-3739/516-623-9282
www.edact.com

Educational Images, Ltd.
PO Box 3456 Westside Station
Elmira, NY 14905-0456
800-527-4264/607-732-1183
www.educationalimages.com

Eli Lilly & Company, Medical Division
Lilly Corporate Center
Indianapolis, IN 46285
317/276-2000
www.lilly.com

Elsevier Health
The Curtis Center, Suite 300E
170 S. Independence Mall W
Philadelphia, PA 19106-3399
800-523-1649/215-238-7883
www.us.elsevierhealth.com

EME Corporation
581 Central Parkway
P.O. Box 1949
Stuart, FL 34995
800-848-2050/772-219-2206
www.emescience.com

Encyclopedia Britannica Educational Corporation
310 South Michigan Avenue
Chicago, IL 60604
800-323-1229/312-294-2104
www.britannica.com

Fisher Scientific Education
3970 John's Creek Court, Suite 500
Suwanee, GA 30024
800-766-7000/770-871-4726
www.fishersci.com

Flinn Scientific, Inc.
PO Box 219
Batavia, IL 60510
800-452-1261/866-452-1436
www.flinnsci.com

Frey Scientific
P.O. Box 8101
100 Paragon Parkway
Mansfield, OH 44903
800-225-FREY/877-256-FREY
www.freyscientific.com

Gold Standard Multimedia
320 West Kennedy Blvd., Suite 400
Tampa, FL 33606
800-375-0943/813-259-1585
www.gsm.com

Guidance Associates
100 South Bedford Road, Suite 120
Mt. Kisco, NY 10549
800-431-1242/914-666-5319
www.guidanceassociates.com

Hawkhill Associates, Inc.
125 East Gilman Street
Madison, WI 53703
800-422-4295/608-251-3924
www.hawkhill.net

Health Care Advances
A Division of NIMCO, Inc.
PO Box 9
102 Highway 81 North
Calhoun, KY 42327-0009
800-962-6662/270-273-5844
www.nimcoinc.com

HW Wilson Company
(publishes Biological and Agricultural Index
Plus, General Science Database)
950 University Avenue
Bronx, NY 10452
800-367-6770/718-588-8400
www.hwwilson.com

Lippincott Williams & Wilkins
530 Walnut Street
Philadelphia, PA 19106-3621
215-521-8300/215-521-8902
www.lww.com

Media Basics Video
Lighthouse Square
PO Box 449
Guilford, CT 06437
800-542-2805/203-458-9816
www.mediabasicsvideo.com

National Geographic Film Library
1145 17th NW
Washington, D.C. 20036
877-730-2022/202-429-5755
www.natgeostock.com

National Geographic Society
P.O. Box 10041
Des Moines, Iowa 50340-0041
888 CALL NGS (888 225 5647)
www.nationalgeographic.com

Nebraska Scientific
3823 Leavenworth Street
Omaha, NE 68105
800-228-7117/402-346-7214
www.nebraskascientific.com

Phoenix Learning Group
2349 Chaffee Drive
St. Louis, MO 63146
800-221-1274
www.phoenixlearninggroup.com

Primal Pictures
159-163 Great Portland Street
London, W1W 5PA, U.K.
880-716-2475/020-7637-1010
www.primalpictures.com

Public Broadcasting Service
1320 Braddock Place
Alexandria, VA 22314
www.pbs.org

RAmEx Ars Medica, Inc.
1511 Sawtelle Blvd. #232
Los Angeles, California 90025-3206
800-633 9281/310-826 9674
www.ramex.com

Research Systems, Inc.
4990 Pearl East Circle
Boulder, CO 80301
303-786-9900
www.rsinc.com

Riverdeep Interactive Learning
500 Redwood Boulevard
Novato, CA 94947
888-242-6747/415-763-4700
www.riverdeep.net

Science Kit and Boreal Laboratories
777 East Park Drive
PO Box 5003
Tonawanda, NY 14150
800-828-7777/800-828-3299
www.sciencekit.com

Scientific American
415 Madison Avenue
New York, NY 10017
800-333-1199/212-754-0550
www.sciam.com

SVE and Churchill Media
6677 North Northwest Highway
Chicago, IL 60631-1304
800-829-1900/800-624-1678
www.svemedia.com

Teacher's Video Company
PO Box 4455
Scottsdale, AZ 85261
480-850-5000
www.teachersvideo.com

Thomson/Gale
(publishes Video Source Book)
27500 Drake Road
Farmington Hills, MI 48331
800-877-4253/248-699-4253
www.galegroup.com

University of California Extension
Center for Media and Independent Learning
2000 Center Street, Fourth Floor
Berkeley, CA 94704-1223
510-642-0460/510-643-9271
http://ucmedia.berkeley.edu

Videodiscovery, Inc.
920 N. 34th
Seattle, WA 98103
800-548-3472/206-285-5400
www.videodiscovery.com

Visible Productions
201 Linden Street, Suite 301
Fort Collins, CO 80524
800-685-4668
http://visiblep.com

VWR International
1310 Goshen Parkway
West Chester, PA 19380
800-932-1700/610-431-9174
www.vwr.com

Test Bank

Chapter 1 The Human Body: An Orientation

Short Answer

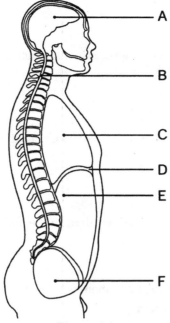

Figure 1.1

Using Figure 1.1, identify the following:

   1) Label A points to the _____ cavity.

   Answer: cranial
   Diff: 1   Page Ref: 20

   2) Label B points to the _____ cavity.

   Answer: spinal
   Diff: 1   Page Ref: 20

   3) Label C points to the _____ cavity.

   Answer: thoracic
   Diff: 1   Page Ref: 20

   4) Label D points to the _____.

   Answer: diaphragm
   Diff: 1   Page Ref: 20

   5) Label E points to the _____ cavity.

   Answer: abdominal
   Diff: 1   Page Ref: 20

   6) Label F points to the _____ cavity.

   Answer: pelvic
   Diff: 1   Page Ref: 20

Fill in the blank or provide a short answer:

7) Groups of cells that have a common function are termed _____ .

Answer: tissues
Diff: 1   Page Ref: 4

8) The larynx is an organ of the _____ system.

Answer: respiratory
Diff: 1   Page Ref: 7

9) The system that functions in the storage of minerals, such as calcium, is called the _____ system.

Answer: skeletal
Diff: 1   Page Ref: 4

10) The breakdown of ingested foods into simple molecules that can then be absorbed into the bloodstream is termed _____ .

Answer: digestion
Diff: 1   Page Ref: 11

11) _____ refers to all of the chemical reactions in the body.

Answer: Metabolism
Diff: 1   Page Ref: 11

12) The ability to sense changes and react to them is termed _____ or _____ .

Answer: irritability; responsiveness
Diff: 1   Page Ref: 11

13) The component of a control system that provides the means for the control center's response (output) is called the _____ .

Answer: effector
Diff: 1   Page Ref: 12–13

14) The study of the body's small structures using a microscope is called _____ .

Answer: microscopic anatomy
Diff: 1   Page Ref: 2

15) A control mechanism that responds to a stimulus by decreasing its intensity is called a _____ mechanism.

Answer: negative feedback
Diff: 1   Page Ref: 13

16) The body's ability to maintain stable internal conditions is referred to as _____ .

Answer: homeostasis
Diff: 1   Page Ref: 12

17) The navel is _____ to the spine.

Answer: ventral or anterior
Diff: 2   Page Ref: 18

18) The armpit area is called the _____ region.

Answer: axillary
Diff: 1   Page Ref: 16–17

19) A cut that is made along the midline is called a _____ section.

Answer: midsagittal or median
Diff: 1   Page Ref: 17

20) The central region of the thoracic cavity containing the heart is called the _____.

Answer: mediastinum
Diff: 1   Page Ref: 20

21) The right and left iliac (inguinal) regions are lateral to the _____ region.

Answer: hypogastric
Diff: 2   Page Ref: 22

22) The cranial and spinal cavities are subdivisions of the _____ cavity.

Answer: dorsal
Diff: 1   Page Ref: 20

23) The _____ system is composed of kidneys, bladder, ureters, and urethra.

Answer: urinary or excretory
Diff: 1   Page Ref: 7

24) Blood is categorized as a _____ because it is compared of similar cells with a common function.

Answer: tissue
Diff: 1   Page Ref: 4

25) Ventral is a directional term synonymous with _____ in humans.

Answer: anterior
Diff: 1   Page Ref: 18

26) The three medial regions of the abdominopelvic cavity are _____, _____, and _____.

Answer: epigastric region, umbilical region, hypogastric region
Diff: 1   Page Ref: 21

27) The function of the _____ system is to control body activities via hormones.

Answer: endocrine
Diff: 1   Page Ref: 5; 7

28) _____ is the process of breaking down ingested food in preparation for absorption.

Answer: Digestion
Diff: 1   Page Ref: 11

29) Blood clotting and the birth of a baby are examples of the _____ feedback mechanism.

Answer: positive
Diff: 1   Page Ref: 13

30) The patellar region is _____ to the popliteal region.

    Answer: ventral or anterior
    Diff: 1   *Page Ref: 16*

31) The abdominal cavity has _____ quadrants and _____ regions.

    Answer: 4; 9
    Diff: 2   *Page Ref: 21*

32) The thoracic cavity is _____ to the abdominopelvic cavity.

    Answer: superior
    Diff: 1   *Page Ref: 20*

33) The epigastric region is _____ to the right hypochondriac region of the abdominopelvic cavity.

    Answer: medial
    Diff: 2   *Page Ref: 21*

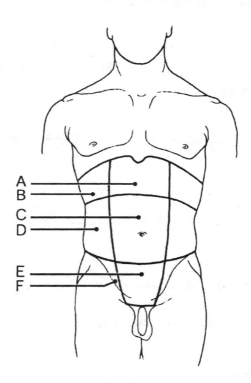

Figure 1.2

Using Figure 1.2, identify the following:

    34) Label A points to the _____ region.

        Answer: epigastric
        Diff: 1   *Page Ref: 21*

    35) Label B points to the _____ region.

        Answer: right hypochondriac
        Diff: 1   *Page Ref: 21*

36) Label C points to the _____ region.

Answer: umbilical
Diff: 1   Page Ref: 21 .

37) Label D points to the _____ region.

Answer: right lumbar
Diff: 1   Page Ref: 21

38) Label E points to the _____ region.

Answer: hypogastric
Diff: 1   Page Ref: 21

39) Label F points to the _____ region.

Answer: right iliac (inguinal)
Diff: 1   Page Ref: 21

Multiple Choice

1) The study of the function of the body and body parts is called:
   A) anatomy
   B) physiology
   C) homeostasis
   D) negative feedback
   E) irritability

Answer: B
Diff: 1   Page Ref: 2

2) Which of the following activities does not represent an anatomical study:
   A) making a section through the heart to observe its interior
   B) examining the surface of a bone
   C) viewing muscle tissue through a microscope
   D) studying how the nerves conduct electrical impulses
   E) observing the parts of a reproducing cell

Answer: D
Diff: 2   Page Ref: 2

3) Which of the following is the correct sequence, going from simplest to most complex, in the levels of structural organization of the human body:
   A) chemical level, cellular level, tissue level, organ level, organ system level, organismal level
   B) chemical level, tissue level, cellular level, organ system level, organ level, organismal level
   C) cellular level, chemical level, tissue level, organ level, organ system level, organismal level
   D) cellular level, tissue level, chemical level, organ level, organ system level, organismal level
   E) cellular level, chemical level, tissue level, organ system level, organismal level, organ level

Answer: A
Diff: 3   Page Ref: 3-4

4) Which of these structures is the most complex:
   A) an organ
   B) a tissue
   C) a molecule
   D) organ system
   E) a cell

   Answer: D
   Diff: 2   *Page Ref: 3–4*

5) The lymphatic system:
   A) responds to internal and external changes by activating appropriate muscles and glands
   B) picks up fluid leaked from blood vessels and returns it to the blood
   C) synthesizes vitamin D
   D) produces heat
   E) secretes hormones that regulate processes such as growth, reproduction, and nutrient use (metabolism) by body cells

   Answer: B
   Diff: 2   *Page Ref: 7*

6) The system that takes in oxygen and releases carbon dioxide to the exterior is the:
   A) respiratory system
   B) cardiovascular system
   C) reproductive system
   D) muscular system
   E) urinary system

   Answer: A
   Diff: 2   *Page Ref: 7*

7) The system that controls and coordinates the body through hormones is the:
   A) integumentary system
   B) skeletal system
   C) nervous system
   D) endocrine system
   E) digestive system

   Answer: D
   Diff: 2   *Page Ref: 7*

8) The muscular system consists of the:
   A) skeletal muscles
   B) muscles of the heart
   C) muscles in the walls of hollow organs
   D) skeletal muscles and the muscles of the heart
   E) muscles of the heart and those in the walls of the hollow organs

   Answer: A
   Diff: 1   *Page Ref: 4*

9) The ovary is part of which of the following two systems:
    A) digestive and endocrine systems
    B) digestive and respiratory systems
    C) reproductive and endocrine systems
    D) reproductive and respiratory systems
    E) endocrine and respiratory systems

Answer: C
Diff: 2   Page Ref: 7

10) Which system covers the external surface of the body and manufactures vitamin D:
    A) endocrine system
    B) integumentary system
    C) nervous system
    D) lymphatic system
    E) skeletal system

Answer: B
Diff: 2   Page Ref: 4; 5

11) Elimination of metabolic wastes from the body is the function of the:
    A) digestive system
    B) urinary system
    C) respiratory system
    D) digestive and urinary systems
    E) digestive and respiratory systems

Answer: B
Diff: 3   Page Ref: 7

12) Which of the following is NOT a necessary life *function*:
    A) maintaining boundaries
    B) movement
    C) responsiveness
    D) nutrients
    E) metabolism

Answer: D
Diff: 2   Page Ref: 10–11

13) Which of the following systems is matched most accurately to the life function it provides:
    A) integumentary system – movement
    B) nervous system – excretion
    C) muscular system – maintaining boundaries
    D) nervous system – responsiveness
    E) respiratory system – digestion

Answer: D
Diff: 1   Page Ref: 4–7

14) Which of these is NOT a survival need:
   A) nutrients
   B) oxygen
   C) water
   D) reproduction
   E) body temperature

Answer: D
Diff: 2   Page Ref: 11–12

15) Which of the following is the correct order of elements in a control system:
   A) receptor, stimulus, afferent pathway, control center, efferent pathway, effector, response
   B) receptor, stimulus, efferent pathway, control center, afferent pathway, effector, response
   C) effector, stimulus, efferent pathway, control center, afferent pathway, receptor, response
   D) stimulus, receptor, afferent pathway, control center, efferent pathway, effector, response
   E) stimulus, receptor, efferent pathway, control center, afferent pathway, effector, response

Answer: D
Diff: 3   Page Ref: 12–13

16) Which of the following elements of a control system detects a change:
   A) control center
   B) stimulus
   C) effector
   D) receptor
   E) efferent pathway

Answer: D
Diff: 1   Page Ref: 12

17) Positive feedback systems:
   A) regulate heart and breathing rates
   B) operate in such a way that the initial stimulus is enhanced and increases
   C) operate in such a way that the initial stimulus is shut off or reduced
   D) regulate heart and breathing rates, and operate in such a way that the initial stimulus is enhanced and increases
   E) regulate heart and breathing rates, and operate in such a way that the initial stimulus is shut off or reduced

Answer: B
Diff: 2   Page Ref: 13

18) Your body thermostat is located in a part of the brain called the hypothalamus. Which of the following elements of a control system does this area in the brain represent:
   A) control center
   B) stimulus
   C) effector
   D) efferent pathway
   E) afferent pathway

Answer: A
Diff: 2   Page Ref: 12

19) In anatomical position:
    A) the body is erect with the feet parallel and the arms hanging at the sides with the palms facing backward
    B) the body is erect with the feet parallel and the arms hanging at the sides with the palms facing forward
    C) the body is lying face up with the feet parallel and the arms at the sides with the palms facing backward
    D) the body is lying face down with the feet parallel and the arms at the sides with the palms facing backward
    E) the body is lying face up with the feet parallel and the arms at the sides with the palms facing forward
Answer: B
Diff: 1   Page Ref: 15

20) Which of the following orientation and directional terms have the same meaning (in humans):
    A) superior and caudal
    B) inferior and cranial
    C) inferior and cephalad
    D) anterior and ventral
    E) anterior and dorsal
Answer: D
Diff: 2   Page Ref: 18

21) Which of the following orientation terms have opposite meanings (in humans):
    A) superficial and proximal
    B) distal and proximal
    C) medial and distal
    D) medial and anterior
    E) posterior and intermediate
Answer: B
Diff: 2   Page Ref: 18

22) Which of the following regional terms means the anterior surface of the elbow:
    A) calcaneal region
    B) scapular region
    C) gluteal region
    D) vertebral region
    E) antecubital region
Answer: E
Diff: 2   Page Ref: 16

23) Sarah fell while ice skating and broke a bone in her carpal region. Where is this region?
    A) hip
    B) lower leg
    C) wrist
    D) shoulder
    E) knee
Answer: C
Diff: 2   Page Ref: 16–17

24) In describing the relationship between the patellar and popliteal regions:
   A) the patellar region is superior to the popliteal region
   B) the patellar region is proximal to the popliteal region
   C) the patellar region is distal to the popliteal region
   D) the patellar region is lateral to the popliteal region
   E) the patellar region is anterior to the popliteal region

Answer: E
Diff: 3   Page Ref: 16–17

25) In describing the relationship of the thoracic and spinal cavities:
   A) the thoracic cavity is superior to the spinal cavity
   B) the thoracic cavity is inferior to the spinal cavity
   C) the thoracic cavity is proximal to the spinal cavity
   D) the thoracic cavity is medial to the spinal cavity
   E) the thoracic cavity is ventral to the spinal cavity

Answer: E
Diff: 3   Page Ref: 20

26) The lungs and heart are in the _____ body cavity.
   A) dorsal
   B) spinal
   C) thoracic
   D) cranial
   E) abdominopelvic

Answer: C
Diff: 1   Page Ref: 20

27) The gluteal region is the:
   A) buttock
   B) shoulder blade region
   C) posterior knee area
   D) posterior surface of the head
   E) curve of the shoulder

Answer: A
Diff: 1   Page Ref: 16–17

28) The region that contains the navel is the:
   A) carpal region
   B) umbilical region
   C) inguinal region
   D) orbital region
   E) anterior knee

Answer: B
Diff: 1   Page Ref: 16–17; 21–22

29) The dorsal body cavity houses the:
    A) urinary and reproductive organs
    B) heart and lungs
    C) digestive and reproductive organs
    D) tongue
    E) spinal cord and brain

Answer: E
Diff: 2   *Page Ref: 20*

30) Which of these regions are associated with the parts of the arm:
    A) femoral, popliteal, patellar
    B) brachial, antecubital, carpal
    C) nasal, oral, occipital
    D) acromial, sacral, gluteal
    E) pelvic, pubic, inguinal

Answer: B
Diff: 2   *Page Ref: 16–17*

31) Which of these regions are NOT associated with the ventral (anterior) portion of the head:
    A) buccal
    B) oral
    C) orbital
    D) occiptal
    E) nasal

Answer: D
Diff: 2   *Page Ref: 16–17*

32) A section that divides the body on the longitudinal plane into equal right and left parts is called:
    A) median (midsagittal)
    B) frontal
    C) transverse
    D) oblique
    E) coronal

Answer: A
Diff: 1   *Page Ref: 17; 19*

33) Which type of section could be used to separate the thoracic cavity from the abdominopelvic cavity:
    A) coronal
    B) sagittal
    C) dorsal
    D) ventral
    E) transverse

Answer: E
Diff: 1   *Page Ref: 17; 19*

34) Which ventral cavity subdivision has no bony protection:
     A) thoracic
     B) pelvic
     C) abdominal
     D) cranial
     E) spinal
   Answer: C
   Diff: 2   Page Ref: 20

35) Which of these regions in the abdominopelvic cavity are medial:
     A) umbilical, right lumbar, and left lumbar regions
     B) epigastric, umbilical, and hypogastric regions
     C) iliac (inguinal), lumbar, and hypogastric regions
     D) epigastric, right, and left hypochondriac regions
     E) right and left iliac (inguinal), and hypogastric regions
   Answer: B
   Diff: 3   Page Ref: 21; 22

36) The stomach, liver, intestines, bladder, rectum, and reproductive organs are housed in the:
     A) cranial cavity
     B) spinal cavity
     C) dorsal cavity
     D) abdominopelvic cavity
     E) thoracic cavity
   Answer: D
   Diff: 2   Page Ref: 20

37) The ribs are located in the:
     A) right and left iliac regions
     B) right and left lumbar regions
     C) right and left pubic regions
     D) right and left hypochondriac regions
     E) right and left inguinal regions
   Answer: D
   Diff: 2   Page Ref: 21; 22

38) Which of the following statements is correct regarding the location of the spleen and stomach:
     A) both of these organs are located in the left upper quadrant
     B) both of these organs are located in the right upper quadrant
     C) the spleen is located in the left upper quadrant and the stomach is located in the right upper quadrant
     D) the spleen is located in the right upper quadrant and the stomach is located in the left upper quadrant
     E) both of these organs are located medially
   Answer: A
   Diff: 3   Page Ref: 21

True/False

1) The highest level of structural organization in humans is the organ level.

   Answer: FALSE
   Diff: 1   Page Ref: 3–4

2) The endocrine system is the fast–acting body control system.

   Answer: FALSE
   Diff: 1   Page Ref: 4; 7

3) The spleen and the tonsils are part of the digestive system.

   Answer: FALSE
   Diff: 2   Page Ref: 7

4) The lymphatic system collects fluids leaked by the cardiovascular system and returns them to the bloodstream.

   Answer: TRUE
   Diff: 1   Page Ref: 7

5) Excretion is the process of removing wastes from the body.

   Answer: TRUE
   Diff: 1   Page Ref: 11

6) Most homeostatic control mechanisms are negative feedback reactions.

   Answer: TRUE
   Diff: 2   Page Ref: 12

7) As body temperature drops below normal, chemical reactions proceed too rapidly and body proteins begin to break down.

   Answer: FALSE
   Diff: 2   Page Ref: 12

8) The sacral region is on the ventral (anterior) body surface.

   Answer: FALSE
   Diff: 1   Page Ref: 16–17

9) The heel of the foot constitutes the plantar region.

   Answer: FALSE
   Diff: 1   Page Ref: 16–17

10) *Proximal* means farther from the origin of a body part.

    Answer: FALSE
    Diff: 2   Page Ref: 18

11) The hypogastric region is directly superior to the umbilical region.

    Answer: FALSE
    Diff: 2   Page Ref: 21–22

12) The thoracic cavity is separated from the abdominopelvic cavity by the diaphragm.

    Answer: TRUE
    Diff: 2   Page Ref: 20

13) The spinal cavity is part of the ventral body cavity.
   Answer: FALSE
   Diff: 2   Page Ref: 20

14) The dorsal body cavity is subdivided into four quadrants and nine regions.
   Answer: FALSE
   Diff: 2   Page Ref: 20–22

15) There is no physical structure that separates the abdominal cavity from the pelvic cavity.
   Answer: TRUE
   Diff: 2   Page Ref: 20

Matching

Match the following:

1) Inferior
   Diff: 1   Page Ref: 18

A) toward the midline

B) away from the body surface

2) Dorsal
   Diff: 1   Page Ref: 18

C) above

3) Lateral
   Diff: 1   Page Ref: 18

D) toward the side

E) behind

4) Deep
   Diff: 2   Page Ref: 18

F) in front of

5) Distal
   Diff: 3   Page Ref: 18

G) close to the origin of the body part
   or the point of attachment of a
   limb to the body trunk

6) Medial
   Diff: 1   Page Ref: 18

H) farther from the origin of a body
   part or the point of attachment of
   a limb to the body trunk

7) Superior
   Diff: 1   Page Ref: 18

I) below

8) Proximal
   Diff: 2   Page Ref: 18

J) toward the body surface

9) Ventral
   Diff: 1   Page Ref: 18

1) I	2) E	3) D	4) B	5) H	6) A
7) C	8) G	9) F			

Match the following:

10) Axillary

    Diff: 1   *Page Ref: 16–17*

11) Tarsal

    Diff: 1   *Page Ref: 16–17*

12) Coxal

    Diff: 2   *Page Ref: 16–17*

13) Orbital

    Diff: 2   *Page Ref: 16–17*

14) Inguinal

    Diff: 2   *Page Ref: 16–17*

15) Umbilical

    Diff: 1   *Page Ref: 16–17*

16) Oral

    Diff: 1   *Page Ref: 16–17*

17) Femoral

    Diff: 1   *Page Ref: 16–17*

18) Patellar

    Diff: 1   *Page Ref: 16–17*

19) Popliteal

    Diff: 1   *Page Ref: 16–17*

A) eye area

B) navel

C) armpit

D) thigh

E) area where thigh meets body trunk

F) anterior knee

G) hip

H) posterior knee area

I) ankle

J) mouth

10) C   11) I   12) G   13) A   14) E   15) B

16) J   17) D   18) F   19) H

Match the following.

20) Slow–acting body control
    system

    Diff: 1   *Page Ref: 4–7*

21) Houses blood cells involved
    in immunity

    Diff: 1   *Page Ref: 4–7*

22) Site of hematopoiesis

    Diff: 1   *Page Ref: 4–7*

23) Regulation of water and
    electrolytes

    Diff: 1   *Page Ref: 4–7*

24) Heat production

    Diff: 1   *Page Ref: 4–7*

25) Responds to stimuli (internal
    and external)

    Diff: 1   *Page Ref: 4–7*

A) skeletal system

B) lymphatic system

C) respiratory system

D) urinary system

E) muscular system

F) nervous system

G) endocrine system

H) digestive system

20) G   21) B   22) A   23) D   24) E   25) F

Essay

1) Distinguish between *anatomy* and *physiology*.
   Answer: Anatomy is the study of the structure and shape of the body and body parts, and their
   relationships to one another. Physiology is the study of how the body and its parts work
   or function.
   Diff: 1   *Page Ref: 2*

2) List, and briefly define, the human body's organization levels from smallest to largest.
   Answer: 1. chemical level:
       a. atoms are the basic building blocks of matter
       b. molecules are units formed by atoms combining

   2. cellular level: cells are the smallest living unit in living organisms

   3. tissue level: tissues are groupings of cells performing a common function

   4. organ level: an organ is a structure consisting of two or more tissue types

   5. organ system level: an organ system describes a group of organs functioning
   cooperatively for a common purpose

   6. organism level: a human organism consists of all of the organ systems of the
   body working together to promote healthy functioning
   (homeostasis)
   Diff: 1   *Page Ref: 3–4*

3) List and explain the eight necessary human life functions.

Answer: 1. Maintenance of boundaries—keeps the internal environment distinct from the external environment; membranes perform this function at the cellular level and skin performs this function for the organism.
2. Movement—includes a change in the position of the body or the propelling of a substance (such as blood, urine, or food) through the body organs; constitutes a major role of the muscular system.
3. Responsiveness (irritability)—the ability to react to stimuli; constitutes a major role of the nervous system.
4. Metabolism—includes all the chemical reactions that occur within the body's cells.
5. Excretion—elimination of carbon dioxide by the lungs and nitrogenous wastes by the kidneys.
6. Digestion—the process of breaking down ingested foodstuffs into simpler molecules that can then be absorbed into the blood for delivery to the body's cells.
7. Growth—an increase in size, which is usually accompanied by an increase in the number of cells.
8. Reproduction—the production of new cells for growth and repair, and also the production of offspring.
Diff: 3   Page Ref: 10–11

4) List and explain the five survival needs of humans.

Answer: 1. Nutrients—include carbohydrates, proteins, and fats, which are taken in via the diet for energy and cell building.
2. Oxygen—required to release energy from food.
3. Water—accounts for over 60% of the body weight, and provides the basis for various body fluids.
4. Appropriate body temperature—when too high or too low, physiological activities cease, primarily because molecules are destroyed or become nonfunctional.
5. Appropriate atmospheric pressure—the force exerted on the surface of the body by the weight of air; is essential for normal operation of the respiratory system and breathing.
Diff: 3   Page Ref: 11–12

5) List and explain the three major body planes and sections.

Answer: 1. Sagittal—cut is made along the longitudinal (lengthwise) plane of the body (or an organ), dividing it into right and left parts.
2. Frontal (coronal)—cut is made along the longitudinal (lengthwise) plane of the body (or an organ), dividing it into anterior and posterior parts.
3. Transverse (cross–section)—cut is made along the transverse (horizontal) plane, dividing the body into superior and inferior parts.
Diff: 2   Page Ref: 17; 19

6) Identify the two dorsal body cavities, and state their locations and the organs contained therein.

Answer: 1. Cranial cavity—the superior posterior space inside the bony skull that houses the brain.
2. Spinal cavity—the inferior posterior space inside the bony vertebral column that houses the spinal cord.
Diff: 2   Page Ref: 22

7) List the four quadrants and nine regions of the abdominopelvic cavity. Explain why this cavity has these subdivisions.

Answer: 1.   The four quadrants are:
   a.   right upper quadrant
   b.   right lower quadrant
   c.   left upper quadrant
   d.   right lower quadrant
2.   The nine regions are:
   a.   epigastric region
   b.   umbilical region
   c.   hypogastric region
   d.   right hypochondriac region
   e.   left hypochondriac region
   f.   right lumbar region
   g.   left lumbar region
   h.   right iliac region
   i.   left iliac region

This cavity has been subdivided into these quadrants and regions because it is large and has many organs.
Diff: 2   *Page Ref: 20–22*

8) Explain how scratching an itch is an example of the negative feedback mechanism.

Answer: 1. Stimulus or input is the itch.
2. A receptor carries the information about the stimulus (itch) to the brain via an afferent pathway.
3. Control center (brain) analyzes this information an turns on an effector which will cancel the stimulus.
4. Information reaches the effector via the efferent pathway from the brain. Muscles move the hand to scratch the itch.
5. Scratching continues until the itch goes away. The brain shuts off the effector once homeostatis is restored.
Diff: 3   *Page Ref: 12–13*

9) Explain the difference between homeostatis and metabolism.

Answer: Homeostasis is the body's attempt to maintain balance during which time internal conditions may vary. Metabolism is all chemical reactions that occur in the body.
Diff: 2   *Page Ref: 11–12*

10) Describe anatomical position. Explain why anatomical position is used.

Answer: Anatomical position is defined as standing erect, feet parallel to the arms, palms facing forward. Anatomical position is used because it is a standard position; it also helps us to avoid confusion. Additionally, anatomical position is a reference point that helps us accurately describe body parts and position.
Diff: 2   *Page Ref: 15*

11) Describe the role of the effector in the negative feedback system.

Answer: The effector is the control center's output and response to the stimulus. The effector's job is to cancel or shut off the control mechanism.
Diff: 1   *Page Ref: 12–13*

Chapter 2 Basic Chemistry

Short Answer

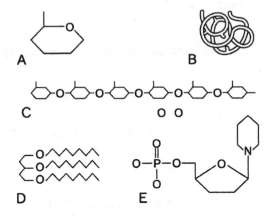

Figure 2.1

Using Figure 2.1, identify the following:

1) The structure of the functional protein is _____.

   Answer: B
   Diff: 3   *Page Ref: 50–51*

2) The structure of the nucleotide is _____.

   Answer: E
   Diff: 3   *Page Ref: 54–56*

3) The structure of the polysaccharide is _____.

   Answer: C
   Diff: 3   *Page Ref: 45*

4) The structure of the monosaccharide is _____.

   Answer: A
   Diff: 3   *Page Ref: 45*

Fill in the blank or provide a short answer:

5) When a change in matter alters the basic nature of the substance, it is called a _____ change.

   Answer: chemical
   Diff: 1   *Page Ref: 27*

6) Inactive or stored energy is called _____ energy.

   Answer: potential
   Diff: 1   *Page Ref: 28*

7) Isotopes differ from each other only in the number of _____ they possess.

   Answer: neutrons
   Diff: 2   *Page Ref: 33*

8) Decomposition of a protein produces _____.

Answer: amino acids
Diff: 3   Page Ref: 40; 49

9) The sum of the protons and neutrons in an atom is called the _____.

Answer: atomic mass number
Diff: 2   Page Ref: 32

10) Compounds that contain carbon–hydrogen bonding are collectively termed _____ compounds.

Answer: organic
Diff: 2   Page Ref: 42

11) Polar molecules, like water, result when electrons are shared _____.

Answer: unequally
Diff: 2   Page Ref: 37

12) The outermost shell of an atom is called the _____ shell.

Answer: valence
Diff: 2   Page Ref: 35

13) An acid is a molecule that releases (donates) _____. State the answer in two ways.

Answer: protons; hydrogen ions
Diff: 2   Page Ref: 43

14) All _____ have an amine (NH_2) group.

Answer: amino acids
Diff: 2   Page Ref: 42

15) Glycogen and starch are examples of a specific category of carbohydrates called _____.

Answer: polysaccharides
Diff: 2   Page Ref: 46

16) A solution with a pH of 11.7 is _____ times more acidic than a solution with a pH of 8.7.

Answer: 1000
Diff: 2   Page Ref: 44

17) Cholesterol is an example of a _____, a specific category of lipids.

Answer: steroids
Diff: 2   Page Ref: 47; 49

18) Enzymes are examples of _____ proteins. State the answer in two ways.

Answer: globular; functional
Diff: 3   Page Ref: 50

19) The building blocks of nucleic acids are called _____.

Answer: nucleotides
Diff: 2   Page Ref: 54

20) The universal energy compound that provides visible energy to cells is _____.

Answer: ATP (adenosine triphosphate)
Diff: 2   Page Ref: 55

Multiple Choice

1) Inactive energy is referred to as:
   A) mechanical energy
   B) potential energy
   C) kinetic energy
   D) radiant energy
   E) electrical energy

Answer: B
Diff: 1   Page Ref: 28

2) An atom with 11 protons, 12 neutrons, and 10 electrons is a(n):
   A) molecule
   B) anion
   C) cation
   D) isotope
   E) radioisotope

Answer: C
Diff: 3   Page Ref: 36

3) The movement of ions across cell membranes is an example of:
   A) radiant energy
   B) chemical energy
   C) electrical energy
   D) mechanical energy
   E) potential energy

Answer: C
Diff: 2   Page Ref: 28

4) Ninety–six percent of the human body is composed of the elements:
   A) carbon, calcium, sodium, and oxygen
   B) carbon, oxygen, iron, and potassium
   C) carbon, oxygen, hydrogen, and nitrogen
   D) calcium, magnesium, potassium, and iron
   E) sodium, potassium, hydrogen, and sulfur

Answer: C
Diff: 2   Page Ref: 29

5) The most abundant element in the human body is:
   A) carbon
   B) oxygen
   C) hydrogen
   D) nitrogen
   E) calcium

Answer: B
Diff: 2   Page Ref: 30

6) The simplest atom—containing one proton, one electron, and no neutrons—is:
   A) carbon
   B) hydrogen
   C) oxygen
   D) nitrogen
   E) sodium

Answer: B
Diff: 1   Page Ref: 31

7) Atomic mass is equivalent to the number of _____ in an atom.
   A) protons
   B) neutrons
   C) electrons
   D) protons and electrons
   E) protons and neutrons

Answer: E
Diff: 2   Page Ref: 32

8) Which of these elements composes bone:
   A) calcium
   B) sulfur
   C) chlorine
   D) iron
   E) iodine

Answer: A
Diff: 2   Page Ref: 30

9) Which of the following is the role of magnesium:
   A) it is present in bone, and is an important cofactor for enzyme activity in a number of
      metabolic reactions
   B) it is needed to make functional thyroid hormones
   C) it is a component of the functional hemoglobin molecule that transports oxygen within
      red blood cells, as well as a component of some enzymes
   D) it is the major extracellular cation in its ionic form, and is important for water balance,
      conduction of nerve impulses, and muscle contraction
   E) it is a major extracellular anion in its ionic form

Answer: A
Diff: 3   Page Ref: 30

10) An atom with an atomic number of 14 will have _____ electrons in its valence shell.
    A) 2
    B) 4
    C) 8
    D) 10
    E) 14

Answer: B
Diff: 3   Page Ref: 32; 35

11) Which of the following statements is correct regarding the electrical charge of subatomic particles:
    A) protons are positively charged, electrons are neutral, and neutrons are negatively charged
    B) protons are positively charged, electrons are negatively charged, and neutrons are neutral
    C) protons are negatively charged, electrons are neutral, and neutrons are negatively charged
    D) protons are negatively charged, electrons are positively charged, and neutrons are neutral
    E) protons are neutral, electrons are negatively charged, and neutrons are positively charged

Answer: B
Diff: 2   Page Ref: 29

12) An atom has 6 protons, 8 neutrons, and 6 electrons. Its atomic mass is:
    A) 2
    B) 6
    C) 8
    D) 14
    E) 20

Answer: D
Diff: 2   Page Ref: 32

13) The atomic number of an atom reveals the number of:
    A) electrons in the atomic nucleus
    B) protons in the atomic nucleus
    C) protons plus neutrons
    D) protons plus electrons
    E) neutrons plus electrons

Answer: B
Diff: 1   Page Ref: 32

14) Isotopes have different numbers of _____; thus they also have different _____.
    A) protons; atomic numbers
    B) neutrons; atomic masses
    C) electrons; atomic numbers
    D) protons; atomis masses
    E) neutrons; atomic numbers

Answer: B
Diff: 2   Page Ref: 33

15) An atom that has lost two electrons is called a(n):
    A) isotope
    B) anion
    C) radioisotope
    D) cation
    E) proton

Answer: D
Diff: 3   Page Ref: 36

16) The subatomic particles that are responsible for the chemical behavior of atoms are the:
    A) protons
    B) neutrons
    C) electrons
    D) isotopes
    E) ions

Answer: C
Diff: 2   *Page Ref: 32*

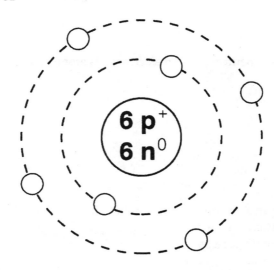

Figure 2.2

17) What is the atomic number of the atom in Figure 2.2:
    A) 2
    B) 3
    C) 4
    D) 6
    E) 12

Answer: D
Diff: 3   *Page Ref: 32*

18) When a pair of electrons is shared equally between two atoms, the bond formed is called a(n):
    A) ionic bond
    B) hydrogen bond
    C) carbon bond
    D) polar covalent bond
    E) nonpolar covalent bond

Answer: E
Diff: 3   *Page Ref: 37*

19) Which of these examples is a compound:
   A) H_2
   B) CH_4
   C) O_2
   D) N_2
   E) 2H

Answer: B
Diff: 2   Page Ref: 34

20) In order to break a disaccharide down into simple sugar units:
   A) water molecules must be added to each bond
   B) water molecules must be removed from each bond
   C) carbon atoms must be added to each bond
   D) carbon atoms must be removed from each bond
   E) water molecules and carbon atoms must be removed from each bond

Answer: A
Diff: 3   Page Ref: 46

21) The reaction A + B → AB is an example of a(n):
   A) exchange reaction
   B) synthesis reaction
   C) decomposition reaction
   D) denaturation reaction
   E) dehydration reaction

Answer: B
Diff: 2   Page Ref: 40

22) Water is useful in body processes because:
   A) it is a good solvent
   B) it acts as an enzyne
   C) it has a low heat capacity
   D) it is a product in hydrolysis reactions
   E) it is chemically inert

Answer: A
Diff: 3   Page Ref: 42

23) The joining of amino acids to form a protein is an example of:
   A) a decomposition reaction
   B) an exchange reaction
   C) a synthesis reaction
   D) a denaturation reaction
   E) a hydrolysis reaction

Answer: C
Diff: 3   Page Ref: 40; 49

24) Which of the following solutions is the weakest acid:
   A) a solution with a pH of 2.4
   B) a solution with a pH of 5.2
   C) a solution with a pH of 6.4
   D) a solution with a pH of 8.6
   E) a solution with a pH of 10.1

   Answer: C
   Diff: 3   *Page Ref: 44*

25) A solution with a pH of 7:
   A) is acidic
   B) releases more hydrogen ions than hydroxyl ions into solution
   C) releases more hydroxyl ions than hydrogen ions into solution
   D) is basic
   E) is neutral

   Answer: E
   Diff: 2   *Page Ref: 44*

26) Which of the following is an example of an inorganic molecule:
   A) a fatty acid
   B) an amino acid
   C) cholesterol
   D) sodium chloride
   E) RNA

   Answer: D
   Diff: 3   *Page Ref: 42–43*

27) Vitamin D and sex hormones are both:
   A) polysaccharides
   B) proteins
   C) nucleic acids
   D) enzymes
   E) steroids

   Answer: E
   Diff: 2   *Page Ref: 49*

28) Glucose and starch are examples of:
   A) carbohydrates
   B) triglycerides
   C) phospholipids
   D) steroids
   E) proteins

   Answer: A
   Diff: 2   *Page Ref: 45–46*

29) Which of the following groups of chemicals includes ONLY monosaccharides:
    A) glucose, fructose, galactose
    B) glucose, fructose, maltose
    C) fructose, maltose, sucrose
    D) fructose, maltose, lactose
    E) maltose, sucrose, lactose

Answer: A
Diff: 2   Page Ref: 45

30) The organic compounds that function in building tissues and acting as enzymes are the:
    A) nucleic acids
    B) carbohydrates
    C) salts
    D) lipids
    E) proteins

Answer: E
Diff: 2   Page Ref: 49

31) Triglycerides:
    A) include lipoid substances such as fat–soluble vitamins (e.g., vitamins A, E, and K), prostaglandins, and lipoproteins
    B) include cholesterol, bile salts, vitamin D, sex hormones, and adrenal cortical hormones
    C) are found in the cell membrane and participate in the transport of lipids in plasma; they are also abundant in the brain and in nervous tissue where they help to form insulating white matter
    D) are found in fat deposits (e.g., subcutaneous tissue around organs), and serve to protect and insulate body organs; they are the major source of stored energy in the body
    E) have a three–dimensional structure that can be easily destroyed by heat, causing them to be denatured and no longer capable of performing their physiological roles

Answer: D
Diff: 2   Page Ref: 46; 47

32) Vitamin D can be described as:
    A) a constituent of orange–pigmented vegetables (carrots) and fruits (tomatoes), and part of the photoreceptor pigment involved in vision
    B) taken in via plant products such as wheat germ and green leafy vegetables; may promote wound healing and contribute to fertility (though not proven in humans)
    C) made available largely by the action of intestinal bacteria; also prevalent in a wide variety of foods, and necessary for the proper clotting of blood
    D) produced in the skin on exposure to UV radiation; necessary for normal bone growth and function
    E) derivatives of fatty acids found in cell membranes; various functions include the stimulation of uterine contractions, the regulation of blood pressure, and the control of motility of the gastrointestinal tract

Answer: D
Diff: 2   Page Ref: 47; 49

33) Which one of the following DNA bases are complementary:
   A) adenine and guanine
   B) guanine and uracil
   C) thymine and guanine
   D) cytosine and adenine
   E) adenine and thymine

   Answer: E
   Diff: 2   *Page Ref:* 55

34) Enzymes:
   A) are essential to virtually every biochemical reaction in the body
   B) help regulate growth and development
   C) are highly specialized proteins that recognize, bind with, and inactivate bacteria, toxins, and some viruses
   D) increase the rates of chemical reactions by at least a millionfold
   E) when absent or destroyed, cause all biochemical reactions to cease

   Answer: D
   Diff: 2   *Page Ref:* 52

35) Which of the following statements about enzymes is true:
   A) they are carbohydrates
   B) they are stable at high temperatures
   C) they are biological catalysts
   D) they are not reuseable
   E) they are required in large amounts in order to be effective

   Answer: C
   Diff: 3   *Page Ref:* 52

36) Saturated fats:
   A) have two fatty acid chains
   B) exist as solids at room temperature
   C) are formed from 4 interlocking carbon rings
   D) contain many double bonds
   E) exist as liquids and are derived from plants

   Answer: B
   Diff: 3   *Page Ref:* 49

37) Which of the following substances below is matched with its correct organic group:
   A) monosaccharides – nucleic acids
   B) DNA – lipids
   C) steroids – carbohydrates
   D) glycerol – proteins
   E) enzymes – proteins

   Answer: E
   Diff: 2   *Page Ref:* 52

38) Enzymes are classified as:
    A) antibodies
    B) hormones
    C) triglycerides
    D) structural proteins
    E) functional proteins

Answer: E
Diff: 2   Page Ref: 52

39) Which of the following statements about RNA is true:
    A) RNA is single stranded
    B) RNA is composed of cytosine, guanine, adenine, and thymine
    C) RNA is found only in the nucleus of the cell
    D) RNA contains deoxyribose
    E) RNA is a double helix

Answer: A
Diff: 2   Page Ref: 55

40) Carbohydrates are built up from their basic building blocks by the:
    A) addition of a water molecule between each unit
    B) removal of a water molecule between every two units
    C) addition of a carbon atom
    D) removal of a carbon atom
    E) process termed "hydrolysis"

Answer: B
Diff: 2   Page Ref: 46

41) The nucleotide chains of DNA are held together by:
    A) carbon bonds
    B) hydrogen bonds
    C) ionic bonds
    D) nonpolar covalent bonds
    E) polar covalent bonds

Answer: B
Diff: 2   Page Ref: 54

42) Which of the following statements about ATP is false:
    A) it drives the transport of certain solutes (e.g., amino acids) across cell membranes
    B) it activates contractile proteins in muscle cells so that cells can shorten and perform mechanical work
    C) it provides the energy needed to drive energy-absorbing chemical reactions
    D) it is a modified nucleotide
    E) its energy is captured in high-energy hydrogen bonds

Answer: E
Diff: 3   Page Ref: 55

43) Glycogen is the storage form of _____ in animals.
   A) protein
   B) lipids
   C) amino acids
   D) glucose
   E) DNA

   Answer: D
   Diff: 2   *Page Ref: 46*

44) _____ are simple sugars containing between 3 and 7 carbon atoms.
   A) Proteins
   B) Monosaccharides
   C) Polysaccharides
   D) Saturated fats
   E) Steroids

   Answer: B
   Diff: 2   *Page Ref: 45*

45) Shell 1 of an atom can hold a maximum of _____ electron(s).
   A) 1
   B) 2
   C) 4
   D) 8
   E) 18

   Answer: B
   Diff: 1   *Page Ref: 35*

46) Trans fats are oils that have been solidified by the addition of:
   A) oxygen atoms
   B) carbon atoms
   C) hydrogen atoms
   D) nitrogen atoms
   E) phosphorus–containing groups

   Answer: C
   Diff: 3   *Page Ref: 49*

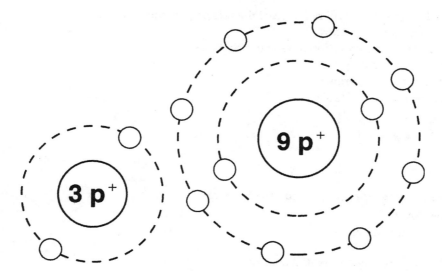

Figure 2.3

47) What type of chemical bond is pictured in Figure 2.3:
    A) nonpolar covalent bond
    B) polar covalent bond
    C) ionic bond
    D) single covalent bond
    E) double covalent bond

Answer: C
Diff: 2   Page Ref: 35–37

48) The sugar found in DNA is:
    A) ribose
    B) sucrose
    C) deoxyribose
    D) lactose
    E) starch

Answer: C
Diff: 1   Page Ref: 55

49) Which of these substances is an enzyme:
    A) glucose
    B) triglyceride
    C) oxidase
    D) nucleotide
    E) omega–3 fatty acid

Answer: C
Diff: 3   Page Ref: 52

50) Which of these factors will not *increase* the rate of a chemical reaction:
     A) increased temperature
     B) increased concentration of reacting particles
     C) presence of catalysts
     D) decreased temperature
     E) decrease in particle size
Answer: D
Diff: 2   Page Ref: 41

True/False

1) Inactive or stored energy is called kinetic energy.
Answer: FALSE
Diff: 1   Page Ref: 28

2) Stored energy is called potential energy.
Answer: TRUE
Diff: 1   Page Ref: 28

3) Negatively charged atoms are called cations.
Answer: FALSE
Diff: 3   Page Ref: 36

4) Atoms are the smallest particles of a compound that still retain the properties of that compound.
Answer: FALSE
Diff: 2   Page Ref: 29; 34

5) Calcium is one of the major elements composing the human body.
Answer: FALSE
Diff: 1   Page Ref: 29; 30

6) Every atom in a molecule has a full valence shell.
Answer: TRUE
Diff: 2   Page Ref: 34–35

7) Water is the single most abundant inorganic compound in the human body.
Answer: TRUE
Diff: 1   Page Ref: 42

8) The lower the pH, the greater the number of hydrogen ions.
Answer: TRUE
Diff: 3   Page Ref: 43; 44

9) Compounds that ionize completely, producing large numbers of hydrogen ions (protons), are termed *weak bases*.
Answer: FALSE
Diff: 2   Page Ref: 43

10) Carbon is found in all inorganic compounds.

   Answer: FALSE
   Diff: 1   Page Ref: 42

11) When a solution produces equal numbers of hydrogen and hydroxyl ions, it is said to be neutral.

   Answer: TRUE
   Diff: 1   Page Ref: 44

12) The normal pH of blood occupies a narrow range around 7.35–7.45.

   Answer: TRUE
   Diff: 2   Page Ref: 44

13) Estrogen and cholesterol are both steroids.

   Answer: TRUE
   Diff: 2   Page Ref: 47; 49

14) Enzymes decrease the rates of chemical reactions.

   Answer: FALSE
   Diff: 2   Page Ref: 52

15) Disruption of the hydrogen bonds of functional proteins leads to their denaturation.

   Answer: TRUE
   Diff: 2   Page Ref: 50–51

Matching

Match the following:

1) A bond in which electrons are completely lost or gained by the atoms involved
   Diff: 2   Page Ref: 35–36

2) A bond in which electrons are shared unequally
   Diff: 2   Page Ref: 36–37

3) A type of bond important in holding different parts of the same molecule together in three–dimensional structure
   Diff: 2   Page Ref: 39

4) A type of covalent bond formed when atoms share two pairs of electrons
   Diff: 2   Page Ref: 38

5) Type of bond exhibited by carbon dioxide
   Diff: 2   Page Ref: 37

A) polar covalent bond

B) nonpolar covalent bond

C) ionic bond

D) hydrogen bond

E) single covalent bond

F) covalent bond

G) double bond

1) C   2) A   3) D   4) E   5) B

Match the following:

6) The particle(s) contributing to
   the atomic mass
   Diff: 1   Page Ref: 32

7) The particle(s) contributing to
   the atomic number
   Diff: 1   Page Ref: 32

8) The particle(s) shared during
   covalent bond formation
   Diff: 1   Page Ref: 35–36

9) The particle(s) that differ
   between isotopes
   Diff: 1   Page Ref: 33

10) The particle(s) located within
    the nucleus
    Diff: 1   Page Ref: 29

11) The particle(s) lost during
    cation formation
    Diff: 2   Page Ref: 36

12) The number of protons is
    equal to the number of these
    subatomic particles
    Diff: 2   Page Ref: 32

A) neutron(s)

B) protons and neutrons

C) proton(s)

D) electron(s)

6) B   7) C   8) D   9) A   10) B   11) D
12) D

Match the following:

13) Building block is the monosaccharide
   Diff: 1   Page Ref: 45

A) proteins

B) lipids

14) DNA, RNA, and ATP are types of these organic compounds
   Diff: 1   Page Ref: 54–55

C) nucleic acids

D) carbohydrates

15) Triglycerides, steroids, and fat–soluble vitamins are types of these organic compounds
   Diff: 1   Page Ref: 46–49

16) Antibodies, some hormones, and enzymes are types of these organic compounds
   Diff: 1   Page Ref: 49–52

17) Building blocks of these organic compounds are amino acids
   Diff: 1   Page Ref: 49

18) Nucleotides form the building blocks of these organic compounds
   Diff: 1   Page Ref: 54

19) Glycogen, glucose, and lactose are examples of these organic compounds
   Diff: 1   Page Ref: 45–46

20) Most of this organic compound group are water insoluble
   Diff: 1   Page Ref: 46

| 13) D | 14) C | 15) B | 16) A | 17) A | 18) C |
| 19) D | 20) B | | | | |

Essay

1) Describe the role of the electron in chemical bond formation.

   Answer: When the valence shell of an atom contains fewer than 8 electrons, an atom will tend to gain, lose, or share electrons with other atoms to reach a stable state. As a result, chemical bonds such as covalent bonds or ionic bonds are formed.
   Diff: 2   Page Ref: 35

2) Compare DNA and RNA from the standpoint of their location, role(s), number of chains, arrangement of nucleotides, and sugars and bases present.

Answer: 1. Location—DNA is located inside the nucleus of the cell; RNA is located inside and outside the nucleus of the cell.
2. Role(s)—DNA undergoes replication prior to cell division to pass on heredity information, and provides instructions for the building of all protein; RNA carries out the orders for protein synthesis issued by DNA.
3. Number of chains—DNA consists of a double chain of nucleotides in the form of a double helix; RNA is a single chain of nucleotides.
4. Arrangement of nucleotides—DNA consists of sugar and phosphate molecules that form uprights of a ladder–like structure, and each rung is formed by two joined bases; in RNA, a base projects from each sugar–phosphate unit in the chain of nucleotides.
5. Sugar—the sugar in DNA is deoxyribose; the sugar in RNA is ribose.
6. Bases—in DNA the bases are adenine (A), thymine (T), guanine (G) and cytosine (C); in RNA the bases are adenine (A), uracil (U), guanine (G) and cytosine (C).

Diff: 3   *Page Ref:* 54–55

3) Discuss the major properties of water that make it so vital to the proper functioning of the body.

Answer: 1. It has a high heat capacity, and absorbs and releases large amounts of heat before its temperature changes appreciably. Therefore, it helps maintain homeostatic body temperature.
2. Because of its polarity, it is an excellent solvent in which electrolytes can ionize. Nutrients, respiratory gases, and wastes can dissolve in water, thereby allowing water to act as a transport and exchange medium in the body. Water is also used as a solvent in specialized molecules that lubricate the body, such as mucus that eases the movement of feces in the digestive tube, saliva that moistens food and prepares it for digestion, and synovial fluids that lubricate bone ends.
3. Water is a reactant in some types of chemical reactions, such as digestion and the breakdown of large biological molecules. Water is added to the bonds of the larger molecules in specific reactions termed hydrolysis reactions.
4. Water serves a protective function by forming a watery cushion (e.g., cerebrospinal fluid cushions the brain and amniotic fluid cushions the fetus).

Diff: 2   *Page Ref:* 42

4) Explain how saturated fats are different from unsaturated fats.

Answer: Saturated fats:
1. tend to be animal fats
2. have all single bonds between carbon atoms
3. may be solid

Unsaturated fats:
1. tend to be plant oils
2. have some double or triple bonds between carbon atoms
3. may be liquid

Diff: 2   *Page Ref:* 49

5) Distinguish between a dehydration synthesis and a hydrolysis reaction.

   Answer: In a dehydration synthesis reaction, a more complex molecule is formed from two simpler ones, and a water molecule is lost as each bond forms. An example of dehydration synthesis is seen when a disaccharide is formed from two monosaccharides. Hydrolysis is the breakdown of a more complex molecule into its building blocks. A water molecule is added to each bond, the bond is broken, and simpler molecules are formed. In the process, water is split into a hydrogen ion and a hydroxyl ion. An example of hydrolysis is seen when a disaccharide is broken down into two monosaccharides.

   Diff: 3   Page Ref: 40; 46

6) Explain why ATP is classified as a nucleic acid.

   Answer: ATP is a modified nucleotide. Nucleotides are the building blocks of nucleic acids. ATP consists of a base (adenine), a sugar (ribose), and three phosphate groups.

   Diff: 2   Page Ref: 55

7) Explain why hydrolysis (decomposition) reactions require the addition of water.

   Answer: Water molecules are added to the bonds of large organic molecules. When water is added to each bond, the bond is broken, and the molecule is broken down.

   Diff: 3   Page Ref: 46

8) Explain why a denatured protein no longer functions.

   Answer: Denaturation results when the three-dimensional shape of a protein is destroyed. The function of a protein depends on its structure. The presence of an active site on the surface of a protein that interacts with other molecules must be intact for the enzyme to work properly.

   Diff: 3   Page Ref: 50–51

9) Explain why enzymes are specific to their substrates.

   Answer: Exzymes, like other proteins, have active sites on their surfaces that chemically interact with other molecules of complementary shape and charge. These active sites must "fit" with the substrate. Enzymes bind to the reacting substrates and structural changes result in a new product.

   Diff: 3   Page Ref: 52

10) Differentiate between a molecule and a compound.

   Answer: Molecules are formed when two or more atoms of the same element combine chemically. Compounds result when two or more different atoms bind together to form a molecule.

   Diff: 2   Page Ref: 34–35

11) Name this type of reaction and briefly explain what is happening in this reaction:

   glucose + fructose → water + sucrose

   Answer: Glucose and fructose are two monosaccharides. Sucrose is a disaccharide. Glucose and fructose are combining to form sucrose. This is an example of a dehydration synthesis reaction. A water molecule is lost from the two simple sugars as the bond forms to create the double sugar.

   Diff: 3   Page Ref: 46

12) List the three parts of a nucleotide.

Answer: Nucleotides contain:
1. a nitrogen–containing base
2. a pentose (5–carbon) sugar
3. a phosphate group

Diff: 1   *Page Ref: 54*

13) Describe the difference between a polar and a nonpolar covalent bond. Give and explain an example of each type of bond.

Answer: 1. In polar covalent bonds, electrons are not shared equally. For instance, water is an example of a polar covalent bond. The electron pairs shared in water spend more time with the oxygen atom causing that end of the molecule to become slightly negative and the hydrogen end to become slightly positive.
2. In nonpolar covalent bonds, electrons are shared equally. For example, the electron pairs in carbon dioxide orbit the entire molecule.

Diff: 3   *Page Ref: 37*

Chapter 3 Cells and Tissues

Short Answer

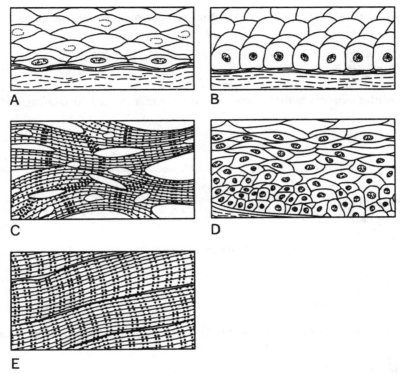

Figure 3.1

Using Figure 3.1, match the following:

1) The illustration of simple cuboidal epithelium is _____.

Answer: B
Diff: 2   Page Ref: 91

2) The illustration of skeletal muscle tissue is _____.

Answer: E
Diff: 3   Page Ref: 99

3) The illustration of stratified squamous epithelium is _____.

Answer: D
Diff: 3   Page Ref: 92

4) The illustration of simple squamous epithelium is _____.

Answer: A
Diff: 2   Page Ref: 91

5) The illustration of cardiac muscle tissue is _____.

Answer: C
Diff: 3   Page Ref: 99

Fill in the blank or provide a short answer:

6) The network of nuclear threads, composed of DNA and protein, that condense to form chromosomes during mitosis is called _____.

Answer: chromatin
Diff: 2   Page Ref: 67

7) The specialized cellular compartments within the cytosol of the cell are collectively called _____.

Answer: organelles
Diff: 2   Page Ref: 69–70

8) Whiplike cellular extensions that move substances along the cell surface are called _____.

Answer: cilia
Diff: 2   Page Ref: 73

9) The phospholipid tails are _____, which make the plasma membrane impermeable to water.

Answer: hydrophobic
Diff: 3   Page Ref: 67–68

10) Tiny finger-like projections of the plasma membrane that increase its surface area are called _____.

Answer: microvilli
Diff: 1   Page Ref: 68–69

11) The membrane connections that prevent the leaking of fluid between cells are called _____.

Answer: tight junctions
Diff: 2   Page Ref: 68–69

12) The rod-shaped bodies that lie at right angles to each other and internally are made up of fine microtubing called _____.

Answer: centrioles
Diff: 2   Page Ref: 73

13) The component of a solution that is present in the smaller amount and is dissolved is the _____.

Answer: solute
Diff: 2   Page Ref: 76

14) The nucleoplasm and cytosol make up the _____ fluid.

Answer: intracellular
Diff: 2   Page Ref: 76

15) The movement of substances through the cell membrane against their concentration gradient is called _____.

Answer: active transport
Diff: 2   Page Ref: 78

16) The random movement of molecules (and ions) down their concentration gradient is called
_____.

Answer: diffusion
Diff: 2   Page Ref: 77

17) In cell division, the term that refers to division of the cytoplasm is _____.
Answer: cytokinesis
Diff: 2   Page Ref: 84

18) The period of the cell cycle when the cell grows and performs its metabolic activities is
_____.

Answer: interphase
Diff: 2   Page Ref: 83

19) After DNA replication has occurred, each of the two strands making up a chromosome is called
a _____.
Answer: chromatid
Diff: 2   Page Ref: 84

20) The DNA segment that carries information for building one protein or polypeptide chain is
called a _____.

Answer: gene
Diff: 2   Page Ref: 86

21) The step, during protein synthesis, of assembling proteins by decoding the information in
messenger RNA is called _____.

Answer: translation
Diff: 3   Page Ref: 86; 88

22) Epithelial tissue consisting of one layer of cells flattened like fish scales is called a _____
epithelium.

Answer: simple squamous
Diff: 2   Page Ref: 90

23) The type of muscle tissue that can be controlled voluntarily is called _____ muscle.

Answer: skeletal
Diff: 2   Page Ref: 98

24) The type of tissue consisting of cells embedded in an extracellular matrix is _____ tissue.

Answer: connective
Diff: 2   Page Ref: 93

25) The type of connective tissue that contains fat stored in adipocytes is called _____.

Answer: adipose tissue
Diff: 1   Page Ref: 97

26) This type of epithelial tissue found lining organs of the digestive system such as the small
intestines is the _____.

Answer: simple columnar
Diff: 2   Page Ref: 90

27) The cell type found in nervous tissue is the _____.

Answer: neuron

Diff: 1   *Page Ref: 98*

28) Tendons and ligaments are common to this type of connective tissue called _____.

Answer: dense fibrous tissue

Diff: 2   *Page Ref: 97*

29) _____ tissue contains cells called fibroblasts that make fibers such as collagen.

Answer: Connective

Diff: 2   *Page Ref: 93*

30) Many layers of cube-shaped cells should be termed _____ epithelial tissue.

Answer: stratified cuboidal

Diff: 2   *Page Ref: 90*

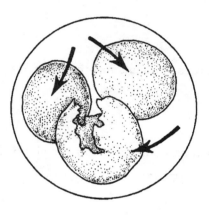

Figure 3.2

31) The cell shown in Figure 3.2 has been placed into a(n) _____ solution.

Answer: hypotonic

Diff: 2   *Page Ref: 77; 80–81*

Multiple Choice

1) Which one of the following is NOT true about the cell membrane:
   A) it consists of two lipid layers
   B) its lipid components are primarily phospholipids and cholesterol
   C) it contains proteins for specialized functions
   D) it regulates the entry and exit of cell materials
   E) it allows water soluble molecules to pass through easily

Answer: E

Diff: 3   *Page Ref: 67–68*

2) The site where ribosomes assemble prior to their migration into the cytoplasm is the:
    A) chromatin
    B) chromosomes
    C) nucleolus
    D) nuclear membrane
    E) plasma membrane

Answer: C
Diff: 1   Page Ref: 67

3) The molecules that make the cell surface fuzzy, sticky, and sugar-rich are the:
    A) cholesterol molecules
    B) glycoproteins
    C) lipid molecules
    D) proteins
    E) phospholipids

Answer: B
Diff: 2   Page Ref: 68

4) The molecules in the cell membrane that serve as receptors or binding sites for hormones or other chemical messengers are the:
    A) glycoproteins
    B) proteins
    C) cholesterol molecules
    D) carbohydrates
    E) lipids

Answer: B
Diff: 3   Page Ref: 68

5) The tiny finger-like projections that increase the surface are of the cell for quicker absorption are called:
    A) desmosomes
    B) gap junctions
    C) inclusions
    D) microvilli
    E) tight junctions

Answer: D
Diff: 2   Page Ref: 68

6) The three major components of the cytoplasm are the:
    A) cytosol, organelles, and inclusions
    B) cytosol, inclusions, and nucleoli
    C) cytosol, organelles, and nucleoli
    D) organelles, inclusions, and nucleoli
    E) organelles, inclusions, and ribosomes

Answer: A
Diff: 2   Page Ref: 69

7) Microvilli are apt to be found in cells that are specialized for:
   A) contraction
   B) protection
   C) absorption
   D) insulation
   E) division

Answer: C
Diff: 3   Page Ref: 68

8) Ribosomes are found:
   A) on smooth endoplasmic reticulum
   B) in the cytoplasm
   C) on the Golgi apparatus
   D) on the rough endoplasmic reticulum
   E) in the cytoplasm and on the rough endoplasmic reticulum

Answer: E
Diff: 3   Page Ref: 71

9) Which organelle uses molecular oxygen to convert and detoxify harmful substances such as alcohol and free radicals:
   A) Golgi apparatus
   B) lysosomes
   C) peroxisomes
   D) ribosomes
   E) secretory vesicles

Answer: C
Diff: 2   Page Ref: 73

10) The movement of fluid through the cell membrane from a high pressure area to a lower pressure area is called:
   A) active transport
   B) bulk transport
   C) osmosis
   D) diffusion
   E) filtration

Answer: E
Diff: 3   Page Ref: 77

11) Two types of passive transport are:
   A) osmosis and endocytosis
   B) endocytosis and diffusion
   C) diffusion and filtration
   D) filtration and exocytosis
   E) exocytosis and endocytosis

Answer: C
Diff: 3   Page Ref: 76

12) Which of the following is NOT an active transport process:
    A) facilitated diffusion
    B) endocytosis
    C) exocytosis
    D) pinocytosis
    E) phagocytosis

Answer: A
Diff: 3   Page Ref: 78–79; 81–83

13) Cells that are specialized to fight disease are called:
    A) nerve cells
    B) macrophages
    C) epithelial cells
    D) oocytes
    E) fibroblasts

Answer: B
Diff: 2   Page Ref: 75

14) Which of the following do not involve the movement of molecules from an area of greater concentration to an area of lower concentration:
    A) diffusion
    B) simple diffusion
    C) facilitated diffusion
    D) filtration
    E) osmosis

Answer: D
Diff: 2   Page Ref: 76–78

15) Two types of endocytosis are:
    A) cellular secretion and solute pumping
    B) solute pumping and active transport
    C) active transport and phagocytosis
    D) phagocytosis and pinocytosis
    E) pinocytosis and passive transport

Answer: D
Diff: 2   Page Ref: 82

16) A solution that contains fewer solutes than the cell is:
    A) hypotonic
    B) hypertonic
    C) intravenous
    D) isotonic
    E) Ringer's lactate

Answer: A
Diff: 1   Page Ref: 80–81

17) A cell whose job is to detoxify harmful or poisonous substances such as alcohol would have many:
    A) nuclei
    B) peroxisomes
    C) lysosomes
    D) rough endoplasmic reticulum
    E) flagella
Answer: B
Diff: 2   *Page Ref: 73*

18) Which of the following processes require the use of carrier molecules:
    A) facilitated diffusion and solute pumping
    B) facilitated diffusion and bulk transport
    C) bulk transport and osmosis
    D) osmosis and filtration
    E) filtration and cellular secretion
Answer: A
Diff: 3   *Page Ref: 77–78*

19) A cell would plump with water and possibly lyse in which of the following solutions:
    A) hypotonic
    B) hypertonic
    C) intravenous
    D) isotonic
    E) Ringer's
Answer: A
Diff: 2   *Page Ref: 80–81*

20) The phase of cell division during which the chromatids are pulled apart and move to the opposite ends of the cell is:
    A) interphase
    B) prophase
    C) metaphase
    D) anaphase
    E) telophase
Answer: D
Diff: 1   *Page Ref: 84*

21) The molecule that carries an amino acid to the ribosome for incorporation into a protein is:
    A) ATP
    B) messenger RNA (mRNA)
    C) ribosomal RNA (rRNA)
    D) DNA
    E) transfer RNA (tRNA)
Answer: E
Diff: 1   *Page Ref: 88*

22) The correct order of phases of the cell cycle is:
    A) prophase, interphase, metaphase, anaphase, telophase
    B) prophase, metaphase, anaphase, telophase
    C) metaphase, anaphase, prophase, telophase
    D) telophase, metaphase, anaphase, prophase
    E) interphase, prophase, metaphase, anaphase, telophase
Answer: E
Diff: 2   *Page Ref: 83–84*

23) The molecule that is made during transcription is:
    A) ATP
    B) messenger RNA (mRNA)
    C) ribosomal RNA (rRNA)
    D) DNA
    E) transfer RNA (tRNA)
Answer: B
Diff: 1   *Page Ref: 86*

24) Which of the following statements about DNA is incorrect:
    A) it contains 2 chains
    B) it contains deoxyribose sugars
    C) it has the base uracil instead of thymine
    D) it never leaves the nucleus
    E) it is replicated in preparation for cell division
Answer: C
Diff: 3   *Page Ref: 83*

25) The molecule that contains anticodons is:
    A) ATP
    B) messenger RNA (mRNA)
    C) ribosomal RNA (rRNA)
    D) DNA
    E) transfer RNA (tRNA)
Answer: E
Diff: 1   *Page Ref: 88*

26) The DNA segment that carries information coding for a particular amino acid is a:
    A) triplet
    B) gene
    C) nucleotide
    D) deoxyribose sugar
    E) phosphate group
Answer: A
Diff: 2   *Page Ref: 86*

27) DNA replication takes place during:
   A) interphase
   B) prophase
   C) metaphase
   D) anaphase
   E) telophase

   Answer: A
   Diff: 2   Page Ref: 83

28) What are the correct base–pairing rules for DNA:
   A) adenine bonds to thymine and guanine bonds to cytosine
   B) adenine bonds to adenine and guanine bonds to guanine
   C) adenine bonds to guanine and thymine bones to cytosine
   D) adenine bonds to cytosine and thymine bonds to guanine
   E) adenine bonds to uracil and guanine bonds to cytosine

   Answer: A
   Diff: 2   Page Ref: 83

29) If the sequence of nitrogenous bases in one strand of DNA is GTA–GCA, the sequence of bases on its complementary DNA strand would be:
   A) CAU–CGU
   B) CAT–CGT
   C) GAU–GCU
   D) GAT–GCT
   E) ACG–ATT

   Answer: B
   Diff: 3   Page Ref: 83

30) Goblet cells are found in:
   A) simple squamous epithelium
   B) simple columnar epithelium
   C) simple cuboidal epithelium
   D) stratified squamous epithelium
   E) transitional epithelium

   Answer: B
   Diff: 2   Page Ref: 90

31) Which type of tissue conducts electrochemical impulses:
   A) epithelial tissue
   B) muscle tissue
   C) nervous tissue
   D) connective tissue
   E) dense tissue

   Answer: C
   Diff: 2   Page Ref: 98

32) Which of the following is NOT connective tissue:
    A) bone
    B) cartilage
    C) blood
    D) skeletal muscle
    E) adipose

Answer: D
Diff: 2   Page Ref: 94–97

33) Which type of epithelial tissue is found lining kidney tubules:
    A) simple cuboidal
    B) stratified squamous
    C) simple squamous
    D) pseudostratified columnar
    E) simple columnar

Answer: A
Diff: 3   Page Ref: 90

34) The tissue that is usually well vascularized and has an extensive extracellular matrix is called:
    A) epithelial tissue
    B) connective tissue
    C) nervous tissue
    D) muscle tissue
    E) brain tissue

Answer: B
Diff: 1   Page Ref: 93

35) The epithelial tissue found in areas subject to considerable friction and abuse, such as the esophagus, is:
    A) pseudostratified columnar epithelium
    B) simple squamous epithelium
    C) simple columnar epithelium
    D) transitional
    E) stratified squamous epithelium

Answer: E
Diff: 2   Page Ref: 90

36) Fat is:
    A) dense connective tissue
    B) loose connective tissue
    C) adipose tissue
    D) areolar tissue
    E) osseous tissue

Answer: C
Diff: 2   Page Ref: 97

37) Identify the type of tissue that is found in lymph nodes, the spleen, and bone marrow:
A) adipose tissue
B) dense connective tissue
C) areolar tissue
D) reticular connective tissue
E) osseous tissue

Answer: D
Diff: 3   Page Ref: 97

38) Glands, such as the thyroid, that secrete their products directly into the blood rather than through ducts are classified as:
A) exocrine
B) endocrine
C) sebaceous
D) ceruminous
E) sudoriferous

Answer: B
Diff: 1   Page Ref: 93

39) Which of these characteristics best describes cardiac muscle tissue:
A) movement is involuntary and cells possess striations
B) attached to the skeleton
C) movement is voluntary and cells possess striations
D) single nucleus and spindle-shaped cells
E) multinucleate and long, cylindrical cells

Answer: A
Diff: 2   Page Ref: 98

40) The type of muscle found in the walls of hollow organs, such as the stomach, and in the walls of blood vessels is:
A) cardiac muscle
B) skeletal muscle
C) smooth muscle
D) both smooth muscle and skeletal muscle
E) both cardiac muscle and skeletal muscle

Answer: C
Diff: 2   Page Ref: 98

41) The type of tissue with a matrix that consists of rows of fibroblasts that manufacture collagen fibers is:
A) dense connective tissue
B) loose connective tissue
C) adipose tissue
D) areolar tissue
E) osseous tissue

Answer: A
Diff: 3   Page Ref: 97

42) The last step in the process of tissue regeneration is:
   A) scab formation
   B) granulation tissue forms
   C) capillaries become very permeable
   D) surface epithelium regenerates
   E) blood clot forms

Answer: D
Diff: 2   Page Ref: 100–101

43) Which cell structure forms an internal framework inside the cell and is made of microtubules, intermediate filaments, and microfilaments:
   A) cytoplasm
   B) plasma membrane
   C) cytoskeleton
   D) nucleus
   E) mitochondria

Answer: C
Diff: 2   Page Ref: 73

44) A cell ingests bacteria. What type of transport is likely responsible for this process:
   A) diffusion
   B) osmosis
   C) exocytosis
   D) endocytosis
   E) filtration

Answer: D
Diff: 2   Page Ref: 81–82

45) Looking into a microscope, you notice cells swimming, propelled by a long tail. What cell structure must these cells have in order to be mobile:
   A) ribosomes
   B) smooth ER
   C) flagella
   D) peroxisomes
   E) cytoplasm

Answer: C
Diff: 2   Page Ref: 73

46) A patient arrives in the hospital extremely dehydrated. In order to fill his cells with fluid, he should be hooked to a(n) _____ intravenous drip.
   A) isotonic
   B) hypotonic
   C) hypertonic
   D) either hypertonic or hypotonic
   E) either isotonic or hyertonic

Answer: B
Diff: 2   Page Ref: 80–81

47) The events of prophase seem to be opposite of those that occur during:
   A) metaphase
   B) interphase
   C) telophase
   D) anaphase
   E) cytokinesis

Answer: C
Diff: 2   Page Ref: 84

48) A cancer drug interferes with the development of mitotic spindle fibers during cell division. Which phase is directly affected:
   A) prophase
   B) telophase
   C) anaphase
   D) metaphase
   E) interphase

Answer: A
Diff: 3   Page Ref: 84

49) Perform transcription on this partial sequence of DNA into mRNA: TTA–GCT–ACT
   A) AAU–CGA–UGA
   B) UUA–CGU–AGU
   C) AAT–CGA–TGA
   D) UUT–CGU–TGU
   E) GGC–TAG–TAG

Answer: A
Diff: 3   Page Ref: 86

50) Facilitated diffusion requires the use of:
   A) ATP
   B) protein channels or molecules
   C) lysosomes
   D) vacuoles
   E) Golgi apparatus

Answer: B
Diff: 2   Page Ref: 77

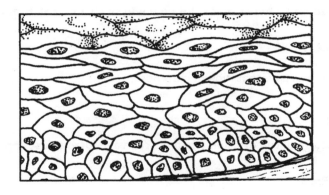

Figure 3.3

51) The tissue shown in Figure 3.3 most likely:
    A) contracts to produce movement
    B) transmits electrochemical impulses
    C) covers and lines body surfaces
    D) stores fat
    E) contains a matrix

Answer: C
Diff: 2   Page Ref: 90; 92

True/False

1) The nonpolar tails of the plasma membrane are hydrophobic.

Answer: TRUE
Diff: 2   Page Ref: 67

2) Desmosomes are junctions that allow cell communication.

Answer: FALSE
Diff: 2   Page Ref: 68–69

3) The Golgi apparatus consists of a stack of flattened membranous sacs associated with swarms of tiny vesicles that are found close to the nucleus.

Answer: TRUE
Diff: 1   Page Ref: 72

4) The process of facilitated diffusion requires energy.

Answer: FALSE
Diff: 2   Page Ref: 76–77

5) The greater the osmotic pressure, the greater the tendency of water to move into that area.

Answer: TRUE
Diff: 3   Page Ref: 80–81

6) The movement of substances from an area of higher hydrostatic pressure to an area of lower hydrostatic pressure is called *diffusion*.

Answer: FALSE
Diff: 1   Page Ref: 77

7) When a cell is placed in a hypertonic solution it will swell and may rupture.

Answer: FALSE
Diff: 2   Page Ref: 80–81

8) Mitotic spindles guide the separation of chromosomes.

Answer: TRUE
Diff: 1   Page Ref: 84

9) Anaphase is the stage of cell division when the cleavage furrow first appears.

Answer: TRUE
Diff: 2   Page Ref: 84

10) Protein synthesis cannot proceed without ribosomes.

Answer: TRUE
Diff: 2   Page Ref: 86–88

11) Translation is the stage in protein synthesis during which a complementary mRNA molecule is synthesized from a DNA template.

Answer: FALSE
Diff: 3   Page Ref: 86–88

12) Stratified epithelium consists of one layer of epithelial cells.

Answer: FALSE
Diff: 1   Page Ref: 90

13) The four primary tissue types are epithelium, muscle, cutaneous, and connective.

Answer: FALSE
Diff: 2   Page Ref: 88

14) The matrix of hyaline cartilage consists of abundant collagen fibers hidden in a rubbery matrix.

Answer: TRUE
Diff: 3   Page Ref: 94

15) Smooth muscle cells are uninucleated spindle-shaped cells that are voluntary.

Answer: FALSE
Diff: 2   Page Ref: 98

Matching

Match the following:

1) Centriole
   Diff: 2   Page Ref: 73

2) Mitochondria
   Diff: 1   Page Ref: 70–71

3) Ribosome
   Diff: 1   Page Ref: 71

4) Lysosome
   Diff: 1   Page Ref: 73

5) Microtubule
   Diff: 2   Page Ref: 73

6) Golgi apparatus
   Diff: 1   Page Ref: 72

7) Nucleolus
   Diff: 2   Page Ref: 67

8) Microvilli
   Diff: 1   Page Ref: 68

9) Smooth ER
   Diff: 1   Page Ref: 71

10) Peroxisomes
   Diff: 2   Page Ref: 73

A) captures energy to produce ATP

B) packages substances for release from cell

C) site of ribosome synthesis

D) determines overall cell shape

E) directs formation of mitotic spindle

F) synthesizes cholesterol and fat

G) digests worn-out or nonusable cell structures

H) uses oxygen to detoxify harmful substances

I) site of protein synthesis

J) increases surface area of plasma membrane for absorption

| 1) E | 2) A | 3) I | 4) G | 5) D | 6) B |
| 7) C | 8) J | 9) F | 10) H | | |

Match the following:

11) Chromosomes move slowly apart toward opposite ends of the cell
   Diff: 2   Page Ref: 84

12) Centrioles separate and move toward opposite sides of the cell
   Diff: 2   Page Ref: 83–84

13) Cytokinesis produces two separate daughter cells
   Diff: 2   Page Ref: 84

A) anaphase

B) metaphase

C) telophase

D) prophase

14) Chromosomes cluster and align at the center of the spindle

Diff: 2   Page Ref: 84

15) Nucleoli appear in each daughter cell

Diff: 2   Page Ref: 84

16) Centromeres split

Diff: 2   Page Ref: 84

17) Chromosomes align at the metaphase plate

Diff: 2   Page Ref: 84

18) Spindle breaks down and disappears

Diff: 2   Page Ref: 84

19) Nuclear envelope and nucleoid break down and disappear

Diff: 2   Page Ref: 84

20) Cleavage furrow squeezes the cell into two parts

Diff: 2   Page Ref: 84

11) A	12) D	13) C	14) B	15) C	16) A
17) B	18) C	19) D	20) C		

Match the following:

21) mRNA

Diff: 2   Page Ref: 86

22) tRNA

Diff: 2   Page Ref: 88

23) DNA

Diff: 3   Page Ref: 86

24) Protein

Diff: 2   Page Ref: 86

A) acts as a template during transcription and is synthesized during translation

B) contains the anticodon and carries amino acids to the ribosome

C) acts as a template during transcription

D) synthesized during transcription and contains the codons

E) synthesized during translation

F) contains the anticodon

21) D	22) B	23) C	24) E

Match the following:

25) Type of tissue that has an apical surface and a basement membrane

Diff: 2   *Page Ref: 89*

26) Type of tissue that consists of living cells surrounded by an extracellular matrix

Diff: 1   *Page Ref: 93*

27) Type of tissue that is specialized to contract and produce movement

Diff: 1   *Page Ref: 97*

28) Type of tissue that can be *simple* or *stratified*

Diff: 2   *Page Ref: 89-90*

29) Type of tissue that consists of neurons and supporting cells

Diff: 1   *Page Ref: 98*

30) Type of tissue that can be described as *voluntary* or *involuntary*

Diff: 2   *Page Ref: 97-98*

31) Type of tissue that contains collagen, elastic, or reticular fibers

Diff: 2   *Page Ref: 93*

32) Type of tissue that makes up endocrine and exocrine glands

Diff: 2   *Page Ref: 93*

33) Type of tissue that is avascular

Diff: 2   *Page Ref: 89*

34) Type of tissue that can be classified as "loose" or "dense"

Diff: 2   *Page Ref: 97*

35) Type of tissue whose two functional characteristics are *irritability* and *conductivity*

Diff: 2   *Page Ref: 98*

A) nervous tissue

B) connective tissue

C) muscle tissue

D) epithelial tissue

25) D	26) B	27) C	28) D	29) A	30) C
31) B	32) D	33) D	34) B	35) A	

Essay

1) List, describe, and state the functions of the three types of membrane junctions.

Answer: 1. Tight junctions are areas where the membranes of adjacent cells fuse together. This creates an impermeable leak-proof cellular sheet and prevents substances from passing between the cells. Tight junctions are found in epithelia lining fluid containing cavities, such as the small intestine.
2. Desmosomes are areas where fine protein filaments extend between two adjacent cells and are anchored in button-like thickenings of the cell membranes called plaque. This type of junction holds adjacent cells together very firmly and is found in areas where cellular sheets are subjected to considerable mechanical stress, such as the skin. Within each cell, the plaques on one side are connected to plaques on the opposite side by thicker protein filaments that act to internally anchor the plaques in place.
3. Gap junctions consist of hollow protein cylinders, called connexons, which extend completely through the plasma membrane of neighboring cells and meet and join together in the extracellular space. This creates a continuous channel for the passage of substances between the interiors of the two adjacent cells. Gap junctions, which promote intercellular communication, are found between the cardiac muscle cells in the heart.

Diff: 3   Page Ref: 68–69

2) Identify the five molecules found in the plasma membrane and state their functions.

Answer: 1. Lipid molecules (phospholipids) provide the medium in which protein molecules float, form the basic fabric of the membrane, and are relatively impermeable to most water-soluble molecules.
2. Cholesterol molecules have a stabilizing effect and help to keep the membrane fluid.
3. Protein molecules are responsible for the most specialized functions of the membrane. They act as enzymes, serve as receptors or binding sites for hormones and other chemical messengers, act as carriers that bind to substances and move them through the cell membrane, and form pores through which water and small molecules can move.
4. Carbohydrate molecules add an identification tag to mark protein molecules, and make the cell membrane a fuzzy, sticky, sugar-rich area.
5. Glycoprotein molecules determine blood type; act as receptors that certain bacteria, viruses, or their toxins can bind to; and play a role in cell-to-cell interactions.

Diff: 3   Page Ref: 67–68

3) List, describe, and state the functions of the three major elements of the cytoplasm.

Answer: 1. The cytosol is a semitransparent fluid that is largely water, and contains dissolved nutrients and a variety of other solutes. Its function is to suspend the organelles and inclusions.
2. Organelles are the "little organs" (specialized cellular compartments) within the cytosol that carry out specific functions for the cell as a whole in order to maintain its life.
3. Inclusions are chemical substances dispersed in the cytoplasm that may or may not be present, depending on the specific cell type. Most are stored nutrients or cell products, which are nonfunctioning units.

Diff: 3   Page Ref: 69

4) Differentiate between the two types of endoplasmic reticulum.

Answer: 1. The rough endoplasmic reticulum (ER):
   a.   is studded with ribosomes
   b.   makes proteins on its ribosomes
2. The smooth ER:
   a.   lacks ribosomes on its surface
   b.   functions in lipid metabolism, drug and pesticide detoxification

Diff: 2   Page Ref: 71–72

5) List the three different types of RNA and identify their functions.

Answer: 1. Messenger RNA (mRNA) carries the "message" containing instructions for protein synthesis from the DNA in the nucleus to the ribosomes in the cytoplasm.
2. Ribosomal RNA (rRNA) forms part of the "ribosomal" structure and helps coordinate the protein building process.
3. Transfer RNA (tRNA) transports an amino acid to the ribosomal site and recognizes the mRNA codons.

Diff: 3   Page Ref: 86; 88

6) Discuss the three steps in protein synthesis.

Answer: 1. Uncoiling of DNA—the DNA segment or gene that specifies one polypeptide or protein uncoils.
2. Transcription (DNA-directed synthesis of mRNA)—one strand of DNA acts as a template for the synthesis of the complementary mRNA molecule, and there is a transfer of information from the DNA's base sequence (code) into the complementary base sequence of mRNA (codon).
3. Translation (RNA-directed synthesis of a polypeptide or protein) involves five steps. First, mRNA leaves the nucleus and attaches to ribosomes. Second, tRNA (anticodon) transports an amino acid to the mRNA strand and recognizes a mRNA molecule (codon). Third, the codon and the anticodon bind. Fourth, the ribosome moves the mRNA strand along as each codon is read sequentially. Finally, as each amino acid is bound to the next by a polypeptide bond, its tRNA is released. The polypeptide or protein chain is released when the termination (stop) codon is read.

Diff: 3   Page Ref: 86; 88

7) Discuss the four stages of mitosis.

Answer: 1. Prophase—chromatin threads coil and shorten so that visible bar-like bodies, called chromosomes, appear. Each chromosome is made up of two strands, called chromatids, which are held together by a centromere. Additionally, the centrioles separate and move toward opposite sides of the cell, directing the assembly of the mitotic spindle (composed of microtubules) between them as they move.
2. Metaphase—the chromosomes cluster and align in the center of the spindle, midway between the centrioles, forming a straight line of chromosomes.
3. Anaphase—the centromeres split and the chromosomes move slowly apart toward opposite ends of the cell. A cleavage furrow appears over the midline of the spindle and eventually pinches the cytoplasmic mass into two parts in a process called cytokinesis.
4. Telophase—the chromosomes reach opposite ends of the cell and their movement ends, and they then uncoil and become chromatin again. A nuclear membrane then forms around each chromatin mass, the spindle breaks down and disappears, and nucleoli re-appear in each of the daughter nuclei. Finally, cytokinesis produces two separate daughter cells.

Diff: 3   Page Ref: 83–84

8) A fat–soluble vitamin, vitamin A, is moving down its concentration gradient into a cell. What type of membrane transport is responsible for its movement? Describe this process.

Answer: Vitamin A is moving via simple diffusion, a type of passive transport. Passive transport requires no energy input from the cell. Vitamin A is moving from an area where it is more concentrated to an area where it is less concentrated. This vitamin is moving without assistance through the plasma membrane.

Diff: 3   Page Ref: 77

9) Since epithelial tissues are avascular, explain how these tissues receive nourishment.

Answer: Epithelial tissues depend on diffusion for food and oxygen. Capillaries in deeper connective tissue carry this nourishment.

Diff: 2   Page Ref: 89

10) Explain why an intravenous solution should be isotonic for a patient.

Answer: Isotonic solutions have the same solute and water concentrations as the cell. Isotonic solutions cause no visible changes in cells since there is not an area more highly concentrated. The use of isotonic intravenous solutions allows red blood cells to retain their normal size and disc–like shape.

Diff: 2   Page Ref: 80

11) Explain the differences among the three types of muscle tissue.

Answer: 1. Skeletal tissue:
  a. is attached to the skeleton
  b. is under voluntary control
  c. is multinucleate
  d. possesses striations
  e. is composed of long, cylindrical cells
2. Cardiac muscle:
  a. is found only in the heart
  b. is under involuntary control
  c. is uninucleate
  d. possesses striations
  e. is composed of cells that are short and branching
  f. possesses intercalated disks that contain gap junctions
3. Smooth muscle:
  a. is found in walls of hollow organs
  b. is uninucleate
  c. lacks striations
  d. possesses cells that are spindle shaped

Diff: 3   Page Ref: 98

Short Answer

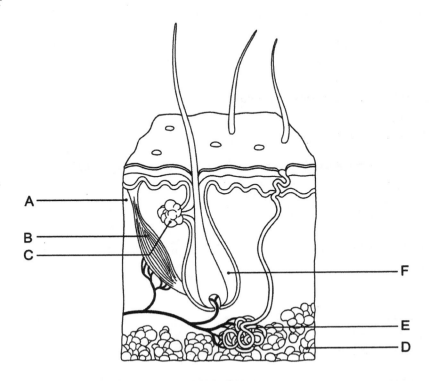

Figure 4.1

Using Figure 4.1, identify the following:

1) The region that contains adipose tissue is indicated by letter _____.

Answer: D
Diff: 2   *Page Ref: 115*

2) The hair follicle is indicated by letter _____.

Answer: F
Diff: 1   *Page Ref: 121*

3) The structure that is responsible for whorled ridges on the epidermal surfaces is indicated by letter _____.

Answer: A
Diff: 1   *Page Ref: 117*

4) The structure that pulls the hair follicle into an upright position is indicated by letter _____.

Answer: B
Diff: 2   *Page Ref: 122*

5) The gland that produces a mixture of oily substances and fragmented cells is indicated by label _____.

Answer: C
Diff: 2   Page Ref: 119

6) The gland that produces sweat is indicated by label _____.

Answer: E
Diff: 2   Page Ref: 119–120

Fill in the blank or provide a short answer:

7) The deepest layer of the dermis is called the _____ layer.

Answer: reticular
Diff: 2   Page Ref: 118

8) In a hair, the outermost single layer of cells that overlap one another like shingles is called the _____.

Answer: cuticle
Diff: 2   Page Ref: 121

9) The part of a hair that projects from the surface of the scalp or skin is called the _____.

Answer: shaft
Diff: 1   Page Ref: 121

10) The sebaceous glands produce _____.

Answer: oil (sebum)
Diff: 1   Page Ref: 119

11) The skin that covers the palms of the hands and the soles of the feet has an extra layer of epidermis called the stratum _____.

Answer: lucidum
Diff: 2   Page Ref: 117

12) The dermis is composed of the reticular and _____ layers.

Answer: papillary
Diff: 1   Page Ref: 117

13) "Goosebumps" are caused by contractions of the _____ muscles.

Answer: arrector pili
Diff: 1   Page Ref: 122

14) The type of burn that involves injury to the epidermis and the upper region of the dermis and is red, blistered, and painful is termed as a _____-degree burn.

Answer: second
Diff: 1   Page Ref: 124

15) The white, cheesy-looking substance that is produced by the sebaceous glands and protects a baby's skin while it is floating in its water-filled sac inside the mother is called _____.

Answer: vernix caseosa
Diff: 1   Page Ref: 127

16) The part of the hair enclosed in the follicle is known as the _____.

Answer: root
Diff: 2   Page Ref: 121

17) The white cresent area located over the nail matrix is called the _____.

Answer: lunula
Diff: 1   Page Ref: 122

18) The layer of the serous membrane that covers an organ is known as the _____ layer.

Answer: visceral
Diff: 3   Page Ref: 112

19) The type of connective tissue membrane found in joints is the _____.

Answer: synovial membrane
Diff: 2   Page Ref: 112

20) The two major categories of membranes are _____ and _____.

Answer: epithelial membranes; connective membranes
Diff: 1   Page Ref: 110

21) Epithelial membranes contain two types of tissue, _____ and _____ tissue.

Answer: epithelial; connective
Diff: 2   Page Ref: 110

Multiple Choice

1) The categories of epithelial tissue membranes are:
    A) synovial, cutaneous, and mucous membranes
    B) synovial, cutaneous, and serous membranes
    C) synovial, mucous, and serous membranes
    D) synovial, mucous, and cutaneous membranes
    E) mucous, cutaneous, and serous membranes

Answer: E
Diff: 2   Page Ref: 110–112

2) Which type of membrane contains fluid between the visceral and perietal layers:
    A) synovial
    B) serous
    C) cutaneous
    D) mucous
    E) connective

Answer: B
Diff: 2   Page Ref: 112

3) Which of the following relationships is incorrect:
   A) visceral peritoneum – covers the outer surface of the small intestine
   B) parietal pericardium – covers the outer surface of the heart
   C) parietal pleura – lines the wall of thoracic cavity
   D) visceral pleura – lines the surface of the lungs
   E) parietal peritoneum – lines the wall of the abdominal cavity

   Answer: B
   Diff: 1   *Page Ref: 112*

4) Which of the following is a connective tissue membrane:
   A) synovial membrane
   B) cutaneous membrane
   C) mucous membrane
   D) serous membrane
   E) pleural membrane

   Answer: A
   Diff: 1   *Page Ref: 112*

5) The only dry membrane is the:
   A) synovial membrane
   B) cutaneous membrane
   C) mucous membrane
   D) serous membrane
   E) basement membrane

   Answer: B
   Diff: 1   *Page Ref: 110*

6) Synovial membranes are found in the:
   A) joint cavities
   B) covering of the heart
   C) lining of the stomach cavity
   D) covering of the brain
   E) lining of the abdominal cavity wall

   Answer: A
   Diff: 1   *Page Ref: 112*

7) Sweat glands associated with hair are:
   A) sebaceous glands
   B) sudoriferous glands
   C) eccrine glands
   D) sebaceous glands and eccrine glands
   E) sudoriferous glands and eccrine glands

   Answer: B
   Diff: 3   *Page Ref: 119*

8) Which of the following is a vital function of the skin:
   A) it converts modified epidermal cholesterol to vitamin D
   B) it aids in the transport of materials throughout the body
   C) the cells of the epidermis store glucose as glycogen for energy
   D) it absorbs vitamin C so that the skin will not be subject to diseases
   E) it aids in desiccation

Answer: A
Diff: 1   Page Ref: 115

9) Although you get wet while swimming, a tough protein within the skin prevents it from soaking up moisture like a sponge. This substance is:
   A) serous fluid
   B) melanin
   C) mucus
   D) carotene
   E) keratin

Answer: E
Diff: 1   Page Ref: 115

10) The epidermis is composed of:
   A) simple columnar epithelium
   B) stratified squamous epithelium
   C) adipose tissue
   D) areolar tissue
   E) dense fibrous connective tissue

Answer: B
Diff: 2   Page Ref: 115

11) The uppermost layer of skin is:
   A) called the dermis
   B) full of keratin
   C) fed by a good supply of blood vessels
   D) called the hypodermis
   E) composed of dense connective tissue

Answer: B
Diff: 2   Page Ref: 115

12) The hypodermis consists of:
   A) simple columnar epithelium
   B) stratified squamous epithelium
   C) adipose tissue
   D) loose connective tissue
   E) dense fibrous connective tissue

Answer: C
Diff: 1   Page Ref: 115

13) A needle would pierce the epidermal layers of the forearm in which order:
    1.   stratum basale
    2.   stratum corneum
    3.   stratum granulosum
    4.   stratum lucidum
    5.   stratum spinosum
  A) 2, 3, 5, 1
  B) 1, 5, 3, 4, 2
  C) 2, 4, 3, 5, 1
  D) 1, 3, 5, 2, 4
  E) 2, 3, 4, 1, 5

Answer: A
Diff: 3   *Page Ref: 115–117*

14) Which of the following homoeostatic imbalances is caused by skin exposure to chemicals:
  A) athlete's foot
  B) cold sores
  C) impetigo
  D) contact dermatitis
  E) cyanosis

Answer: D
Diff: 2   *Page Ref: 123*

15) The "tanning" effect (darkening of the skin) that occurs when a person is exposed to the sun is due to:
  A) melanin
  B) keratin
  C) oil
  D) Langerhans cells
  E) sweat

Answer: A
Diff: 1   *Page Ref: 117*

16) The layer of the epidermis in which cells first die because of their inability to get nutrients and oxygen is the:
  A) stratum spinosum
  B) stratum granulosum
  C) stratum basale
  D) stratum corneum
  E) stratum lucidum

Answer: E
Diff: 2   *Page Ref: 115–117*

17) Melanocytes are found in the:
  A) stratum spinosum
  B) stratum lucidum
  C) stratum corneum
  D) stratum basale
  E) stratum granulosum

Answer: D
Diff: 2   *Page Ref: 117*

18) A splinter penetrates to the deepest layer of the epidermis on your foot. This layer is:
    A) stratum basale
    B) stratum corneum
    C) stratum granulosum
    D) stratum lucidum
    E) stratum spinosum

Answer: A
Diff: 3   Page Ref: 115–116

19) Epidermal cells that are actively mitotic and replace superficial cells that are continually rubbed off are:
    A) stratum granulosum cells
    B) stratum corneum cells
    C) stratum lucidum cells
    D) stratum spinosum cells
    E) stratum germinativum cells

Answer: E
Diff: 2   Page Ref: 116

20) Nutrients reach the surface of the skin (epidermis) through the process of:
    A) absorption
    B) evaporation
    C) filtration
    D) diffusion
    E) osmosis

Answer: D
Diff: 1   Page Ref: 116

21) Which of the following is NOT a true statement about the papillary layer of the dermis:
    A) it is the deepest layer of the skin
    B) it produces the pattern for fingerprints
    C) it contains nerve endings that respond to touch and temperature stimuli
    D) it is highly vascular
    E) it is located immediately beneath the epidermis

Answer: A
Diff: 1   Page Ref: 117–118

22) In order to warm the body up when cold:
    A) vitamin D is synthesized
    B) sudoriferous glands release sweat
    C) sebaceous glands release oil
    D) the arrector pili muscles contract to stand hairs upright
    E) melanin is produced

Answer: D
Diff: 2   Page Ref: 122

23) Finger–like upward projections of the dermis into the epidermis are called:
   A) hair follicles
   B) hair bulbs
   C) Meissner's corpuscles
   D) dermal papillae
   E) Pacinian corpuscles

   Answer: D
   Diff: 2   Page Ref: 117

24) Nails are composed of:
   A) melanin
   B) hemoglobin
   C) keratin
   D) sebum
   E) carotene

   Answer: C
   Diff: 1   Page Ref: 122

25) The secretions of the eccrine glands are:
   A) primarily uric acid
   B) 99% water, sodium chloride, and trace amounts of wastes, lactic acid, and vitamin C
   C) fatty substances, proteins, antibodies, and trace amounts of minerals and vitamins
   D) solely metabolic wastes
   E) basic

   Answer: B
   Diff: 2   Page Ref: 120

26) The secretion of sweat is stimulated:
   A) by high temperatures
   B) when the air temperature drops
   C) by hormones, especially male sex hormones
   D) as a protective coating when one is swimming
   E) both by high temperatures and by hormones, especially male hormones

   Answer: E
   Diff: 3   Page Ref: 120

27) Sudoriferous glands are important for:
   A) production of keratin
   B) keeping skin and hair cells soft and flexible
   C) production of sweat
   D) body heat regulation
   E) production of vitamin D

   Answer: D
   Diff: 1   Page Ref: 119–120

28) Inflammation of the hair follicles and sebaceous glands is called:
   A) impetigo
   B) alopecia
   C) psoriasis
   D) boils
   E) contact dermatitis

   Answer: D
   Diff: 2   Page Ref: 123

29) What is the first threat to life from a massive third-degree burn:
   A) infection
   B) dehydration
   C) unbearable pain
   D) loss of immune function
   E) blood loss

   Answer: B
   Diff: 2   Page Ref: 124

30) A physician estimates the volume of fluid lost in a severely burned patient by:
   A) measuring urinary output and fluid intake
   B) observing the tissues that are usually moist
   C) blood analysis
   D) using the "rule of nines"
   E) performing enzyme studies

   Answer: D
   Diff: 1   Page Ref: 124

31) Which of the following is an indication of melanoma:
   A) a symmetrical mole
   B) a pigmented spot that has smooth borders
   C) a spot on the skin that is smaller than the size of a pencil eraser
   D) a pigmented spot that is black
   E) a pigmented spot that contains areas of different colors

   Answer: E
   Diff: 1   Page Ref: 126

32) Acne and seborrhea are caused by problems with:
   A) eccrine glands
   B) nail beds
   C) sudoriferous glands
   D) sebaceous glands
   E) hair follicles

   Answer: D
   Diff: 2   Page Ref: 119

33) Male pattern baldness has a genetic switch that turns on in response to:
   A) age
   B) size
   C) weight
   D) male hormones
   E) female hormones

   Answer: A
   Diff: 1   Page Ref: 127

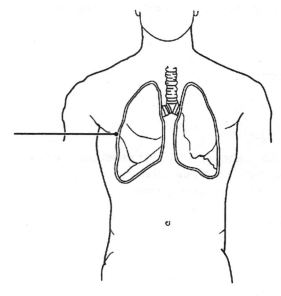

Figure 4.2

34) The membrane shown in Figure 4.2 is:
   A) cutaneous membrane
   B) synovial membrane
   C) pericardium, a serous membrane
   D) mucous membrane
   E) pleura, a serous membrane

   Answer: E
   Diff: 2   Page Ref: 111–112

True/False

1) Membranes that line body cavities that have openings to the exterior of the body are called mucous membranes.

   Answer: TRUE
   Diff: 1   Page Ref: 110–112

2) The serous membrane that covers the external surface of both lungs is called the visceral pleura.

   Answer: TRUE
   Diff: 1   Page Ref: 112

3) When an individual is exposed to extremely low air temperatures, the capillaries of the skin will dilate so that blood will flush into skin capillary beds and heat will be dissipated.

Answer: FALSE
Diff: 3   *Page Ref: 118*

4) The outermost layer of the epidermis is the stratum basale.

Answer: FALSE
Diff: 1   *Page Ref: 115–116*

5) The pinkish hue of healthy individuals with fair skin is the result of the crimson color of oxygenated hemoglobin circulating in the dermal capillaries and reflecting through the dermis.

Answer: TRUE
Diff: 2   *Page Ref: 118*

6) The major portion of the skin is comprised of the dermis.

Answer: TRUE
Diff: 1   *Page Ref: 117*

7) The epidermis is made up of stratified squamous epithelium.

Answer: TRUE
Diff: 2   *Page Ref: 115*

8) Skin is also known as a synovial membrane.

Answer: FALSE
Diff: 1   *Page Ref: 110; 114*

9) A serous membrane is composed of a layer of simple squamous epithelium resting on a thin layer of areolar connective tissue.

Answer: TRUE
Diff: 1   *Page Ref: 112*

10) Eccrine and apocrine glands are the two types of sebaceous glands.

Answer: FALSE
Diff: 1   *Page Ref: 119*

11) Melanin is found in the uppermost layer of skin and helps prevent water loss.

Answer: FALSE
Diff: 1   *Page Ref: 117*

12) Hair is produced by the hair bulb and is composed primarily of dead keratinized cells.

Answer: TRUE
Diff: 1   *Page Ref: 121*

13) The thickened, proximal area of the nail is called the nail matrix, and it is responsible for nail growth.

Answer: TRUE
Diff: 1   *Page Ref: 122*

14) The reason that the nail bed appears pink is the presence of a large number of melanocytes in the underlying dermis.

Answer: FALSE
Diff: 1   *Page Ref: 122*

15) Joe just burned his hand on a hot pot. A blister forms and the burn is painful; Joe's burn would best be described as a third-degree burn.

Answer: FALSE
Diff: 1   *Page Ref: 124*

16) The nail is actually a modification of the skin and corresponds to the hooves of animals.

Answer: TRUE
Diff: 1   *Page Ref: 122*

17) The downy type of hair covering a newborn is called vernix caseosa.

Answer: FALSE
Diff: 2   *Page Ref: 127*

18) The ABCD rule is used for classifying burns.

Answer: FALSE
Diff: 2   *Page Ref: 126*

19) In first-degree burns, only the epidermis is damaged.

Answer: TRUE
Diff: 2   *Page Ref: 124*

20) Squamous cell carcinoma arises from cells of the stratum spinosum.

Answer: TRUE
Diff: 1   *Page Ref: 126*

Matching

Match the following:

1) Acne

   Diff: 1   *Page Ref: 119*

2) Cold sores

   Diff: 2   *Page Ref: 123*

3) Psoriasis

   Diff: 2   *Page Ref: 123*

4) Athlete's foot

   Diff: 1   *Page Ref: 123*

5) Basal cell carcinoma

   Diff: 2   *Page Ref: 125-126*

6) Malignant melanoma

   Diff: 2   *Page Ref: 126*

7) Third-degree burns

   Diff: 2   *Page Ref: 124*

8) Seborrhea

   Diff: 2   *Page Ref: 119*

9) Impetigo

   Diff: 2   *Page Ref: 123*

10) Alopecia

   Diff: 2   *Page Ref: 127*

11) Decubitus ulcers

   Diff: 2   *Page Ref: 118*

A) partial-thickness burn

B) cancer of skin pigment cells

C) full-thickness burn

D) bedsores

E) fluid-filled blisters caused by herpes simplex virus

F) hair thinning and some degree of baldness

G) malignancy of the lowest epidermal layer

H) overproduction of skin cells causing dry, silvery scales

I) infection of the sebaceous glands accompanied by skin pimples

J) fungus infection between toes

K) staphylococcus bacterial infection causing water-filled lesions around the mouth and nose

L) overactivity of sebaceous glands that results in dandruff

1) I	2) E	3) H	4) J	5) G	6) B
7) C	8) L	9) K	10) F	11) D	

Match the following:

12) Papillary layer

   Diff: 2   *Page Ref: 117*

13) Hair root

   Diff: 2   *Page Ref: 121*

14) Matrix

   Diff: 2   *Page Ref: 121*

15) Medulla

   Diff: 2   *Page Ref: 121*

16) Apocrine gland

   Diff: 2   *Page Ref: 120*

17) Eccrine gland

   Diff: 2   *Page Ref: 119–120*

18) Dermal sheath

   Diff: 2   *Page Ref: 121*

A) part of the hair enclosed in the follicle

B) lower layer of the dermis

C) upper layer of the dermis

D) central core of each hair

E) sudoriferous glands largely confined to the axillary region

F) part of the hair projecting from the skin surface

G) divides to form hair cells

H) sudoriferous glands found all over the body

I) outermost covering of the hair follicle

12) C   13) A   14) G   15) D   16) E   17) H
18) I

Match the following:

19) Type of membrane that is dry

Diff: 1   *Page Ref: 110*

A) serous membrane

B) synovial membrane

20) Type of membrane adapted
for absorption or secretion

Diff: 2   *Page Ref: 110*

C) mucous membrane

D) cutaneous membrane

21) Type of membrane that has no
epithelial cells at all

Diff: 1   *Page Ref: 112*

22) Type of membrane that
contains a visceral and a
partietal layer

Diff: 2   *Page Ref: 112*

23) Only example of a connective
tissue membrane

Diff: 1   *Page Ref: 112*

24) Type of membrane that lines
open body cavities

Diff: 1   *Page Ref: 110*

25) Peritoneum, pericardium, and
pleura are examples of this
type of membrane

Diff: 1   *Page Ref: 112*

19) D   20) C   21) B   22) A   23) B   24) C
25) A

Essay

1) Explain the ABCD rule.

Answer: The ABCD rule describes the appearance of the most serious form of skin cancer,
melanoma. The "A" is for asymmetry. In melanoma, the two sides of the pigmented spot
or mole do not match. The "B" is for border irregularity. In melanoma, the borders of the
lesion are not smooth but exhibit indentations. The "C" is for color. In melanoma, the
pigmented spot contains areas of different colors (blacks, browns, tans, and sometimes
blues and reds). The "D" is for diameter. In melanoma, the spot is larger than 6 mm in
diameter (the size of a pencil eraser).

Diff: 3   *Page Ref: 126*

2) Distinguish between the appearances of partial-thickness and full-thickness burns.

Answer: *Partial thickness burns* are burns that don't completely damage both layers of skin, and include first- and second-degree burns. In first-degree burns only the epidermis is damaged, with redness and swelling and some pain. These burns typically heal in two to three days without special attention. Second-degree burns involve injury to the epidermis and upper region of the dermis. They are characterized by redness, blisters, and pain. Ordinarily, no permanent scars result if care is taken to prevent infection. *Full-thickness burns* destroy the entire thickness of skin and are also termed third-degree burns. In third-degree burns, the burned area appears blanched (gray-white) or blackened. The burned area is not painful since nerve endings in the area are destroyed. Regeneration is not possible, therefore skin grafting must be done to cover underlying exposed tissues.

Diff: 2   *Page Ref: 123-125*

3) Explain how the skin helps regulate body temperature.

Answer: The nervous system is responsible for controlling all temperature-regulating functions of the skin. When the temperature in the external environment is high, heat loss occurs as the nervous system activates sweat glands. Perspiration is produced, which evaporates from the skin surface, causing heat to be dissipated. At the same time, the nervous system causes blood to be flushed into skin capillary beds so that heat radiates from the body surface. In contrast, when the temperature in the external environment is low, the nervous system prevents blood from entering the skin capillary system and radiation to the body exterior is prevented so that perspiration does not occur. At the same time, blood is prevented from entering deeper tissues and the core temperature of the body is maintained.

Diff: 3   *Page Ref: 118; 120*

4) Define and explain the function of the arrector pili.

Answer: The arrector pili are small bands of smooth muscle cells that connect each side of a hair follicle to the dermal tissue. They are activated by cold or fright and, when contracted, pull the hair follicle into an upright position, dimpling the skin surface with "goose bumps."

Diff: 1   *Page Ref: 122*

5) Identify four changes that occur to the skin and subcutaneous connective tissue as a result of aging, and state how these changes can be delayed.

Answer: 1. The amount of subcutaneous tissue below the skin decreases, leading to an intolerance to cold in the elderly.
2. Because of decreased oil production and declining numbers of collagen fibers, the skin becomes drier and may become itchy and bothersome.
3. Thinning of the skin makes it more susceptible to bruising and other types of injuries.
4. A decrease in elasticity of the skin, along with the loss of subcutaneous fat, allows bags to form under the eyes and causes jowls to sag.
To delay these changes, the skin should be kept clean and shielded from the sun, and a healthy diet with plenty of fluids should be maintained.

Diff: 3   *Page Ref: 127*

6) List and describe the three types of epithelial membranes.

Answer: 1. Cutaneous membrane is:
    a. skin
    b. dry
    c. composed of keratinizing stratified squamous epithelium and the underlying connective tissue is often dense and fibrous.
  2. Mucous membrane:
    a. is moist
    b. is found lining all body cavities that open to the exterior
    c. often contains stratified squamous epithelium or simple columnar epithelium
  3. Serous membrane:
    a. is composed of two layers (visceral layer covers the organ in the cavity while the parietal layer lines a specific portion of the wall of the ventral body cavity)
    b. covers organs in body cavities that are closed to the exterior
    c. is contructed of simple squamous epithelium overlying a thin layer of areolar connective tissue

Diff: 2   *Page Ref: 110–112*

7) Explain how the skin functions to protect deeper tissues.

Answer: Skin contains:
  1. keratin which toughens cells and serves as a barrier to mechanical damage and chemical damage; keratin also serves to waterproof the skin to prevent desiccation
  2. acidic oily secretions that prevent bacterial damage
  3. melanin to protect from UV damage
  4. receptors to detect heat, cold, and pain; serves as a protection against thermal damage

Diff: 2   *Page Ref: 115–119*

8) Thirteen–year–old John has been diagnosed with acne. Expain to him what causes acne.

Answer: Acne is an active infection of the sebaceous glands accompanied by pimples on the skin. Sebaceous glands release sebum, or oil, onto the skin's surface.

Diff: 1   *Page Ref: 119*

Chapter 5 The Skeletal System

Short Answer

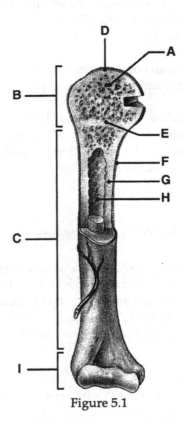

Figure 5.1

Using Figure 5.1, identify the following:

1) Spongy bone is indicated by letter _____.

   Answer: A
   Diff: 1   Page Ref: 135–137

2) The area that causes the lengthwise growth of a long bone is indicated by letter _____.

   Answer: E
   Diff: 2   Page Ref: 135–137

3) The area that serves as a storage area for fat in adults is indicated by letter _____.

   Answer: H
   Diff: 2   Page Ref: 135–137

4) The diaphysis is indicated by letter _____.

   Answer: C
   Diff: 2   Page Ref: 135–137

5) The distal epiphysis is indicated by letter _____.

   Answer: I
   Diff: 2   Page Ref: 135–137

6) The area that contains glassy hyaline cartilage that provides a smooth slippery surface which decreases friction is indicated by letter _____.

Answer: D
Diff: 2   Page Ref: 135–137

Fill in the blank or provide a short answer:

7) Blood cell formation is called _____.

Answer: hematopoiesis
Diff: 1   Page Ref: 135

8) _____ are giant cells that destroy bone.

Answer: Osteoclasts
Diff: 1   Page Ref: 140

9) Cube–shaped bones that contain mostly spongy bone are called _____ bones.

Answer: short
Diff: 1   Page Ref: 135

10) The disease in children whose diets lack calcium or vitamin D, where the bones fail to calcify, is called _____.

Answer: rickets
Diff: 1   Page Ref: 142

11) A round or oval hole through a bone, which contains blood vessels and/or nerves, is called a _____.

Answer: foramen
Diff: 1   Page Ref: 138

12) A large rounded projection on a bone is called a _____.

Answer: tuberosity
Diff: 1   Page Ref: 138

13) A fracture where the bone breaks cleanly but does not penetrate the skin is termed a _____ fracture.

Answer: simple or closed
Diff: 1   Page Ref: 142

14) An increase in bone diameter is called _____ growth.

Answer: appositional
Diff: 1   Page Ref: 140

15) The only freely movable bone in the skull is the _____.

Answer: mandible
Diff: 2   Page Ref: 149

16) The part of the ethmoid bone that contains holey areas with fibers that carry impulses from the olfactory receptors of the nose to the brain is the _____.

Answer: cribriform plate
Diff: 2   Page Ref: 148

17) The external acoustic (auditory) meatus is found on the _____ bone.

Answer: temporal
Diff: 2   *Page Ref: 145*

18) The heel bone is called the _____.

Answer: calcaneus
Diff: 1   *Page Ref: 166*

19) The head of the humerus fits into the _____ of the scapula.

Answer: glenoid cavity
Diff: 2   *Page Ref: 160*

20) The disease in which uric acid accumulates in the blood and may be deposited as needle–shaped crystals in the soft tissues of joints is called _____.

Answer: gout
Diff: 1   *Page Ref: 174*

21) The elbow joint is an example of a _____ joint in which movement occurs in only one plane.

Answer: hinge
Diff: 1   *Page Ref: 171*

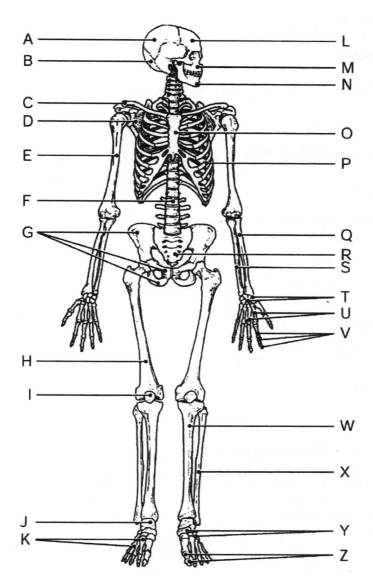

Figure 5.2

Using Figure 5.2, identify the following:

22) The frontal bone is indicated by letter _____.

Answer: L
Diff: 1   Page Ref: 145

23) The femur is indicated by letter _____.

Answer: H
Diff: 1   Page Ref: 144

24) The fibula is indicated by letter _____.

Answer: X
Diff: 1   Page Ref: 144

25) The sternum is indicated by letter _____.

Answer: O
Diff: 1   Page Ref: 144

26) The radius bone is indicated by letter _____.

Answer: Q
Diff: 1   Page Ref: 144

27) The mandible is indicated by letter _____.

Answer: N
Diff: 1   Page Ref: 149

28) The scapula is indicated by letter _____.

Answer: D
Diff: 1   Page Ref: 144

29) The phalanges of the foot are indicated by letter _____.

Answer: Z
Diff: 1   Page Ref: 144

30) The sacrum is indicated by letter _____.

Answer: R
Diff: 1   Page Ref: 144

Multiple Choice

1) The most important minerals stored in bones are:
   A) calcium and iron
   B) sodium and phosphorus
   C) sodium and potassium
   D) calcium and phosphorus
   E) calcium and potassium

Answer: D
Diff: 1   Page Ref: 135

Figure 5.3

2) The type of tissue shown in Figure 5.3 is found mostly in:
   A) articular cartilage
   B) yellow marrow
   C) the diaphysis
   D) the epiphysis
   E) short bones

Answer: C
Diff: 3   Page Ref: 137; 139

3) Which of the following groups of bones in the human body, categorized according to shape, is correct:
   A) wrist and ankle bones – long bones
   B) arm and leg bones – short bones
   C) skull bones – flat bones
   D) coxal bones – irregular bones
   E) cranium – sesamoid bones

Answer: D
Diff: 2   Page Ref: 135

4) Which of the following bone categories is composed of two layers of compact bone sandwiching a layer of spongy bone between them:
   A) compact bone
   B) irregular bone
   C) flat bone
   D) long bone
   E) sesamoid bone

Answer: C
Diff: 1   Page Ref: 135

5) The periosteum is secured to the underlying bone by dense connective tissue fibers called:
   A) Volkmann's canals
   B) a bony matrix with hyaline cartilage
   C) Sharpey's fibers
   D) endochondral bone
   E) articular cartilage

   Answer: C
   Diff: 1   *Page Ref: 135*

6) In adults, the function of the yellow marrow is to:
   A) store adipose tissue
   B) form blood cells
   C) store calcium and phosphorus
   D) cause lengthwise growth in long bones
   E) decrease friction at joint surfaces

   Answer: A
   Diff: 3   *Page Ref: 136*

7) The presence of an epiphyseal plate indicates that:
   A) bone is dead
   B) bone length is no longer increasing
   C) bone diameter is increasing
   D) bone diameter is decreasing
   E) bone length is increasing

   Answer: E
   Diff: 2   *Page Ref: 136*

8) Osteons are characteristic of _____.
   A) articular cartilage
   B) spongy bone
   C) compact bone
   D) yellow marrow
   E) Sharpey's fibers

   Answer: C
   Diff: 3   *Page Ref: 137; 139*

9) The bone cells within lacunae receive nourishment from blood vessels through passageways called:
   A) Haversian canals
   B) perforating canals
   C) lamellae
   D) medullary cavities
   E) canaliculi

   Answer: E
   Diff: 1   *Page Ref: 139*

10) A shallow, basin-like depression in a bone often serving as an articular surface is a:
    A) sinus
    B) meatus
    C) fossa
    D) foramen
    E) groove

Answer: C
Diff: 1   Page Ref: 138

11) A round or oval opening through a bone is a:
    A) facet
    B) fossa
    C) foramen
    D) fissure
    E) trochanter

Answer: C
Diff: 1   Page Ref: 138

12) Which of these are bone-forming cells:
    A) osteocytes
    B) canaliculi
    C) osteoclasts
    D) osteoblasts
    E) lamellae

Answer: D
Diff: 2   Page Ref: 140

13) The canal that runs through the core of each osteon contains:
    A) cartilage and lamellae
    B) osteoclasts and osteoblasts
    C) yellow marrow and Sharpey's fibers
    D) blood vessels and nerve fibers
    E) red marrow

Answer: D
Diff: 1   Page Ref: 139

14) The small cavities in bone tissue where osteocytes are found are called:
    A) lacunae
    B) Volkmann's canals
    C) Haversian canals
    D) trabeculae
    E) lamellae

Answer: A
Diff: 1   Page Ref: 138-139

15) What kind of tissue is the forerunner of long bones in the embryo:
    A) elastic connective tissue
    B) dense fibrous connective tissue
    C) fibrocartilage
    D) hyaline cartilage
    E) loose fibrous connective tissue

Answer: D
Diff: 1   Page Ref: 140

16) Which of the following is an example of a bone that forms from fibrous membranes:
    A) the parietal bone
    B) the radius
    C) the humerus
    D) the femur
    E) the tibia

Answer: A
Diff: 3   Page Ref: 135; 145

17) The factor(s) that determine *where* bone matrix is to be remodeled is (are):
    A) sex hormones
    B) growth hormone
    C) stresses of gravity and muscle pull on the skeleton
    D) parathyroid hormone (PTH)
    E) calcium level of the blood

Answer: C
Diff: 2   Page Ref: 140

18) There are four stages in the healing of a bone fracture. Which of the following best illustrates the sequence of these stages:
    1. bony callus formation   3. fibrocartilage callus formation
    2. bone remodeling   4. hematoma formation
    A) 4, 3, 2, 1
    B) 4, 3, 1, 2
    C) 1, 2, 3, 4
    D) 1, 3, 4, 2
    E) 1, 3, 2, 4

Answer: B
Diff: 2   Page Ref: 143

19) What type of cell does parathyroid hormone (PTH) activate:
    A) osteocyte
    B) osteoblast
    C) osteoclast
    D) periosteum
    E) lacunae

Answer: C
Diff: 2   Page Ref: 140

20) A compound fracture can be described as when:
    A) the bone is crushed
    B) the broken bone ends are forced into each other
    C) the broken bone is exposed to the outside
    D) the bone is broken into many fragments
    E) adjacent bones fracture simultaneously
Answer: C
Diff: 2   Page Ref: 143

21) A bone fracture where the bone is broken into many fragments is a:
    A) compound fracture
    B) simple fracture
    C) comminuted fracture
    D) compression fracture
    E) greenstick fracture
Answer: C
Diff: 1   Page Ref: 142

22) A fracture that is common in children, whose bones have relatively more collagen in their
    matrix and are more flexible than those of adults, is a(n):
    A) impacted fracture
    B) spiral fracture
    C) depressed fracture
    D) greenstick fracture
    E) open fracture
Answer: D
Diff: 2   Page Ref: 142

23) A fracture that is common in osteoporotic bones is a(n):
    A) impacted fracture
    B) compression fracture
    C) spiral fracture
    D) depressed fracture
    E) simple fracture
Answer: B
Diff: 2   Page Ref: 142

24) The axial skeleton contains:
        1.   skull
        2.   arms and legs
        3.   ribs and sternum
        4.   vertebrae
        5.   pelvic girdles
    A) 1, 3, 4, 5
    B) 1, 3, 4
    C) 2, 5
    D) 2, 3, 4, 5
    E) 1, 2, 3, 5
Answer: B
Diff: 2   Page Ref: 145

25) The suture found between the parietal and temporal bone is the:
   A) squamous suture
   B) lambdoid suture
   C) sagittal suture
   D) coronal suture
   E) both the squamous suture and the sagittal suture

Answer: A
Diff: 2   Page Ref: 145

26) All of the following facial bones are paired except one. Which of the following is the unpaired facial bone:
   A) palatine
   B) lacrimal
   C) vomer
   D) maxillae
   E) zygomatic

Answer: C
Diff: 2   Page Ref: 145–149

27) The middle nasal conchae are part of the:
   A) maxillae
   B) sphenoid bone
   C) nasal bone
   D) vomer bone
   E) ethmoid bone

Answer: E
Diff: 2   Page Ref: 147–148

28) Which of these bones is NOT associated with the foot:
   A) talus
   B) calcaneus
   C) metatarsals
   D) tarsals
   E) metacarpals

Answer: E
Diff: 2   Page Ref: 165–166

29) The hyoid bone is unique because:
   A) it is the only bone of the body that does not directly articulate with any other bone
   B) it has an unusual shape
   C) it is covered with mucosa
   D) it has no specific function
   E) it largely consists of cartilage

Answer: A
Diff: 1   Page Ref: 149

30) The sella turcica is part of the _____ bone.
    A) parietal
    B) ethmoid
    C) sphenoid
    D) temporal
    E) frontal

Answer: C
Diff: 2   *Page Ref: 145*

31) There are _____ vertebrae in the neck region.
    A) five thoracic
    B) seven lumbar
    C) seven cervical
    D) twelve thoracic
    E) five lumbar

Answer: C
Diff: 2   *Page Ref: 150*

32) Transverse foramina are found in the:
    A) sacrum
    B) coccyx
    C) thoracic vertebrae
    D) lumbar vertebrae
    E) cervical vertebrae

Answer: E
Diff: 3   *Page Ref: 155*

33) The atlas is the:
    A) last lumbar vertebra
    B) first thoracic vertebra
    C) part of the sacrum
    D) second cervical vertebra
    E) first cervical vertebra

Answer: E
Diff: 1   *Page Ref: 155*

34) Which is the correct order of ribs, from superior to inferior:
    A) floating ribs, true ribs, false ribs
    B) floating ribs, false ribs, true ribs
    C) true ribs, false ribs, floating ribs
    D) true ribs, floating ribs, false ribs
    E) false ribs, floating ribs, true ribs

Answer: C
Diff: 2   *Page Ref: 157–158*

35) The sternum is the result of fusion of three bones called the:
   A) ischium, ilium, coccyx
   B) pubis, ischium, ilium
   C) manubrium, body, xiphoid process
   D) jugular notch, sternal angle, xiphisternal joint
   E) true ribs, manubrium, xiphoid process

Answer: C
Diff: 3   *Page Ref: 157*

36) The greater trochanter is located on the:
   A) radius
   B) humerus
   C) fibula
   D) tibia
   E) femur

Answer: E
Diff: 2   *Page Ref: 164*

37) The tailbone is the:
   A) ischium
   B) sacrum
   C) pubis
   D) coccyx
   E) patella

Answer: D
Diff: 1   *Page Ref: 157*

38) Which of the following is correct of the female pelvis when comparing it with the male pelvis:
   A) the angle of the female pubic arch is smaller
   B) the distance between the female ischial spines is greater
   C) the distance between the female ischial tuberosities is less
   D) the female iliac bones are less flared
   E) the female pelvis as a whole is deeper, and the bones are heavier and thicker

Answer: B
Diff: 3   *Page Ref: 164*

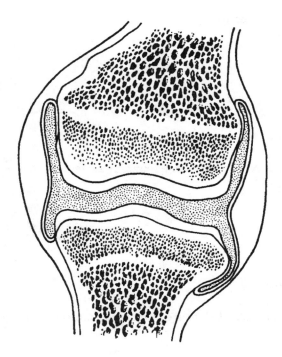

Figure 5.4

39) The type of joint shown in Figure 5.4 is:
    A) a suture
    B) a fibrous joint
    C) an amphiarthrotic joint
    D) a cartilaginous joint
    E) a synovial joint

Answer: E
Diff: 3   *Page Ref: 170–171*

40) A structure found on the femur is the:
    A) anterior crest
    B) trochlea
    C) lateral malleolus
    D) intercondylar fossa
    E) medial malleolus

Answer: D
Diff: 3   *Page Ref: 164*

41) Articulations permitting only slight degrees of movement are _____, whereas articulations permitting no movement are called _____.
    A) amphiarthroses; synarthroses
    B) synarthroses; amphiarthroses
    C) diarthroses; amphiarthroses
    D) amphiarthroses; diarthroses
    E) diarthroses; synarthroses

Answer: A
Diff: 2   *Page Ref: 166; 168–170*

42) Fingers and toes are referred to as:
   A) tarsals
   B) metacarpals
   C) phalanges
   D) metatarsals
   E) carpals

Answer: C
Diff: 2   *Page Ref: 162; 166*

43) Which of these bones is NOT a long bone found in the leg:
   A) femur
   B) patella
   C) fibula
   D) metatarsals
   E) tibia

Answer: B
Diff: 2   *Page Ref: 164–166*

44) Four of the five answers listed below are parts of the same anatomical area. Select the exception.
   A) humerus
   B) radius
   C) scapula
   D) fibula
   E) clavicle

Answer: D
Diff: 2   *Page Ref: 158–161*

45) Bone formation can be referred to as:
   A) osteoporosis
   B) rickets
   C) ossification
   D) gout
   E) osteoarthritis

Answer: C
Diff: 2   *Page Ref: 140*

True/False

1) Hematopoiesis refers to the formation of blood cells within the red marrow cavities of certain bones.

Answer: TRUE
Diff: 1   *Page Ref: 135*

2) The diaphysis of a long bone is composed of spongy bone.

Answer: FALSE
Diff: 1   *Page Ref: 135*

3) All flat bones are formed from hyaline cartilage.

Answer: FALSE
Diff: 1   *Page Ref: 135*

4) Osteoblasts respond to the parathyroid hormone (PTH).

Answer: FALSE
Diff: 2   *Page Ref: 140*

5) The master gland of the body (pituitary gland) is housed in a saddlelike depression in the temporal bone called the *sella turcica*.

Answer: FALSE
Diff: 2   *Page Ref: 145*

6) Ribs numbered 11 and 12 are true ribs because they have no anterior attachments.

Answer: FALSE
Diff: 1   *Page Ref: 158*

7) The zygomatic bones form the cheekbones.

Answer: TRUE
Diff: 1   *Page Ref: 149*

8) The spinal cord passes through the body of each vertebra.

Answer: FALSE
Diff: 1   *Page Ref: 155*

9) Most of the stress on the vertebral column occurs on the sturdiest vertebrae in the sacral region.

Answer: FALSE
Diff: 2   *Page Ref: 155*

10) In anatomical position, the lateral lower leg bone is the fibula.

Answer: TRUE
Diff: 1   *Page Ref: 165*

11) There are seven cervical, twelve thoracic, and five lumbar vertebrae.

Answer: TRUE
Diff: 2   *Page Ref: 155*

12) Spinal curvatures that are present at birth are called primary curvatures (the cervical and lumbar curvatures) and those that develop later are secondary curvatures (the thoracic and sacral curvatures).

Answer: FALSE
Diff: 2   *Page Ref: 151; 154*

13) The heaviest, strongest bone in the body is the femur.

Answer: TRUE
Diff: 1   *Page Ref: 164*

14) Fontanels allow for growth of the brain.

Answer: TRUE
Diff: 1   *Page Ref: 150*

Matching

Match the following:

1) An incomplete fracture or cracking of the bone without actual separation of the parts (common in children)
   Diff: 1   Page Ref: 142

2) Fracture where bone fragments into many pieces
   Diff: 1   Page Ref: 142

3) Fracture in which broken bone ends are forced into each other
   Diff: 1   Page Ref: 142

4) Type of fracture in which bone is crushed
   Diff: 1   Page Ref: 142

5) Type of fracture in which the broken bone portion is pressed inward
   Diff: 1   Page Ref: 142

A) impacted

B) depressed

C) compression

D) comminuted

E) greenstick

1) E   2) D   3) A   4) C   5) B

Match the following:

6) Cells that can dissolve the bony matrix
   Diff: 1   Page Ref: 140

7) Layers of calcification that are found in bone
   Diff: 1   Page Ref: 139

8) Small channels that radiate through the matrix of bone
   Diff: 1   Page Ref: 139

9) Cells that can build bony matrix
   Diff: 2   Page Ref: 140

10) Area where bone growth takes place
    Diff: 2   Page Ref: 136

A) osteoblasts

B) canaliculi

C) epiphyseal line

D) lacunae

E) osteoclasts

F) Sharpey's fibers

G) osteocytes

H) osteons

I) lamellae

J) epiphyseal plate

6) E   7) I   8) B   9) A   10) J

Match the following:

    11) Wrist joint
       Diff: 1   *Page Ref: 170–171*

    12) Shoulder joint
       Diff: 1   *Page Ref: 171–172*

    13) Elbow joint
       Diff: 1   *Page Ref: 171*

    14) Knuckle joints
       Diff: 1   *Page Ref: 171*

    15) Joint between atlas and axis
       Diff: 1   *Page Ref: 171*

A) pivot joint

B) ball–and–socket joint

C) plane joint

D) hinge joint

E) condyloid jont

F) saddle joint

11) C   12) B   13) D   14) E   15) A

Match the following:

    16) Patella
       Diff: 2   *Page Ref: 135–136*

    17) Femur
       Diff: 2   *Page Ref: 135–136*

    18) Carpals
       Diff: 2   *Page Ref: 135–136*

    19) Ulna
       Diff: 2   *Page Ref: 135–136*

    20) Atlas
       Diff: 2   *Page Ref: 135–136*

    21) Sternum
       Diff: 2   *Page Ref: 135–136*

    22) Fibula
       Diff: 2   *Page Ref: 135–136*

    23) Coxal bone
       Diff: 2   *Page Ref: 135–136*

    24) True ribs
       Diff: 2   *Page Ref: 135–136*

    25) Parietal bones
       Diff: 2   *Page Ref: 135–136*

A) irregular bone

B) long bone

C) short bone

D) flat bone

E) short and sesamoid bone

16) E	17) B	18) C	19) B	20) A	21) D
22) B	23) A	24) D	25) D		

Essay

1) Explain the five functions of the skeletal system.

   Answer: 1. Support—the skeletal system forms the body's internal structural framework. The bones of the legs act as pillars to support the body trunk when we stand, and the rib cage supports the thoracic wall.
   2. Movement—the skeletal muscles, attached to bones by tendons, use the bones as levers to move the body and its parts.
   3. Protection—bones, such as the skull, thorax, and pelvis, protect the enclosed soft body organs.
   4. Storage—fat is stored in the internal cavities of bones. Bones also serve as a storehouse for minerals, the most important being calcium and phosphorus.
   5. Hematopoiesis—blood cell formation occurs within the red marrow of certain bones.
   Diff: 2   *Page Ref: 134–135*

2) List and discuss the structures of a long bone.

   Answer: 1. Diaphysis—the shaft of the long bone: a) it is made of compact bone; b) it is covered by a fibrous connective tissue membrane, the periosteum. The periosteum is securely held to the compact bone beneath by connective tissue fibers called perforating or Sharpey's fibers; c) it contains a hollow cavity called the medullary cavity that stores adipose tissue as yellow marrow, and is the site of hematopoiesis (red blood cell formation) in infants when it contains red marrow.
   2. Epiphyses—somewhat rounded ends of the long bone: each epiphysis has an outer layer of compact bone covering an inner core of spongy bone. The external surface is covered by a layer of hyaline cartilage, instead of a periosteum, called articular cartilage. This provides for a smooth, gliding joint.
   3. Epiphyseal line/plate—the junction between the epiphyses and the diaphysis. During growth years is made of hyaline cartilage and is called the epiphyseal plate. It causes the lengthwise growth of the bone. By the end of puberty, long bones stop lengthening when the plate has been replaced by bone. It now appears as a thin bony ridge and is called the epiphyseal line.
   Diff: 1   *Page Ref: 135–136*

3) List and explain the steps in the repair process of a simple fracture.

Answer: Step 1 is hematoma formation. A hematoma, or bloodfilled swelling, forms when bone breaks and blood vessels rupture. Bone cells are deprived of nutrition and die.

Step 2 is fibrocartilaginous callus formation. The site of damage experiences growth of new capillaries into the clotted blood and disposal of dead tissue by phagocytes. Connective tissue cells of various types form a mass of repair tissue called fibrocartilage callus. This fibrocartilage callus contains several elements: some cartilage matrix, some bony matrix, and collagen fibers. This fibrocartilage callus acts to splint the broken bone, closing the gap.

Step 3 is bony callus formation. As more osteoblasts and osteoclasts migrate into the area and multiply, fibrocartilage is gradually replaced by a callus of spongy bone (the bony callus).

Step 4 is bone remodeling. Over the next few months, bony callus is remodeled in response to the mechanical stresses placed on it, so that it forms a strong, permanent patch at the fracture site.

Diff: 2   *Page Ref: 143*

4) Discuss the two factors that cause bone remodeling throughout life.

Answer: 1. Calcium levels in the bloodstream determine when bone is to be broken down. When calcium levels in the bloodstream drop below normal, the parathyroid glands produce and release parathyroid hormone (PTH) into the blood. PTH activates osteoclasts (giant bone-destroying cells in bone) to break down bone and release calcium into the blood. Conversely, when calcium levels in the bloodstream are too high, osteoblasts (bone-forming cells in bone) are activated and calcium is deposited in bone matrix as hard calcium salts.

2. Stresses of muscle pull and gravity acting on the skeleton determine where bone matrix is to be broken down or formed so that the skeleton can remain strong for as long as possible. Long bones grow in length and in thickness as the body increases in size and as a result of the activity of bulky muscles. At these sites, osteoblasts (bone-forming cells) lay down new matrix and become trapped within it. Once they are trapped, they become osteocytes or true bone cells.

Diff: 3   *Page Ref: 140*

5) Define fontanel and discuss its functions. Identify the four fontanels in the infant and cite their locations.

Answer: Fontanels are fibrous membranes connecting the cranial bones of the infant skull. They serve two functions: they allow the fetal skull to be compressed slightly during childbirth and they allow the infant brain to grow during the later part of pregnancy and early infancy. The four fontanels are:

1. Anterior fontanel—this is the largest fontanel and is located between the pareital bones and the frontal bone. It is diamond-shaped.

2. Mastoid fontanel—superior to the posterior part of the temporal bone on a lateral view of the cranium.

3. Posterior fontanel—smaller, triangular fontanel located posteriorly on the lateral view of the cranium.

4. Sphenoidal fontanel—superior to the anterior part of the temporal bone on the lateral view of the cranium.

Diff: 3   *Page Ref: 149-150*

6) List some of the features of a female pelvis that make it different from a male pelvis.

Answer: The female pelvis:
a. has a larger and more circular inlet.
b. is shallower than the male pelvis.
c. has lighter and thinner bones.
d. has a shorter and less curved sacrum.
e. has a more rounded pubic arch.
f. has shorter ischial spines that are also farther apart.

Diff: 2   *Page Ref: 164*

7) If 6–year–old Sarah fell and broke her femur, damaging the proximal epiphyseal plate, what might she expect as she grows older? What is an epiphyseal plate and why is it significant to this situation?

Answer: The epiphyseal plate is a flat plate of hyaline cartilage seen in young growing bone. Epiphyseal plates cause the lengthwise growth of long bone. Since this child is still growing and has not completed puberty, she may expect impaired growth in that one epiphyseal plate. Lucky for Sarah, there is an epiphyseal plate located at both the distal and proximal ends of the femur. The healthy distal plate can continue to grow.

Diff: 3   *Page Ref: 136; 140*

8) Differentiate the roles of osteoclasts, osteoblasts, and osteocytes in bone.

Answer: 1. Osteoclasts are giant bone–destroying cells that break down bone matrix and release calcium ions into the blood. They are activiated by a hormone called parathyroid hormone (PTH).
2. Osteoblasts are bone–forming cells. They add bone tissue to growing bones.
3. Osteocytes are mature bone cells. In their former lives, they were osteoblasts that laid down bone matrix, but became trapped in it.

Diff: 2   *Page Ref: 137; 140*

9) Explain how atlas and axis are different from other vertebrae. Discuss the roles they play in the body.

Answer: 1. Unlike all other vertebra, atlas (C1) has no body. Axis (C2) has a large process called the dens or odontoid process.
2. The structural differences of these two vertebrae allow you to rotate your head from side to side to indicate "no." The joint between these two vertebrae is a pivot joint.

Diff: 2   *Page Ref: 155*

10) Differentiate among the three types of joints based on structural and functional classification. Provide examples of each type of joint.

Answer: 1. Synarthroses are immovable joints. These joints are structurally classified as fibrous joints since the bones are united by fibrous tissue. Skull sutures are one example of a fibrous joint.
2. Amphiarthroses are slightly movable joints. These joints are structurally classified as cartilaginous joints since the bone ends are connected by cartilage. The pubic symphysis and intervertebral joints are two examples.
3. Diathroses are freely movable joints. These joints are structurally classified as synovial joints since the articulating bone ends are separated by a joint cavity containing synovial fluid. There are many examples of synovial joints, including the elbow, knee, and shoulder.

Diff: 3   *Page Ref: 166; 168–169*

Short Answer

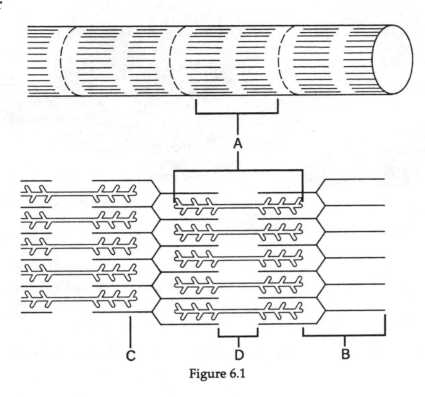

Figure 6.1

Using Figure 6.1, match the following:

1) The I band within a skeletal muscle fiber is indicated by letter _____.

   Answer: B
   Diff: 1   Page Ref: 188

2) The A band within a skeletal muscle fiber is indicated by letter _____.

   Answer: A
   Diff: 2   Page Ref: 188

3) The lighter central area of the A band is indicated by letter _____.

   Answer: D
   Diff: 2   Page Ref: 188

4) The thin filament is indicated by letter _____.

   Answer: C
   Diff: 2   Page Ref: 188

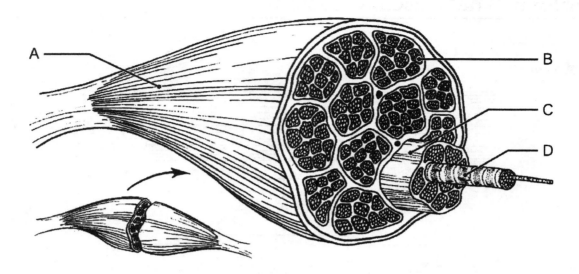

Figure 6.2

Using Figure 6.2, match the following:

5) The connective tissue "overcoat" that wraps the entire muscle is indicated by letter _____.

Answer: A
Diff: 1   Page Ref: 185

6) The connective tissue that wraps a fascicle, or bundle of muscle fibers, is indicated by letter _____.

Answer: C
Diff: 2   Page Ref: 185

7) The muscle fiber is indicated by letter _____.

Answer: D
Diff: 1   Page Ref: 185

8) The endomysium that wraps individual muscle fibers is indicated by letter _____.

Answer: B
Diff: 1   Page Ref: 185

Fill in the blank or provide a short answer:

9) Only _____ muscle cells are cylindrical and multinucleated.

Answer: skeletal
Diff: 1   Page Ref: 184

10) The muscle tissue that normally exhibits voluntary contractions is _____ muscle.

Answer: skeletal
Diff: 1   Page Ref: 185

11) Only _____ muscle cells possess intercalated discs.

Answer: cardiac
Diff: 1   Page Ref: 186

12) Skeletal muscle is often attached to bone by strong, cordlike structures called _____.

Answer: tendons
Diff: 1   Page Ref: 185

13) The _____ zone of a sarcomere contains no actin filaments while the skeletal muscle is at rest (noncontractile state).

Answer: H
Diff: 1   Page Ref: 187; 189

14) The heads of the myosin myofilaments are called _____ when they link the thick and thin filaments together during skeletal muscle contraction.

Answer: cross bridges
Diff: 1   Page Ref: 189

15) The gap between the motor neuron and the muscle fiber it supplies at the neuromuscular junction is called the _____.

Answer: synaptic cleft
Diff: 1   Page Ref: 189

16) When a skeletal muscle is fully contracted, the _____ are closer to the thick filaments.

Answer: Z discs
Diff: 2   Page Ref: 192

17) The only energy source that can be used to directly power muscle activity is _____.

Answer: ATP
Diff: 2   Page Ref: 195

18) A smooth, sustained contraction is called _____.

Answer: tetanus
Diff: 1   Page Ref: 194

19) The _____ of a muscle is attached to the immovable or less movable bone.

Answer: origin
Diff: 1   Page Ref: 198–199

20) The movement that is commonly seen in a ball-in-socket joint, that includes a combination of flexion, extension, abduction, and adduction, is called _____.

Answer: circumduction
Diff: 2   Page Ref: 199

21) The muscle that has the major responsibility for causing a particular movement is the _____.

Answer: prime mover
Diff: 1   Page Ref: 202

22) The arrangement of fascicles in orbicularis oris is _____.

Answer: circular
Diff: 1   Page Ref: 204; 207

23) The muscle referred to as the "smiling" muscle because it raised the corners of the mouth upward is the _____.

Answer: zygomaticus
Diff: 2   Page Ref: 207

24) The _____ muscle runs deep to the external oblique muscle.

Answer: internal oblique
Diff: 1   Page Ref: 209

25) The quadriceps femoris muscle group is composed of the three vastus muscles and the _____ muscle.

Answer: rectus femoris
Diff: 2   Page Ref: 214

26) An inherited disease that causes muscles to degenerate and atrophy is known as _____.

Answer: muscular dystrophy
Diff: 2   Page Ref: 221

Multiple Choice

1) Muscle tissue that has involuntary regulation of contraction is:
    A) cardiac muscle only
    B) smooth muscle only
    C) skeletal muscle only
    D) cardiac muscle and smooth muscle
    E) cardiac muscle and skeletal muscle

Answer: D
Diff: 2   Page Ref: 185–186

2) The muscle tissue type that consists of single, very long, cylindrical, multinucleate cells with very obvious striations is:
    A) cardiac muscle only
    B) smooth muscle only
    C) skeletal muscle only
    D) cardiac and smooth muscle
    E) cardiac and skeletal muscle

Answer: C
Diff: 2   Page Ref: 183–185

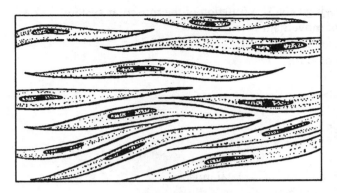

Figure 6.3

3) The type of muscle tissue pictured in Figure 6.3 is:
    A) skeletal muscle
    B) voluntary
    C) striated
    D) found only in the heart
    E) smooth muscle

Answer: E
Diff: 2   Page Ref: 184

4) The plasma membrane of a muscle cell is called the:
    A) sarcolemma
    B) sarcomere
    C) myofilament
    D) sarcoplasm
    E) sarcoplasmic reticulum

Answer: A
Diff: 3   Page Ref: 187

5) Which of the following does not describe cardiac muscle tissue:
    A) uninucleate
    B) striations
    C) involuntary
    D) rhythmic contractions
    E) attached to bones

Answer: E
Diff: 2   Page Ref: 186

6) What type of membrane wraps a fascicle:
    A) endomysium
    B) epimysium
    C) aponeuroses
    D) perimysium
    E) tendons

Answer: D
Diff: 2   Page Ref: 185

7) Which of the following is NOT a function of the muscular system:
  A) production of movement
  B) maintenance of posture
  C) stabilization of joints
  D) generation of heat
  E) hematopoiesis

Answer: E
Diff: 1   Page Ref: 187

8) A sarcomere is:
  A) the nonfunctional unit of skeletal muscle
  B) the contractile unit between two Z discs
  C) the area between two intercalated discs
  D) the wavy lines on the cell, as seen in a microscope
  E) a compartment in a myofilament

Answer: B
Diff: 2   Page Ref: 187

9) Which one of the following is composed of myosin protein:
  A) thick filaments
  B) thin filaments
  C) all myofilaments
  D) Z discs
  E) light bands

Answer: A
Diff: 2   Page Ref: 187–189

10) Place these structures of the skeletal muscle in order from largest to smallest:
  1. fascicle
  2. myofilament
  3. muscle fiber (cell)
  4. myofibril
  5. sarcomere
  A) 1, 3, 4, 5, 2
  B) 1, 4, 3, 2, 5
  C) 2, 5, 4, 3, 1
  D) 3, 1, 2, 4, 5
  E) 3, 2, 5, 4, 1

Answer: A
Diff: 3   Page Ref: 185–189

11) The axon terminals of a nerve cell and the sarcolemma of a skeletal muscle cell join at the:
  A) motor unit
  B) neuromuscular junction
  C) synaptic cleft
  D) action potential
  E) myofibril

Answer: B
Diff: 3   Page Ref: 189

12) Which one of the following functions do calcium ions perform during skeletal muscle
    contraction:
    A) increase the action potential transmitted along the sarcolemma
    B) release the inhibition on Z discs
    C) expose myosin binding sites on the actin
    D) cause ATP binding to actin
    E) bind to regulatory proteins on the myosin filaments, changing both their shape and their
       position on the thick filaments

Answer: C
Diff: 2　　　*Page Ref: 193*

13) The mechanical force of contraction is generated by:
    A) shortening of the thick filaments
    B) shortening of the thin filaments
    C) a sliding of thin filaments past thick ones
    D) the "accordian-like" folding of thin and thick filaments
    E) the temporary disappearance of thin filaments

Answer: C
Diff: 2　　　*Page Ref: 192*

14) Acetylcholine is:
    A) an ion pump on the postsynaptic membrane
    B) a source of energy for muscle contraction
    C) a component of thick myofilaments
    D) an oxygen-binding protein
    E) a neurotransmitter that stimulates skeletal muscle

Answer: E
Diff: 1　　　*Page Ref: 189*

15) The gap between the axon terminal of a motor neuron and the sarcolemma of a skeletal muscle
    cell is called the:
    A) motor unit
    B) sarcomere
    C) neuromuscular junction
    D) synaptic cleft
    E) cross bridge

Answer: D
Diff: 2　　　*Page Ref: 189*

16) Neurotransmitters are released upon stimulation from a nerve impulse by the:
    A) myofibrils
    B) motor unit
    C) thick filaments
    D) axon terminals of the motor neuron
    E) sarcolemma of the muscle cell

Answer: D
Diff: 2　　　*Page Ref: 189*

17) An elaborate and specialized network of membranes in skeletal muscle cells that function in calcium storage is the:
   A) sarcolemma
   B) mitochondria
   C) intermediate filament network
   D) myofibrillar network
   E) sarcoplasmic reticulum

Answer: E
Diff: 1   Page Ref: 189

18) During skeletal muscle contraction, myosin cross bridges attach to active sites of:
   A) myosin filaments
   B) actin filaments
   C) Z discs
   D) thick filaments
   E) the H zone

Answer: B
Diff: 1   Page Ref: 192

19) The major function of the sarcoplasmic reticulum in skeletal muscle contraction is to:
   A) make and store phosphocreatine
   B) synthesize actin and myosin myofilaments
   C) provide a source of myosin for the contraction process
   D) regulate intracellular calcium concentration
   E) store ATP

Answer: D
Diff: 2   Page Ref: 189

20) The striations that give skeletal muscle its characteristic striped appearance are produced, for the most part, by:
   A) a difference in the thickness of the sarcolemma
   B) the arrangement of myofilaments
   C) the sarcoplasmic reticulum
   D) the T tubules
   E) the "cocked" positions of the heads of the thick filaments

Answer: B
Diff: 2   Page Ref: 189

21) Which of these events must occur first to trigger the skeletal muscle to generate an action potential and contract:
   A) sodium ions rush into the cell
   B) acetylcholine (ACh) causes temporary permeability to sodium
   C) diffusion of potassium ions out of the cell
   D) operation of the sodium-potassium pump
   E) acetylcholinesterase (AchE) breaks down acetylcholine (ACh)

Answer: B
Diff: 3   Page Ref: 189-190

22) A skeletal muscle twitch differs from a tetanic contraction in that:
   A) the tetanic contraction is considered abnormal, while the twitch is a normal muscle response
   B) the tetanic contraction is caused by a single stimulus, while the twitch is caused by very rapid multiple stimuli
   C) the muscle twitch is prolonged and continuous while a tetanic contraction is brief and "jerky"
   D) the muscle twitch occurs only in small muscles while a tetanic contraction occurs in large muscle groups
   E) the muscle twitch is a brief and "jerky" movement, while the tetanic contraction is prolonged and continuous

Answer: E
Diff: 3   Page Ref: 194

23) Creatine phosphate (CP) functions within the muscle cells by:
   A) forming a temporary chemical compound with myosin
   B) forming a chemical compound with actin
   C) inducing a conformational change in the myofilaments
   D) storing energy that will be transferred to ADP to resynthesize ATP as needed
   E) storing energy that will be transferred to ATP to resynthesize ADP as needed

Answer: D
Diff: 2   Page Ref: 195

24) The condition of skeletal muscle fatigue can be best explained by:
   A) the all–or–none law
   B) the inability to generate sufficient quantities of ATP due to feedback regulation of synthesis
   C) insufficient intracellular quantities of ATP due to excessive consumption
   D) a total lack of ATP
   E) inadequate numbers of mitochondria

Answer: C
Diff: 1   Page Ref: 195–196

25) Which one of the following muscle actions would NOT be classified as an ISOTONIC contraction:
   A) pushing against a stationary wall
   B) lifting a glass of water to your mouth
   C) writing a letter
   D) tying your shoe
   E) throwing a ball

Answer: A
Diff: 1   Page Ref: 197

26) Anaerobic glycolysis occurs without:
   A) ATP
   B) oxygen
   C) lactic acid
   D) carbon dioxide
   E) glucose

Answer: B
Diff: 3   Page Ref: 195

27) Which of these pathways to regenerate ATP during muscle activity is the fastest:
    A) direct phosphorylation of ADP by creatine phosphate
    B) aerobic respiration
    C) anaerobic glycolysis and lactic acid formation
    D) oxidative phosphorylation
    E) both aerobic respiration and anaerobic glycolysis

Answer: C
Diff: 3   Page Ref: 195

28) The insertion of the gluteus maximus is the:
    A) sacrum
    B) tibia
    C) ilium
    D) calcaneus
    E) femur

Answer: E
Diff: 2   Page Ref: 211

29) Which of the following muscles closes the jaw:
    A) the buccinator
    B) the masseter
    C) the frontalis
    D) the sternocleidomastoid
    E) the masseter and the temporalis

Answer: E
Diff: 2   Page Ref: 207

30) Sandra is playing the piano for her recital. Which muscle is not involved in the movement of her hands and/or fingers:
    A) flexor carpi radialis
    B) flexor carpi ulnaris
    C) extensor digitorum
    D) extensor digitorum longus
    E) extensor carpi radialis

Answer: D
Diff: 2   Page Ref: 219

31) Which of the following muscles inserts on the calcaneus:
    A) the semitendinosus
    B) the sartorius
    C) the tibialis anterior
    D) the soleus
    E) the iliopsoas

Answer: D
Diff: 2   Page Ref: 214; 219

32) Which one of the following does NOT compress the abdomen:
   A) internal oblique
   B) external oblique
   C) transversus abdominis
   D) latissimus dorsi
   E) rectus abdominis

Answer: D
Diff: 2   Page Ref: 209

33) A muscle located on the ventral (anterior) side of the body is the:
   A) pectoralis major
   B) occipitalis
   C) gastrocnemius
   D) gluteus medius
   E) latissimus dorsi

Answer: A
Diff: 1   Page Ref: 208

34) A nursing infant develops a powerful sucking muscle that adults also use for whistling or blowing a trumpet called the:
   A) platysma
   B) masseter
   C) zygomaticus
   D) buccinator
   E) temporalis

Answer: D
Diff: 1   Page Ref: 207

35) Which of these muscles is not responsibile for flexion or extension of the arm?
   A) biceps brachii
   B) triceps brachii
   C) brachialis
   D) platysma
   E) latissimus dorsi

Answer: D
Diff: 3   Page Ref: 210; 211

36) A muscle group that works with and assists the action of a prime mover is a(n):
   A) antagonist only
   B) fixator only
   C) synergist only
   D) antagonist and synergist
   E) antagonist and fixator

Answer: C
Diff: 1   Page Ref: 202

37) Which of the following muscles is not involved in dorsiflexion and/or plantar flexion of the foot:

    A) gastrocnemius
    B) tibialis anterior
    C) extensor digitorum longus
    D) soleus
    E) iliopsoas

Answer: E
Diff: 3   Page Ref: 212; 214

38) Which one of the following is the action of the orbicularis oris:

    A) closes, purses, and protrudes the lips
    B) pulls the lower lip down and back
    C) draws the eyebrows together
    D) allows blinking, squinting, and various other protective mechanisms for the eye
    E) closes the jaw

Answer: A
Diff: 1   Page Ref: 207

39) Paralysis of which of the following would make an individual unable to flex the thigh:

    A) biceps femoris
    B) vastus medialis
    C) vastus lateralis
    D) vastus intermedius
    E) iliopsoas and rectus femoris

Answer: E
Diff: 2   Page Ref: 212; 214

40) Which one of the following muscles is involved in abduction of the arm at the shoulder joint:

    A) deltoid
    B) biceps brachii
    C) triceps brachii
    D) latissimus dorsi
    E) pectoralis major

Answer: A
Diff: 2   Page Ref: 210

41) Which of the following muscles adducts the thigh:

    A) peroneus muscles
    B) gluteus maximus
    C) sartorius
    D) quadriceps group
    E) adductor muscles

Answer: E
Diff: 1   Page Ref: 214

42) While doing "jumping jacks" during an exercise class, your arms and legs move laterally away from the midline of your body. This motion is called:
    A) extension
    B) flexion
    C) abduction
    D) adduction
    E) circumduction
Answer: C
Diff: 1   Page Ref: 199

43) Which of the following muscles are antagonists:
    A) biceps brachii and triceps brachii
    B) bicpes femoris and biceps brachii
    C) vastus medialis and vastus lateralis
    D) masseter and temporalis
    E) gastrocnemius and soleus
Answer: A
Diff: 3   Page Ref: 211

44) Paralysis of which of the following would make an individual unable to flex the knee:
    A) hamstring muscle group
    B) gluteal muscle group
    C) gastrocnemius
    D) sartorius
    E) iliopsoas
Answer: A
Diff: 3   Page Ref: 214

45) Which one of the following is NOT a criteria generally used in naming muscles:
    A) relative size of the muscle
    B) number of origins of the muscle
    C) shape of the muscle
    D) method of attachment of the muscle to bone
    E) action of the muscle
Answer: D
Diff: 2   Page Ref: 204

True/False

1) Skeletal muscle is considered involuntary because it is the only type of muscle usually subject to conscious control.
Answer: FALSE
Diff: 1   Page Ref: 183; 185

2) The epimysium covers individual muscle fibers.
Answer: FALSE
Diff: 1   Page Ref: 185

3) Skeletal muscles need nerve stimulation for contraction to occur.
Answer: TRUE
Diff: 1   Page Ref: 189

4) A nerve cell and all the muscle cells that it stimulates are referred to as a motor unit.

Answer: TRUE
Diff: 1   Page Ref: 189

5) A contraction in which a skeletal muscle does not shorten but its tension increases is called isometric.

Answer: TRUE
Diff: 1   Page Ref: 197

6) Cardiac muscle fibers are relatively short, tapering cells within a single centrally located nucleus.

Answer: FALSE
Diff: 1   Page Ref: 186

7) The neurotransmitter used by the nervous system to activate skeletal muscle cells is acetylcholine.

Answer: TRUE
Diff: 1   Page Ref: 189

8) Thick filaments are made of a protein called actin.

Answer: FALSE
Diff: 1   Page Ref: 189

9) One of the important functions of skeletal muscle is to generate heat.

Answer: TRUE
Diff: 1   Page Ref: 187

10) Lactic acid results from aerobic respiration.

Answer: FALSE
Diff: 2   Page Ref: 195

11) A sustained partial contraction of skeletal muscle is called muscle tone.

Answer: TRUE
Diff: 1   Page Ref: 197

12) An aponeurosis is a ropelike piece of muscle fascia that forms indirect connections to muscles of the leg.

Answer: FALSE
Diff: 1   Page Ref: 185

13) A muscle twitch results when the muscle is stimulated so rapidly that no evidence of relaxation is seen.

Answer: FALSE
Diff: 2   Page Ref: 194

14) The effect of the neurotransmitter on the muscle cell membrane is to temporarily modify its permeability of ions such as Na^+ and K^+.

Answer: TRUE
Diff: 2   Page Ref: 189–190

15) When a muscle fiber contracts, the I bands diminish in size, the H zones disappear, and the A bands move closer together but do not diminish in length.

Answer: TRUE
Diff: 2   *Page Ref: 192*

16) The insertion of the biceps brachii muscle is on the radius.

Answer: FALSE
Diff: 2   *Page Ref: 211*

17) A prime mover of the arm that acts in adduction is the deltoid.

Answer: FALSE
Diff: 1   *Page Ref: 210*

18) The deepest muscle of the abdominal wall is the transversus abdominis.

Answer: TRUE
Diff: 2   *Page Ref: 209*

19) Dorsiflexion and plantar flexion are synergistic actions.

Answer: FALSE
Diff: 1   *Page Ref: 202*

20) Plantar flexion at the ankle joint is accomplished by the tibialis anterior muscle.

Answer: FALSE
Diff: 2   *Page Ref: 214*

21) The bicpes brachii muscle is named for the two heads that orginiate from the shoulder girdle.

Answer: TRUE
Diff: 2   *Page Ref: 211*

22) There are 206 skeletal muscles in the human body.

Answer: FALSE
Diff: 1   *Page Ref: 198*

23) Supination and pronation refer to up and down movements of the foot at the ankle.

Answer: FALSE
Diff: 2   *Page Ref: 202*

Matching

Match the following:

1) The distance between two Z discs

Diff: 2   *Page Ref: 187–188*

2) Otherwise known as thick filaments

Diff: 2   *Page Ref: 189*

3) Contains only the actin filaments

Diff: 2   *Page Ref: 187–188*

4) Both actin and myosin are found in this band

Diff: 1   *Page Ref: 187–188*

5) The type of filament that is studded with myosin heads

Diff: 1   *Page Ref: 189*

6) Tiny contractile unit that shortens during muscle contraction

Diff: 2   *Page Ref: 187; 192*

7) Actin filaments are anchored to these disclike membranes

Diff: 1   *Page Ref: 189*

8) Lighter central portion of the A band

Diff: 2   *Page Ref: 187*

A) sarcomere

B) myosin filaments

C) A band

D) I band

E) Z discs

F) H zone

G) actin filaments

1) A	2) B	3) D	4) C	5) B	6) A
7) E	8) F				

Match the following:

9) Serves as the actual "go" signal for muscle contraction

   Diff: 2   Page Ref: 193

10) Neurotransmitter substance released at motor end plates by the motor neuron

   Diff: 2   Page Ref: 189

11) Normally stored in the sarcoplasmic reticulum

   Diff: 2   Page Ref: 189

12) A metabolic pathway that produces water, carbon dioxide, and ATP, and provides for a large amount of ATP per glucose because oxygen is used

   Diff: 3   Page Ref: 195

13) A reserve, high–energy compound used to convert ADP to ATP by the transfer of a high–energy phosphate group

   Diff: 2   Page Ref: 195

14) Destroys acetylcholine (ACh)

   Diff: 2   Page Ref: 190

A) calcium ions

B) aerobic respiration

C) anaerobic respiration

D) creatine phosphate

E) sodium ions

F) potassium ions

G) enzymes

H) acetylcholine

9) A   10) H   11) A   12) B   13) D   14) G

Match the following:

15) Type of movement that decreases the angle of the joint

   Diff: 2   Page Ref: 199

16) Type of movement that results when the forearm rotates laterally so that the palm faces anteriorly

   Diff: 2   Page Ref: 202

17) The movement of a limb toward the body midline

   Diff: 2   Page Ref: 199

A) abduction

B) pronation

C) adduction

D) flexion

E) rotation

F) extension

G) supination

18) Type of movement that increases the angle of the joint

Diff: 2   Page Ref: 199

19) The movement of a bone around its longitudinal axis

Diff: 2   Page Ref: 199

20) The movement of a limb away from the body midline

Diff: 2   Page Ref: 199

21) Type of movement that results when the forearm rotates medially so the palm faces posteriorly

Diff: 2   Page Ref: 202

22) Primary action of the deltoid

Diff: 2   Page Ref: 210

23) Primary action of the adductor muscles

Diff: 2   Page Ref: 214

24) Primary action of the erector spinae

Diff: 2   Page Ref: 210

25) Primary action of the rectus abdominis

Diff: 2   Page Ref: 209

15) D	16) G	17) C	18) F	19) E	20) A
21) B	22) A	23) C	24) F	25) D	

Essay

1) Compare skeletal, smooth, and cardiac muscles as to their body location, microscopic anatomy, regulation of contraction, speed of contraction, and rhythmicity.

   Answer: Body location—skeletal muscle is attached to bones or to skin (some facial muscles); cardiac muscle is located in the walls of the heart; smooth muscle is found in the walls of hollow visceral organs (other than the heart).
   Microscopic anatomy—skeletal muscle consists of very long, cylindrical, multinucleated cells with very obvious striations; cardiac muscle consists of branching chains of cells that are uninucleated and possess striations; smooth muscle consists of single fusiform uninucleated cells that lack striations.
   Regulation of contraction—skeletal muscle is voluntary via nervous system controls, but this normal voluntary control can be overridden by involuntary reflex arcs (as explained in later chapters); cardiac muscle is involuntary via the heart pacemaker, nervous system controls, and hormones; smooth muscle is involuntary via nervous system controls, hormones, other chemicals, and stretching.
   Speed of contraction—skeletal muscle is slow to fast; cardiac muscle is slow; smooth muscle is the slowest.
   Rhythmicity—skeletal muscle is arrhythmic; cardiac muscle is rhythmic; smooth muscle is sometimes rhythmic.

   Diff: 3   *Page Ref: 183–186*

2) Describe the events that occur from the time that a motor neuron releases acetylcholine at the neuromuscular junction until muscle cell contraction occurs.

   Answer: Acetylcholine is released, which diffuses through the synaptic cleft and attaches to receptors on the sarcolemma. The sarcolemma permeability to sodium ions increases briefly, causing sodium ions to rush into the muscle cell, which changes the electrical conditions of the resting sarcolemma. An action potential is initiated and sweeps over the entire sarcolemma. Calcium ions are released from storage areas inside the sarcoplasmic reticulum of the muscle cell. They attach to the myofilaments, which triggers the sliding of the myofilaments and causes a muscle cell contraction.

   Diff: 3   *Page Ref: 189–192*

3) List the seven criteria that are used in naming muscles and give an example of each.

   Answer: 1. Direction of the muscle fibers (e.g., external oblique)
   2. Relative size of the muscle (e.g., maximus, minimus, longus)
   3. Location of the muscle (e.g., temporalis, frontalis)
   4. Number of origins (e.g., biceps, triceps, quadriceps)
   5. Location of the muscle's origin and insertion (e.g., the sternocleidomastoid muscle has its origin on the sternum [sterno] and clavicle [cleido] and inserts on the mastoid process of the temporal bone)
   6. Shape of the muscle (e.g., the deltoid muscle is roughly triangular—deltoid means "triangular")
   7. Action of the muscle (e.g., the adductor muscles of the thigh all bring about its adduction, and the extensor muscles of the wrist all extend the wrist)

   Diff: 3   *Page Ref: 202; 204*

4) What is the effect of aging on skeletal muscles?

Answer: With aging, the amount of connective tissue in muscle increases and the amount of skeletal muscle tissue decreases, thus the muscles become stringier (more sinewy). Since skeletal muscle represents a larger portion of body weight, it begins to decline in elderly persons as this normal loss of muscle mass occurs. Another result of the loss in muscle mass is a decrease in muscle strength—strength decreases by about 50% by the age of 80. Regular exercise can help offset the effects of aging on the muscular system, and frail elders who begin to "pump iron" can rebuild muscle mass and significantly increase their functional strength.

Diff: 3   *Page Ref: 221*

5) Explain the steps in the sliding filament theory of muscle contraction, following the spreading of an action potential along the sarcolemma.

Answer: An action potential triggers the sarcoplasmic reticulum to release calcium ions into the sarcoplasm of the muscle cell. The calcium ions bind to regulatory proteins on the actin filaments, changing both their shape and their position on the actin filaments. This action allows myosin receptor sites on the thin actin filaments to become exposed. The myosin heads attach to the myosin binding sites on the actin filaments. Energized by ATP, the myosin heads swivel toward the center of the sarcomere, attaching and detaching several times. In the process the thin actin filaments are pulled toward the center of the sarcomere. As this event occurs simultaneously in sarcomeres throughout the cell, the muscle cell shortens. When the action potential ends, the calcium ions are reabsorbed back into the sarcoplasmic reticulum storage areas, causing the regulatory proteins to resume their original shape and position. Since the myosin heads now have nothing to attach to, the muscle cell relaxes and returns to its original length.

Diff: 3   *Page Ref: 192–193*

6) Fascicle arrangements produce skeletal muscles with different structures and functional properties, and determine their individual range of motion and power. List the seven different fascicle arrangements of human skeletal muscles and give a specific example of each:

Answer: 1. Circular—orbicularis oris, orbicularis oculi
2. Convergent—pectoralis major
3. Parallel—sartorius
4. Unipennate—extensor digitorum longus
5. Multipennate—deltoid
6. Fusiform—biceps brachii
7. Bipennate—rectus femoris

Diff: 3   *Page Ref: 204–206*

7) List the "five golden rules" of gross skeletal muscle activity.

Answer: 1. With few exceptions, all muscles cross at least one joint.
2. Typically, the bulk of the muscle lies proximal to the joint crossed.
3. All muscles have at least two attachments: the origin and the insertion.
4. Muscles can only pull: they never push.
5. During contraction, the muscle insertion moves toward the origin.

Diff: 3   *Page Ref: 198*

8) Explain how isometric and isotonic contractions differ, using examples of each.

Answer: 1. Isometric contractions are contractions in which the muscles do not shorten. An example of an isometric contraction is pushing against a wall with bent elbows. The muscles cannot shorten since the wall doesn't move.

2. Isotonic contractions occur when muscles shorten and movement occurs due to the sliding of the myofilaments. Flexion and extension of the arm are just two examples of isotonic contractions.

Diff: 2   *Page Ref: 197*

9) Explain the difference between a motor unit and a neuromuscular junction.

Answer: 1. The motor unit is the one neuron and all of the skeletal muscle cells it stimulates.

2. The neuromuscular junction occurs between the axon terminals of one neuron and the sarcolemma of a skeletal muscle cell.

Diff: 2   *Page Ref: 189*

10) Explain how muscle movements mature in a baby, using examples of each.

Answer: 1. Muscle development proceeds in a cephalic/caudal direction. For instance, babies can raise their heads before they can walk.

2. Muscle control proceeds in a proximal/distal direction. For instance, babies can perform gross movements like wave "bye-bye" before they can use the pincher grasp to pick up a pin.

Diff: 2   *Page Ref: 221*

Short Answer

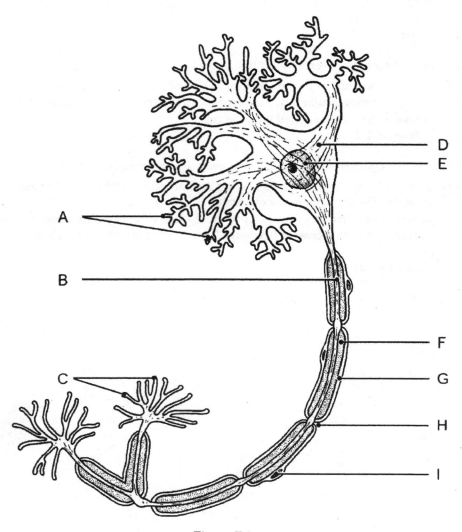

Figure 7.1

Using Figure 7.1, identify the following:

1) The neural processes that convey incoming messages toward the cell body are indicated by letter _____.

Answer: A
Diff: 2   *Page Ref:* 232–233

2) The metabolic center of the neuron is indicated by letter _____.

Answer: D
Diff: 2   *Page Ref:* 232–233

3) The axon terminals are indicated by letter _____.

Answer: C
Diff: 1   Page Ref: 232–233

4) The axon is indicated by letter _____.

Answer: B
Diff: 1   Page Ref: 232–233

5) The gaps between Schwann cells are indicated by letter _____.

Answer: H
Diff: 2   Page Ref: 232–234

6) The nucleus of the neuron is indicated by letter _____.

Answer: E
Diff: 1   Page Ref: 232–233

Fill in the blank or provide a short answer:

7) The autonomic nervous system is also referred to as the _____ nervous system since it controls activities of smooth and cardiac muscles and glands.

Answer: involuntary
Diff: 1   Page Ref: 230

8) _____ cells form the myelin sheaths around nerve fibers in the PNS.

Answer: Schwann
Diff: 1   Page Ref: 232

9) That part of the Peripheral Nervous System (PNS) that is voluntary and conducts impulses from the Central Nervous System (CNS) to the skeletal muscles is the _____ nervous system.

Answer: somatic
Diff: 2   Page Ref: 230

10) Cells found in the CNS that cling to neurons and anchor them to blood vessels are called _____.

Answer: astrocytes
Diff: 1   Page Ref: 230–231

11) The gaps between Schwann cells found at regular intervals in peripheral system neurons are called _____.

Answer: nodes of Ranvier
Diff: 1   Page Ref: 232; 234

12) Myelinated regions of the CNS are referred to as _____ matter.

Answer: white
Diff: 1   Page Ref: 234

13) Bundles of nerve fibers (neuron processes) running through the CNS are called _____, whereas in the PNS they are called _____.

Answer: tracts; nerves
Diff: 2   Page Ref: 234

14) The cell bodies of the _____ neurons are always located within the CNS.

Answer: motor
Diff: 2   *Page Ref: 236*

15) Neurons with two processes, an axon and a dendrite, are structurally classified as _____ neurons.

Answer: bipolar
Diff: 1   *Page Ref: 237*

16) All motor and association neurons are classified structurally as _____ neurons.

Answer: multipolar
Diff: 2   *Page Ref: 236–237*

17) When there are fewer positive ions sitting on the inner face of the neuron's plasma membrane than there are on the outer face of the tissue fluid that surrounds it, the membrane is said to be _____.

Answer: polarized
Diff: 3   *Page Ref: 237*

18) A type of reflex that stimulates the skeletal muscles is called a _____ reflex.

Answer: somatic
Diff: 1   *Page Ref: 240*

19) The thalamus, hypothalamus, and epithalamus collectively constitute the _____.

Answer: diencephalon (interbrain)
Diff: 2   *Page Ref: 246*

20) The brain dysfunction where blood supply to a region (or regions) of the brain is blocked and vital brain tissue dies, as by a blood clot or a ruptured blood vessel, is called _____.

Answer: cerebrovascular accident (CVA), commonly called a stroke
Diff: 2   *Page Ref: 252; 254*

21) The brain and spinal cord are protected and cushioned by three connective tissue membranes that are collectively called _____.

Answer: meninges
Diff: 2   *Page Ref: 249*

22) The area in the center of the gray matter of the spinal cord that contains cerebrospinal fluid —fluid that continues down the fourth ventricle—is called the _____.

Answer: central canal
Diff: 2   *Page Ref: 256*

23) The primary motor area of the brain allows us to consciously control our _____ muscles.

Answer: skeletal
Diff: 1   *Page Ref: 243*

24) Diminished effectiveness of the sympathetic nervous system that can cause a type of low blood pressure during rapid changes in body position (such as when elderly persons stand up quickly after sitting or lying down) is called _____.

Answer: orthostatic hypotension
Diff: 2   *Page Ref: 273*

25) The perineurium is a coarse connective wrapping that defines the boundary of a fiber bundle called a(n) _____.

Answer: fascicle
Diff: 1   Page Ref: 258

26) The fissure in the brain that separates the two cerebral hemispheres is called the _____.

Answer: longitudinal fissure
Diff: 2   Page Ref: 242

27) The hypothalamus regulates the _____ gland.

Answer: pituitary
Diff: 2   Page Ref: 246

28) The large fiber tract that allows communication between the two cerebral hemispheres is called the _____.

Answer: corpus callosum
Diff: 2   Page Ref: 242

29) The progressive degenerative disease that results in dementia associated with a shortage of acetylcholine and structural changes in brain areas involving cognition and memory is called _____.

Answer: Alzheimer's disease
Diff: 2   Page Ref: 253

30) Cerebrospinal fluid is formed from blood by the _____.

Answer: choroid plexuses
Diff: 1   Page Ref: 251

31) A _____ is a type of traumatic brain injury that results in marked tissue destruction.

Answer: contusion
Diff: 2   Page Ref: 252

32) The only major nerve out of the cervical plexus that supplies the diaphragm and muscles of the shoulder and neck is the _____ nerve.

Answer: phrenic
Diff: 2   Page Ref: 264

33) _____ disease results from a degeneration of the dopamine–releasing neurons of the substantia nigra.

Answer: Parkinson's
Diff: 2   Page Ref: 253–254

34) The _____ is a connective tissue wrapping around fasicles of neuron fibers.

Answer: perineurium
Diff: 1   Page Ref: 258

35) Sweat glands that produce perspiration when stimulated are innervated only by the _____ fibers.

Answer: sympathetic
Diff: 3   Page Ref: 269

36) The only pair of cranial nerves to extend to the thoracic and abdominal cavities is the
_____ nerves.

Answer: vagus
Diff: 1   *Page Ref: 260*

37) Cranial nerve III is known as the _____ nerve.

Answer: oculomotor
Diff: 2   *Page Ref: 259*

38) The _____ division of the ANS activates when we are frightened or stressed.

Answer: sympathetic
Diff: 2   *Page Ref: 266*

39) One of the last areas of the CNS to mature is the _____, which regulates body
temperature.

Answer: hypothalamus
Diff: 2   *Page Ref: 273*

40) The cranial nerve responsible for controlling tongue movements is the _____ nerve,
number _____.

Answer: hypoglossal; XII
Diff: 3   *Page Ref: 260*

41) Each spinal nerve divides into a dorsal and a ventral _____.

Answer: ramus
Diff: 2   *Page Ref: 262*

42) The _____ nerve, the largest nerve in the body, splits into the common fibular and tibial
nerves.

Answer: sciatic
Diff: 2   *Page Ref: 264*

Multiple Choice

1) The term *central nervous system* refers to the:
    A) autonomic and peripheral nervous systems
    B) brain, spinal cord, and cranial nerves
    C) brain and cranial nerves
    D) spinal cord and spinal nerves
    E) brain and spinal cord

Answer: E
Diff: 1   *Page Ref: 229*

2) The peripheral nervous system consists of:
    A) spinal nerves only
    B) the brain only
    C) cranial nerves only
    D) the brain and spinal cord
    E) the spinal and cranial nerves

Answer: E
Diff: 1   *Page Ref: 229*

3) Which of these cells are not a type of neuroglia found in the CNS:
   A) astrocytes
   B) microglia
   C) Schwann cells
   D) ependymal cells
   E) oligodendrocytes

Answer: C
Diff: 2   *Page Ref: 230–232*

4) The Schwann cell forms a myelin sheath around the:
   A) dendrites
   B) cell body
   C) nucleus
   D) axon
   E) nodes of Ranvier

Answer: D
Diff: 1   *Page Ref: 232*

5) The neuron processes that normally receive incoming stimuli are called:
   A) axons
   B) dendrites
   C) neurolemmas
   D) Schwann cells
   E) satellite cells

Answer: B
Diff: 1   *Page Ref: 232*

6) Collections of nerve cell bodies inside the CNS are called:
   A) ganglia
   B) tracts
   C) nerves
   D) nuclei
   E) tracts or ganglia

Answer: A
Diff: 2   *Page Ref: 234*

7) Which one of the following best describes the waxy-appearing material called *myelin*:
   A) an outer membrane on a neuroglial cell
   B) a lipid–protein (lipoprotein) cell membrane on the outside of axons
   C) a mass of white lipid material that surrounds the cell body of a neuron
   D) a mass of white lipid material that insulates the axon of a neuron
   E) a mass of white lipid material that surrounds the dendrites of a neuron

Answer: D
Diff: 2   *Page Ref: 232*

8) Which of the following sensory receptors is a touch receptor:
   A) Golgi tendon organ
   B) Meissner's corpuscle
   C) Pacinian corpuscle
   D) naked nerve endings
   E) muscle spindles

Answer: B
Diff: 2   *Page Ref: 235–236*

9) A neuron with a cell body located in the CNS whose primary function is connecting other neurons is called a(n):
   A) efferent neuron
   B) afferent neuron
   C) association neuron
   D) glial cell
   E) satellite cell

Answer: C
Diff: 1   *Page Ref: 236*

10) White matters refers to myelinated fibers in the:
    A) CNS
    B) PNS
    C) ANS
    D) SNS
    E) both ANS and SNS

Answer: A
Diff: 2   *Page Ref: 234–235*

11) Impulse conduction is fastest in neurons that are:
    A) myelinated
    B) unmyelinated
    C) sensory
    D) motor
    E) cerebral

Answer: A
Diff: 2   *Page Ref: 232*

12) Bipolar neurons are commonly:
    A) motor neurons
    B) called neuroglia
    C) found in ganglia
    D) found in the eye and nose
    E) more abundant in adults than in children

Answer: D
Diff: 1   *Page Ref: 237*

13) An action potential:
   A) is essential for nerve impulse propagation
   B) involves the influx of negative ions to depolarize the membrane
   C) involves the outflux of negative ions to depolarize the membrane
   D) involves the outflux of positive ions to depolarize the membrane
   E) is initiated by potassium ion movements

Answer: A
Diff: 2   Page Ref: 237–239

14) Immediately after an action potential is propagated, which one of the following ions rapidly diffuses out of the cell into the tissue fluid:
   A) sodium
   B) chloride
   C) calcium
   D) potassium
   E) magnesium

Answer: D
Diff: 2   Page Ref: 239

15) An action potential is caused by an influx of these ions into the cell:
   A) potassium
   B) sodium
   C) calcium
   D) magnesium
   E) both potassium and sodium

Answer: B
Diff: 2   Page Ref: 237–239

16) The ability to respond to a stimulus is termed:
   A) polarized
   B) irritability
   C) depolarized
   D) conductivity
   E) all–or–none response

Answer: B
Diff: 1   Page Ref: 237

17) The diffusion of potassium ions out of a neuron causes it to experience:
   A) an action potential
   B) depolarization
   C) repolarization
   D) a graded potential
   E) a nerve impulse

Answer: C
Diff: 2   Page Ref: 239

18) Which one of the following is the correct sequence of events that follows a threshold potential:
1. the membrane becomes depolarized
2. sodium channels open and sodium ions diffuse inward
3. the membrane becomes repolarized
4. potassium channels open and potassium ions diffuse outward while sodium is actively transported out of the cell

   A) 3, 2, 4, 1
   B) 2, 1, 4, 3
   C) 2, 1, 3, 4
   D) 1, 2, 4, 3
   E) 4, 1, 3, 2

Answer: B
Diff: 3   *Page Ref: 237–239*

19) Which one of the following describes saltatory conduction:
   A) occurs only if the myelin sheath is continuous
   B) occurs only if nodes of Ranvier are lacking
   C) occurs only in the absence of axon hillocks
   D) is faster than conduction on an unmyelinated fiber
   E) is slower than conduction on an unmyelinated fiber

Answer: D
Diff: 2   *Page Ref: 239*

20) The gap between two communicating neurons is termed:
   A) synaptic cleft
   B) cell body
   C) effector
   D) Schwann cell
   E) node of Ranvier

Answer: A
Diff: 2   *Page Ref: 239–240*

21) The substance that is released at axonal endings to propagate a nervous impulse is called:
   A) an ion
   B) nerve glue
   C) a neurotransmitter
   D) the sodium–potassium pump
   E) an action potential

Answer: C
Diff: 1   *Page Ref: 239*

22) Which of the following is the correct sequence in a typical reflex arc:
   A) effector, afferent neuron, integration center, efferent neuron, receptor
   B) receptor, afferent neuron, integration center, efferent neuron, effector
   C) effector, efferent neuron, integration center, afferent neuron, receptor
   D) receptor, efferent neuron, integration center, afferent neuron, effector
   E) receptor, afferent neuron, efferent neuron, integration center, effector

Answer: B
Diff: 3   *Page Ref: 240*

23) Muscles and glands are:
    A) receptors
    B) effectors
    C) myelinated
    D) part of the peripheral nervous system
    E) part of the central nervous system

Answer: B
Diff: 1   *Page Ref: 240*

24) The three major parts of the brain stem are the:
    A) cerebrum, cerebellum, and diencephalon
    B) thalamus, epithalamus, and hypothalamus
    C) dura mater, arachnoid mater, and pia mater
    D) midbrain, pons, and medulla oblongata
    E) basal nuclei, pineal body, and choroid plexus

Answer: D
Diff: 2   *Page Ref: 247–248*

25) The elevated ridges of tissue on the surface of the cerebral hemispheres are known as
_____ while the shallow grooves are termed _____.
    A) sulci; gyri
    B) gyri; sulci
    C) ganglia; gyri
    D) tracts; ganglia
    E) receptors; effectors

Answer: B
Diff: 2   *Page Ref: 242*

26) The olfactory area is found within the:
    A) occipital lobe
    B) temporal lobe
    C) frontal lobe
    D) parietal lobe
    E) pyramidal tract

Answer: B
Diff: 2   *Page Ref: 243*

27) Sally has a brain injury; she knows what she wants to say but can't vocalize the words. The part
of her brain that deals with the ability to speak is the:
    A) longitudinal fissure
    B) gyrus
    C) central sulcus
    D) Broca's area
    E) primary motor area

Answer: D
Diff: 3   *Page Ref: 243*

28) The midbrain, pons, and medulla oblongata are housed in the:
   A) diencephalon
   B) hypothalamus
   C) brain stem
   D) pineal gland
   E) cerebellum

Answer: C
Diff: 2   Page Ref: 247–248

29) Lobe that contains the primary motor area that enables voluntary control of skeletal muscle movements:
   A) parietal lobe
   B) temporal lobe
   C) occipital lobe
   D) frontal lobe
   E) diencephalon

Answer: D
Diff: 2   Page Ref: 243

30) The pituitary gland is most closely associated with the:
   A) hypothalamus
   B) thalamus
   C) pineal gland
   D) midbrain
   E) medulla oblongata

Answer: A
Diff: 2   Page Ref: 246

31) Cerebrospinal fluid circulates through all of the following except:
   A) subarachnoid space
   B) corpus callosum
   C) cerebral aqueduct
   D) fourth ventricle
   E) lateral ventricles

Answer: B
Diff: 3   Page Ref: 250–251

32) The area of the brain stem that plays a role in consciousness and the awake/sleep cycles is the:
   A) thalamus
   B) reticular activating system (RAS)
   C) pineal gland
   D) limbic system
   E) cerebellum

Answer: B
Diff: 2   Page Ref: 248

33) Control of temperature, endocrine activity, **metabolism**, and thirst are functions associated with the:
   A) medulla oblongata
   B) cerebellum
   C) hypothalamus
   D) thalamus
   E) cerebrum

Answer: C
Diff: 2   Page Ref: 246-247

34) The vital centers for the control of visceral activities such as heart rate, breathing, blood pressure, swallowing, and vomiting are located in the:
   A) pons
   B) medulla oblongata
   C) midbrain
   D) cerebrum
   E) hypothalamus

Answer: B
Diff: 1   Page Ref: 248

35) Loss of muscle coordination results from damage to the:
   A) cerebrum
   B) hypothalamus
   C) cerebellum
   D) thalamus
   E) midbrain

Answer: C
Diff: 3   Page Ref: 248

36) Which one of the following represents the correct sequence from outermost to innermost layers of the meninges:
   A) pia mater, dura mater, arachnoid mater
   B) pia mater, arachnoid mater, dura mater
   C) arachnoid mater, dura mater, pia mater
   D) dura mater, pia mater, arachnoid mater
   E) dura mater, arachnoid mater, pia mater

Answer: E
Diff: 2   Page Ref: 249-251

37) The subarachnoid space lies directly between the:
   A) arachnoid mater and dura mater
   B) arachnoid mater and pia mater
   C) skull and arachnoid mater
   D) arachnoid mater and cerebrum
   E) arachnoid mater and cerebellum

Answer: B
Diff: 2   Page Ref: 251

38) The cerebrospinal fluid:
   A) is secreted by the arachnoid villi
   B) enters the four ventricles after filling and circulating through the subarachnoid space
   C) is secreted mostly by the ependymal cells lining the brain ventricles
   D) is continually formed mostly by the choroid plexuses
   E) is identical in composition to whole blood

   Answer: D
   Diff: 2   Page Ref: 251

39) The blood–brain barrier is effective against the passage of:
   A) water
   B) nutrients such as glucose
   C) alcohol
   D) anesthetics
   E) metabolic waste such as urea

   Answer: E
   Diff: 2   Page Ref: 252

40) Which of the following is a traumatic brain injury:
   A) cerebrovascular accident (CVA)
   B) Alzheimer's disease
   C) aphasia
   D) cerebral edema
   E) Parkinson's disease

   Answer: D
   Diff: 2   Page Ref: 252–255

41) The gray matter of the spinal cord:
   A) surrounds the central canal
   B) contains myelinated fiber tracts
   C) is made up of the dorsal, lateral, and ventral columns
   D) surrounds the white matter of the spinal cord
   E) always carries sensory information to the brain

   Answer: A
   Diff: 3   Page Ref: 256

42) Cell bodies of the sensory neurons of the spinal nerves are located in:
   A) the dorsal root ganglia of the spinal cord
   B) the ventral root ganglia of the spinal cord
   C) the thalamus
   D) the hypothalamus
   E) sympathetic ganglia

   Answer: A
   Diff: 3   Page Ref: 256

43) Which one of the following is the correct sequence of nerves that exit the spinal cord, going from superior to inferior:
   A) thoracic spinal nerves, cervical spinal nerves, lumbar spinal nerves, sacral spinal nerves
   B) cervical spinal nerves, lumbar spinal nerves, thoracic spinal nerves, sacral spinal nerves
   C) thoracic spinal nerves, cervical spinal nerves, sacral spinal nerves, lumbar spinal nerves
   D) cervical spinal nerves, thoracic spinal nerves, sacral spinal nerves, lumbar spinal nerves
   E) cervical spinal nerves, thoracic spinal nerves, lumbar spinal nerves, sacral spinal nerves

Answer: E
Diff: 3   Page Ref: 255

44) Which one of the following is the correct sequence in connective tissue sheaths, going from outermost to innermost layer:
   A) epineurium, endoneurium, perineurium
   B) epineurium, perineurium, endoneurium
   C) perineurium, epineurium, endoneurium
   D) perineurium, endoneurium, epineurium
   E) endoneurium, epineurium, perineurium

Answer: B
Diff: 2   Page Ref: 258

45) Afferent nerves are called _____, and motor nerves are called _____.
   A) motor nerves; sensory nerves
   B) peripheral nerves; cranial nerves
   C) mixed nerves; motor nerves
   D) sensory nerves; efferent nerves
   E) cranial nerves; peripheral nerves

Answer: D
Diff: 2   Page Ref: 258

46) The function of the olfactory nerve concerns:
   A) hearing
   B) vision
   C) chewing
   D) smell
   E) eye movement

Answer: D
Diff: 2   Page Ref: 259

47) The nerve that contains sensory fibers that are involved in hearing is:
   A) cranial nerve II
   B) cranial nerve III
   C) cranial nerve V
   D) cranial nerve VIII
   E) cranial nerve IX

Answer: D
Diff: 3   Page Ref: 260

48) Spinal nerves exiting the cord from the level of L4 to S4 form the:
   A) lumbar plexus
   B) femoral plexus
   C) sacral plexus
   D) thoracic plexus
   E) obturator plexus
   Answer: C
   Diff: 2   *Page Ref: 263–264*

49) Damage to this nerve results in "wristdrop," the inability to extend the hand at the wrist:
   A) phrenic
   B) axillary
   C) obturator
   D) radial
   E) femoral
   Answer: D
   Diff: 3   *Page Ref: 264*

50) Which of the nerves plexuses originates from ventral rami $L_1–L_4$:
   A) sacral
   B) spinal
   C) lumbar
   D) brachial
   E) cervical
   Answer: C
   Diff: 3   *Page Ref: 264*

51) Which of the nerve plexuses serves the shoulder and arm:
   A) sacral
   B) phrenic
   C) lumbar
   D) brachial
   E) cervical
   Answer: D
   Diff: 2   *Page Ref: 264–265*

52) The sciatic nerve is the largest nerve in the body resulting from a combination of which two nerves:
   A) pudendal and femoral nerves
   B) femoral and tibial nerves
   C) pudendal and common peroneal nerves
   D) common fibular and tibial nerves
   E) pudendal and tibial nerves
   Answer: D
   Diff: 1   *Page Ref: 264*

53) The sympathetic and parasympathetic nervous systems are subdivisions of the:
    A) central nervous system
    B) voluntary nervous system
    C) autonomic nervous system
    D) somatic nervous system
    E) peripheral nervous system

Answer: C
Diff: 1   *Page Ref: 230; 266*

54) In contrast to the somatic nervous system, the autonomic nervous system:
    A) has two motor neurons
    B) has two afferent neurons
    C) stimulates its effector cells
    D) has both afferent and efferent fibers
    E) has centers in the brain and spinal cord

Answer: A
Diff: 3   *Page Ref: 230; 262*

55) Which one of these effectors is NOT directly controlled by the autonomic nervous system:
    A) smooth muscle
    B) cardiac muscle
    C) skeletal muscle
    D) most glands
    E) abdominal organs

Answer: C
Diff: 2   *Page Ref: 262*

56) Preparing the body for the "fight-or-flight" response during threatening situations is the role of the:
    A) sympathetic nervous system
    B) cerebrum
    C) parasympathetic nervous system
    D) somatic nervous system
    E) afferent nervous system

Answer: A
Diff: 1   *Page Ref: 270*

57) Which of the following effects is characteristic of the parasympathetic nervous system:
    A) decreases activity of the digestive system
    B) stimulates sweat glands to produce perspiration
    C) decreases urine output
    D) increases metabolic rate
    E) decreases heart rate

Answer: E
Diff: 3   *Page Ref: 269*

58) The effects of the sympathetic nervous system are essentially opposite of the:
   A) central nervous system
   B) parasympathetic nervous system
   C) autonomic nervous system
   D) motor division
   E) sensory division

   Answer: B
   Diff: 2   Page Ref: 230; 270

59) Sympathetic division fibers leave the spinal cord in the:
   A) craniosacral regions, and the postganglionic fibers secrete norepinephrine
   B) thoracolumbar region, and the postganglionic fibers secrete acetylcholine
   C) craniosacral region, and the postganglionic fibers secrete acetylcholine
   D) thoracolumbar region, and the postganglionic fibers secrete norepinephrine
   E) craniosacral region, and the preganglionic fibers secrete norepinephrine

   Answer: D
   Diff: 3   Page Ref: 267–269

60) Sympathetic nervous system stimulation causes:
   A) decreased blood glucose, increased GI peristalsis, and increased heart rate and blood pressure
   B) increased blood glucose, increased GI peristalsis, and decreased heart rate and blood pressure
   C) increased blood glucose, decreased GI peristalsis, and increased heart rate and blood pressure
   D) decreased blood glucose, increased GI peristalsis, and decreased heart rate and blood pressure
   E) decreased blood glucose, decreased GI peristalsis, and decreased heart rate and blood pressure

   Answer: C
   Diff: 3   Page Ref: 269

61) Which one of the following statements about aging is most accurate:
   A) the brain reaches its maximum weight around the seventh decade of life
   B) synaptic connections are too fixed to permit a great deal of learning after the age of 35
   C) despite some neuronal loss, an unlimited number of neural pathways are available and ready to be developed; therefore, additional learning can occur throughout life
   D) learning throughout the adult and aging years is supported primarily by glial proliferation
   E) increased efficiency of the sympathetic nervous system enhances the ability to learn

   Answer: C
   Diff: 2   Page Ref: 272–273

True/False

1) Myelination of nerve fibers in the central nervous system is the job of the oligodendrocyte.
   Answer: TRUE
   Diff: 1   Page Ref: 230–232

2) Oligodendrocytes produce myelin sheaths in the PNS.

Answer: FALSE
Diff: 2   Page Ref: 230–232

3) The nodes of Ranvier are found at regular intervals only on myelinated, peripheral nerve fibers.

Answer: TRUE
Diff: 2   Page Ref: 232–234

4) Cell bodies of sensory neurons are always located in ganglia lying outside the central nervous system.

Answer: TRUE
Diff: 1   Page Ref: 234

5) An afferent sensory neuron carries stimuli from the central nervous system to the effector.

Answer: FALSE
Diff: 1   Page Ref: 235

6) Sensory neurons carry information away from the CNS.

Answer: FALSE
Diff: 1   Page Ref: 235

7) Bipolar neurons are rare in adults.

Answer: TRUE
Diff: 2   Page Ref: 237

8) The all–or–none phenomenon as applied to nerve conduction states that the whole nerve cell must be stimulated for conduction to take place.

Answer: FALSE
Diff: 2   Page Ref: 239

9) Reflexes are rapid, predictable, and automatic responses to stimuli.

Answer: TRUE
Diff: 1   Page Ref: 240

10) Saltatory conduction occurs due to the presence of salt (NaCl) around the neuron.

Answer: FALSE
Diff: 3   Page Ref: 239

11) A polarized neuron has fewer positive ions inside in comparison to the outside of the neuron.

Answer: TRUE
Diff: 2   Page Ref: 237

12) Difficulty in breathing may reflect damage to respiratory centers located in the cerebellum.

Answer: FALSE
Diff: 2   Page Ref: 248

13) One of the major functions of the pons is to produce releasing factors that control the function of the anterior pituitary.

Answer: FALSE
Diff: 2   Page Ref: 246

14) Part of the diencephalon structure is formed by the hypothalamus.

Answer: TRUE
Diff: 1   *Page Ref: 246*

15) Cerebrospinal fluid circulates within the ventricles of the brain and also in the subarachnoid space outside the brain.

Answer: TRUE
Diff: 1   *Page Ref: 251*

16) The collection of spinal nerves at the inferior end of the spinal cord is called the cauda equina.

Answer: TRUE
Diff: 2   *Page Ref: 256*

17) There is no possibility of damaging the spinal cord below the third lumbar vertebra.

Answer: TRUE
Diff: 2   *Page Ref: 255*

18) The glossopharyngeal nerve is the only cranial nerve pair that contains sensory fibers.

Answer: FALSE
Diff: 3   *Page Ref: 259–260*

19) Cranial nerve XI is the accessory nerve that controls tongue movement.

Answer: FALSE
Diff: 3   *Page Ref: 259–260*

20) There are 31 pairs of cranial nerves and 12 pairs of spinal nerves.

Answer: FALSE
Diff: 1   *Page Ref: 258; 262*

21) The musculocutaneous nerve is a major nerve of the brachial plexus.

Answer: TRUE
Diff: 2   *Page Ref: 264*

22) Sympathetic postganglionic fibers release norepinephrine and the preganglionic axon releases acetyocholine.

Answer: TRUE
Diff: 3   *Page Ref: 269*

23) In contrast to the parasympathetic division, the sympathetic division has numerous ganglionic neurons in the gray matter of the spinal cord.

Answer: FALSE
Diff: 2   *Page Ref: 266–268*

24) Most body organs are innervated by only the sympathetic division of the nervous system.

Answer: FALSE
Diff: 2   *Page Ref: 266–270*

25) Neurons in adults do not undergo mitosis.

Answer: TRUE
Diff: 1   *Page Ref: 273*

Matching

Match the following:

1) Period when the interior of the cell becomes less negative due to an influx of sodium ions

   Diff: 3   Page Ref: 237–239

2) Specific period during which potassium ions diffuse out of the neuron due to a change in membrane permeability

   Diff: 3   Page Ref: 237–239

3) Termed a nerve impulse when transmitted

   Diff: 3   Page Ref: 237–239

4) Period when the neuron is at rest; it has a more negative interior in comparison to the positive exterior

   Diff: 2   Page Ref: 237–239

5) Local depolarization is also known as this term

   Diff: 3   Page Ref: 237–239

A) action potential

B) repolarization

C) graded potential

D) polarization

E) depolarization

1) E   2) B   3) A   4) D   5) C

Match the following:

6) Auditory area

   Diff: 2   Page Ref: 242–243

7) Primary sensory cortex

   Diff: 2   Page Ref: 242–243

8) Somatic motor cortex

   Diff: 2   Page Ref: 242–243

9) Motor speech area

   Diff: 2   Page Ref: 242–243

10) Premotor area

   Diff: 2   Page Ref: 242–243

11) Visual area

   Diff: 2   Page Ref: 242–243

A) basal nuclei

B) interbrain

C) midbrain

D) frontal lobe

E) parietal lobe

F) occipital lobe

G) corticospinal tract

H) temporal lobe

I) pyramidal tract

6) H   7) E   8) D   9) D   10) D   11) F

Match the following:

12) Composed of cerebral peduncles and the corpora quadrigemina
Diff: 2   *Page Ref: 248*

13) Contains centers that control heart rate, blood pressure, breathing, swallowing, and vomiting
Diff: 2   *Page Ref: 248*

14) Gland that hangs from the hypothalamus
Diff: 2   *Page Ref: 246*

15) Regulates body temperature, water balance, and metabolism
Diff: 2   *Page Ref: 246*

16) Relay station for sensory impulses passing to the sensory cortex
Diff: 3   *Page Ref: 246*

17) Motor control of the visceral organs
Diff: 3   *Page Ref: 248*

A) reticular formation

B) midbrain

C) hypothalamus

D) medulla oblongata

E) thalamus

F) pituitary gland

12) B   13) D   14) F   15) C   16) E   17) A

Match the following:

18) Cranial nerve IV

    Diff: 1   *Page Ref: 259–260*

19) Moves eyes laterally

    Diff: 2   *Page Ref: 259–260*

20) Cranial nerve II

    Diff: 1   *Page Ref: 259–260*

21) Controls lens shape and pupil size

    Diff: 2   *Page Ref: 259–260*

22) Cranial nerve IX

    Diff: 1   *Page Ref: 259–260*

23) Promotes digestive activity and regulates heart activity

    Diff: 2   *Page Ref: 259–260*

24) Cranial nerve VII

    Diff: 1   *Page Ref: 259–260*

25) Fibers emerge from the medulla and run to the throat

    Diff: 3   *Page Ref: 259–260*

A) Trigeminal

B) Vestibulocochlear

C) Oculomotor

D) Trochlear

E) Glossopharyngeal

F) Accessory

G) Facial

H) Abducens

I) Optic

J) Olfactory

K) Vagus

L) Hypoglossal

18) D   19) H   20) I   21) C   22) E   23) K
24) G   25) L

Essay

1) List and explain the three general functions of the nervous system

    Answer: 1. Sensory (input) function—the nervous system uses millions of sensory receptors to monitor changes (stimuli) inside and outside the body; the gathered information is called the sensory function.
    2. Integrative function—the nervous system processes and interprets sensory input and makes decisions about what should be done and the magnitude to which it should be done at each moment.
    3. Motor (output) function—the process of reaction to stimuli; the body responds by activating muscles that can produce motion or glands that can produce and secrete hormones.

    Diff: 2   *Page Ref: 228–229*

2) List and describe the two principal divisions of the peripheral nervous system and their subdivisions.

Answer: 1. Sensory (afferent) division—consists of nerve fibers that convey impulses to the central nervous system from sensory receptors located in various parts of the body (i.e., skin, skeletal muscle, visceral organs). This is further subdivided into:
  a. Somatic sensory (afferent) fibers—consist of nerve fibers that convey impulses from the skin, skeletal muscle, and joints to the central nervous system.
  b. Visceral sensory (afferent) fibers—consist of nerve fibers that convey impulses from the visceral organs to the central nervous system.

2. Motor (efferent) division—consists of nerve fibers that convey impulses from the central nervous system to effected organs called effectors (i.e., muscles and glands). This is further subdivided into:
  a. Somatic (voluntary) nervous system—carries impulses from the central nervous system to effectors (skeletal muscles); allows for conscious control of skeletal muscle.
  b. Autonomic (involuntary) nervous system—carries impulses from the central nervous system to smooth and cardiac muscle and glands; has two subdivisions—the parasympathetic and sympathetic nervous systems.

Diff: 3   Page Ref: 229–230

3) List and explain the four major events that take place during the conduction of a nerve impulse beginning with the resting membrane.

Answer: 1. Electrical condition of a resting (polarized) membrane—in a resting membrane, the external face of the membrane is slightly positive; its internal face is slightly negative. The chief extracellular ion is sodium, whereas the chief intracellular ion is potassium. A polarized membrane is relatively impermeable to both ions.
2. Depolarization and generation of an action potential—a stimulus changes the permeability of a "patch" of the membrane, and sodium ions diffuse rapidly into the cell. This changes the polarity of the membrane (the outside becomes more negative). If the stimulus is strong enough, an action potential is initiated.
3. Propagation of an action potential—depolarization of the first membrane patch causes permeability changes in the adjacent membrane and the events described in "2" (above) are repeated. Thus the action potential propagates rapidly along the entire length of the membrane.
4. Repolarization—potassium ions diffuse out of the cell as membrane permeability changes again, restoring the negative charge on the inside of the membrane and the positive charge on the outside surface. Repolarization occurs in the same direction as depolarization. The ionic conditions of the resting state are later restored by the activity of the sodium–potassium pump.

Diff: 3   Page Ref: 237–239

4) List the four events that lead to transmission of an impulse across a synapse.

Answer: 1. The impulse arrives at the synaptic knob of the presynaptic neuron.
2. The synaptic vesicle fuses with the presynaptic neuron membrane and the chemical neurotransmitter is released via exocytosis.
3. The neurotransmitter is released, travels across the synaptic cleft, and binds to receptor sites on the postsynaptic neuron. If sufficient neurotransmitter is released, the entire series of events involved in the conduction of a nerve impulse will occur in the postsynaptic neuron.
4. The electrical changes prompted by neurotransmitter binding are very brief because the neurotransmitter is quickly removed from the synapse either by re-uptake into the axonal terminal or by enzymatic breakdown.

Diff: 3   *Page Ref: 239–240*

5) Compare the sympathetic and parasympathetic branches of the autonomic nervous system with respect to the location of the centers, location of the ganglia, neurotransmitters, and their specific effects.

Answer: 1. Location of the Centers
Sympathetic Nervous System—centers are located in the gray matter of the spinal cord from T_1 to L_2 (therefore it is also called the thoracolumbar nervous system).

Parasympathetic Nervous System—centers are located in the brain (in nuclei of several of the cranial nerves) and in the sacral region of the spinal cord (S_2 to S_4).

2. Location of Ganglia
Sympathetic Nervous System—ganglia are located in a sympathetic chain or trunks located just outside the spinal cord on each side. Accordingly, preganglionic neurons have short axons and postganglionic neurons have long axons.
Parasympathetic Nervous System—ganglia are located in terminal ganglia, a short distance from the organs served. Accordingly, preganglionic neurons have long axons and postganglionic neurons have short axons.

3. Neurotransmitters
Sympathetic Nervous System—preganglionic axons are cholinergic fibers (produce acetylcholine) and postganglionic axons are adrenergic fibers (produce norepinephrine).
Parasympathetic Nervous System—both preganglionic and postganglionic axons are cholinergic fibers (produce acetylcholine).

4. General Effects—generally speaking, the sympathetic and parasympathetic branches of the autonomic nervous system are antagonistic: on any one organ, these two branches have opposite and counter-balancing effects.
Sympathetic Nervous System—often referred to as the "fight or flight" nervous system; it is active when in an emergency or a threatening situation.
Parasympathetic Nervous System—often referred to as the "rest and digest" nervous system; it is most active when the body is not threatened in any way and is functioning to conserve body energy and promote normal digestion and elmination.

Diff: 3   *Page Ref: 230;262; 266–270*

6) Explain how multiple sclerosis affects nerve functioning.

Answer: People with multiple sclerosis (MS) experience destruction of their myelin sheaths. As destruction progresses, the electrical current is short-circuited. The person affected with MS may experience visual and speech disturbances and lose muscle control.

Diff: 1   *Page Ref: 234*

7) List and describe the protective structures found in the CNS.

Answer: 1. The brain and spinal cord are protected by a bony skull and a bony vertebral column.

2. There are three layers of membranes (meninges) covering the structures in the CNS.

a. The outermost dura mater surround the brain. This double–layered membrane is a leathery covering.

b. The middle membrane layer is the arachnoid mater, which has a cobweb appearance.

c. The pia mater is the innermost layer, which clings to the surface of the brain and spinal cord.

3. Cerebrospinal fluid forms a water cushion that circulates in and around the brain and spinal cord. The CSF protects the CNS from blows and other trauma. Also, remember from a previous chapter that water has a high heat capacity that prevents changes in temperature.

Diff: 2   *Page Ref: 248–251*

8) Describe the cells that form myelin sheaths in the CNS and PNS.

Answer: 1. In the CNS, oligodendrocytes wrap their extensions around nerve fibers producing myelin sheaths. Oligodendrocytes can wrap as many as 60 different nerve fibers at the same time.

2. In the PNS, Schwann cells wrap around the axons of nerve fibers.

Diff: 1   *Page Ref: 232*

Chapter 8 Special Senses

Short Answer

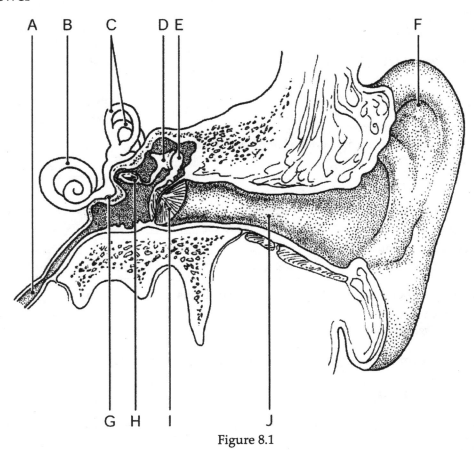

Figure 8.1

Using Figure 8.1, identify the following:

1) The auricle (pinna) is indicated by the letter _____.

Answer: F
Diff: 1   Page Ref: 294–295

2) The tympanic membrane is indicated by letter _____.

Answer: I
Diff: 1   Page Ref: 294–295

3) The semicircular canals are indicated by letter _____.

Answer: C
Diff: 1   Page Ref: 294–295

4) The cochlea is indicated by letter _____.

Answer: B
Diff: 1   Page Ref: 294–295

5) The pharyngotympanic (auditory) tube is indicated by letter _____.

Answer: A
Diff: 1   Page Ref: 294–295

6) The malleus (hammer) is indicated by letter _____.

Answer: E
Diff: 1   Page Ref: 294–295

7) The stapes (stirrup) is indicated by letter _____.

Answer: H
Diff: 1   Page Ref: 294–295

Fill in the blank or provide a short answer:

8) _____ glands are located on the lateral end of each eye.

Answer: Lacrimal
Diff: 1   Page Ref: 282

9) The six muscles attached to the outer surface of the eye that produce gross eye movements and make it possible for the eyes to follow objects are the _____.

Answer: extrinsic muscles
Diff: 2   Page Ref: 282

10) The area of sharpest visual acuity that normally contains only cones is the _____.

Answer: fovea centralis
Diff: 1   Page Ref: 286

11) Rods and cones are called _____ because they respond to light.

Answer: photoreceptors
Diff: 2   Page Ref: 284

12) The lens divides the eye into two segments, the _____ and the _____ segments.

Answer: anterior (aqueous); posterior (vitreous)
Diff: 2   Page Ref: 289

13) Aqueous humor is reabsorbed into venous blood at the sclera–cornea conjunction through the _____.

Answer: scleral venous sinus or canal of Schlemm
Diff: 3   Page Ref: 289

14) The eye condition resulting from the inability of the aqueous humor to drain from the eye is called _____.

Answer: glaucoma
Diff: 2   Page Ref: 289

15) The upside–down image formed on the retina as a result of the light-bending activity of the lens is the _____.

Answer: real image
Diff: 3   Page Ref: 290

16) Fibers from the medial side of each eye cross over to the opposite side of the brain at the

_____.

Answer: optic chiasma
Diff: 2   Page Ref: 291

17) The overlapping of the two visual fields that provides for depth perception (3–D vision) results

in _____.

Answer: binocular vision
Diff: 3   Page Ref: 291

18) Loss of the same side of the visual field of both eyes from damage to the visual cortex on one

side only is called _____.

Answer: hemianopia
Diff: 3   Page Ref: 291

19) Earwax is produced by _____.

Answer: ceruminous glands
Diff: 2   Page Ref: 294

20) The three subdivisions of the bony labyrinth of the internal ear are _____, _____,

and _____.

Answer: cochlea, vestibule, semicircular canals
Diff: 3   Page Ref: 295

21) The stirrup bone of the internal ear is also known as _____.

Answer: stapes
Diff: 1   Page Ref: 295

22) The cochlear nerve transmits impulses to the auditory cortex located in the _____.

Answer: temporal lobe
Diff: 2   Page Ref: 300

23) A division of the cranial nerve, the _____ transmits information to the cerebellum about

equilibrium.

Answer: vestibular nerve
Diff: 3   Page Ref: 297

24) Tiny stones made of calcium salts that roll in response to changes in gravitational pull are

called _____.

Answer: otoliths
Diff: 3   Page Ref: 297

25) The serious inner ear condition that causes nausea, vertigo, and progressive deafness is called

_____.

Answer: Meniere's syndrome
Diff: 3   Page Ref: 300

26) The receptors for taste and smell are classified as _____.

Answer: chemoreceptors
Diff: 1   Page Ref: 301

27) The small, peglike projections of the tongue's surface are called _____.

Answer: papillae
Diff: 2   *Page Ref: 302*

28) Bitter receptors on the tongue's taste buds respond to _____.

Answer: alkaloids
Diff: 2   *Page Ref: 302*

29) After age 40 the lens of the eye becomes less elastic; this condition is called _____.

Answer: presbyopia
Diff: 2   *Page Ref: 304*

30) A condition in which ear ossicles fuse is known as _____.

Answer: otosclerosis
Diff: 3   *Page Ref: 304*

Multiple Choice

1) The oily secretions that lubricate the eye are produced by the:
    A) ceruminous glands
    B) lacrimal glands
    C) tarsal glands
    D) apocrine glands
    E) ciliary glands

Answer: C
Diff: 2   *Page Ref: 282*

2) Tarsal glands associated with the edges of the eyelids are considered modified:
    A) ceruminous glands
    B) sweat glands
    C) lacrimal glands
    D) sebaceous glands
    E) apocrine glands

Answer: D
Diff: 3   *Page Ref: 282*

3) The highly contagious bacterial infection known as "pinkeye" is caused by bacterial or viral irritation of the:
    A) choroid
    B) conjunctiva
    C) cornea
    D) retina
    E) sclera

Answer: B
Diff: 2   *Page Ref: 282*

4) The gland that produces tears in the eye is called the:
    A) tarsal gland
    B) ceruminous gland
    C) sebaceous gland
    D) lacrimal gland
    E) ciliary gland

Answer: D
Diff: 1   Page Ref: 282

5) Which cranial nerve is responsible for moving the eye laterally:
    A) cranial nerve VI (abducens)
    B) cranial nerve III (oculomotor)
    C) cranial nerve II (optic)
    D) cranial nerve IV (trochlear)
    E) cranial nerve VIII (vestibulocochlear)

Answer: D
Diff: 3   Page Ref: 284

6) Inflammation of the conjunctiva involves which of the following:
    A) circular band surrounding the pupil
    B) delicate membrane lining the eyelids and covering the front of the eyeball
    C) glands that produce tears
    D) portion of the eye that contains the optic nerve
    E) extrinsic eye muscles

Answer: B
Diff: 2   Page Ref: 282

7) The fibrous outermost tunic seen anteriorily as the "white of the eye" is the:
    A) cornea
    B) choroid
    C) retina
    D) sclera
    E) fovea centralis

Answer: D
Diff: 1   Page Ref: 283

8) The transparent central anterior portion of the sclera through which light enters the eye is called the:
    A) choroid
    B) cornea
    C) iris
    D) pupil
    E) retina

Answer: B
Diff: 1   Page Ref: 283

9) The middle coat of the eyeball that contains pigment which prevents light from scattering in the eyeball is the:
   A) choroid
   B) cornea
   C) retina
   D) pupil
   E) sclera

   Answer: A
   Diff: 1   *Page Ref: 283*

10) Which layer of the eye contains rods and cones:
   A) sclera
   B) retina
   C) choroid
   D) iris
   E) optic nerve

   Answer: B
   Diff: 2   *Page Ref: 284*

11) The pigmented portion of the eye that has a rounded opening through which light passes is the:
   A) iris
   B) lens
   C) cornea
   D) sclera
   E) retina

   Answer: A
   Diff: 2   *Page Ref: 283–284*

12) The three sets of color receptors within the retina are sensitive to wavelengths of visible light that are:
   A) red, green, and yellow
   B) red, blue, and yellow
   C) green, yellow, and purple
   D) orange, green, and purple
   E) blue, green, and red

   Answer: E
   Diff: 2   *Page Ref: 288*

13) The greatest visual acuity is found at the:
   A) optic disc
   B) fovea centralis
   C) iris
   D) ciliary body
   E) lens

   Answer: B
   Diff: 2   *Page Ref: 286*

14) The aqueous humor of the eye is reabsorbed into venous blood through the:
    A) inferior larimal canal
    B) nasolacrimal duct
    C) scleral venous sinus (canal of Schlemm)
    D) ciliary body
    E) pupil

Answer: C
Diff: 1   *Page Ref: 289*

15) Which one of the following is NOT true of color blindness:
    A) it is sex-linked, inherited homeostatic imbalance
    B) it results from lack of cones
    C) it occurs most often in women
    D) it is caused by a defect in genes on the X (female) sex chromosome
    E) lack of red or green receptors is the most common type

Answer: C
Diff: 3   *Page Ref: 288*

16) The gel-like substance that reinforces the eyeball and prevents it from collapsing inward is the:
    A) aqueous humor
    B) ciliary body
    C) choroid coat
    D) vitreous humor
    E) canal of Schlemm

Answer: D
Diff: 1   *Page Ref: 289*

17) What structure of the eye focuses light on the retina:
    A) iris
    B) sclera
    C) lens
    D) choroid
    E) optic chiasma

Answer: C
Diff: 2   *Page Ref: 288*

18) The inability to see distant objects is termed "nearsighted" or:
    A) emmetropia
    B) hyperopia
    C) myopia
    D) astigmatism
    E) presbyopia

Answer: C
Diff: 2   *Page Ref: 292*

19) Eyes suddenly exposed to bright light experience:
   A) convergence
   B) accommodation pupillary reflex
   C) photopupillary reflex
   D) eyestrain
   E) hemianopia

   Answer: C
   Diff: 2   Page Ref: 293

20) Which one of the following correctly lists the order of the parts through which light passes as it enters the eye:
   A) cornea, aqueous humor, lens, vitreous humor
   B) aqueous humor, cornea, lens, vitreous humor
   C) vitreous humor, lens, aqueous humor, cornea
   D) cornea, lens, aqueous humor, vitreous humor
   E) lens, aqueous humor, cornea, vitreous humor

   Answer: A
   Diff: 3   Page Ref: 288–289

21) Receptors stimulated by the physical forces that cause movement of fluid or vibration within the body are:
   A) chemoreceptors
   B) mechanoreceptors
   C) thermoreceptors
   D) proprioceptors
   E) gustatory receptors

   Answer: B
   Diff: 2   Page Ref: 294

22) Sound waves entering the external auditory canal hit the eardrum, also known as the:
   A) tympanic membrane
   B) pinna
   C) auricle
   D) oval window
   E) ossicles

   Answer: A
   Diff: 1   Page Ref: 294

23) Hair cells that function as hearing receptors are located within the:
   A) auditory tube
   B) spiral organ of Corti
   C) oval window
   D) auricle
   E) ossicles

   Answer: B
   Diff: 1   Page Ref: 298

24) The pathway of vibrations through the ossicles from the tympanic membrane, or eardrum, to the oval window is:
  A) malleus, incus, stapes
  B) incus, malleus, stapes
  C) stapes, incus, malleus
  D) malleus, stapes, incus
  E) stapes, malleus, incus
  Answer: A
  Diff: 3   Page Ref: 295

25) Equilibrium receptors are located in the:
  A) ossicles
  B) external ear
  C) middle ear
  D) tympanic membrane
  E) inner ear
  Answer: E
  Diff: 2   Page Ref: 296

26) An ear infection following an illness such as a cold has passed from the throat through the auditory tube to the:
  A) eardrum
  B) semicircular canals
  C) inner ear
  D) middle ear
  E) outer ear
  Answer: D
  Diff: 3   Page Ref: 294

27) The auditory ossicle called the "anvil" is also called the:
  A) malleus
  B) incus
  C) stapes
  D) bony labyrinth
  E) cochlea
  Answer: B
  Diff: 1   Page Ref: 295

28) Which one of the following is NOT part of the inner ear?
  A) cochlea
  B) vestibule
  C) semicircular canals
  D) ossicles
  E) membranous labyrinth
  Answer: D
  Diff: 1   Page Ref: 295–296

29) Dynamic equilibrium receptors are found in the:
    A) cochlea
    B) semicircular canals
    C) malleus
    D) oval window
    E) vestibule

Answer: B
Diff: 2   *Page Ref: 297*

30) Hearing receptors within the spiral organ of Corti are called:
    A) hair cells
    B) rod cells
    C) cone cells
    D) Corti cells
    E) ceruminous cells

Answer: A
Diff: 1   *Page Ref: 298*

31) The portion of the bony labyrinth responsible for static equilibrium is the:
    A) vestibule
    B) semicircular canals
    C) cochlea
    D) oval window
    E) ossicles

Answer: A
Diff: 3   *Page Ref: 296*

32) Sensorineural deafness occurs when there is damage or degeneration of receptor cells of the:
    A) semicircular canals
    B) spiral organ of Corti
    C) ossicles
    D) spiral organ of Corti or cochlear nerve
    E) round window

Answer: D
Diff: 3   *Page Ref: 300*

33) Gustatory hairs are to taste as olfactory hairs are to:
    A) sight
    B) hearing
    C) dynamic equilibrium
    D) smell
    E) both hearing and dynamic equilibrium

Answer: D
Diff: 2   *Page Ref: 301-302*

34) Which one of the following is NOT a primary taste sensation:
   A) sweet
   B) salty
   C) pungent
   D) bitter
   E) sour

Answer: C
Diff: 1   Page Ref: 302

35) Which one of the following nerves serves the anterior tongue:
   A) cochlear
   B) vestibular
   C) glossopharyngeal
   D) vagus
   E) facial

Answer: E
Diff: 3   Page Ref: 302

36) Which one of the following cranial nerves is NOT involved in either taste or smell:
   A) facial nerve (VII)
   B) vestibular (VIII)
   C) glossopharyngeal (IX)
   D) vagus (X)
   E) olfactory nerve (I)

Answer: B
Diff: 3   Page Ref: 297

37) Stimulation of sour receptors occurs in response to:
   A) lemons
   B) beef steak
   C) sugar
   D) salt
   E) saccharine

Answer: A
Diff: 3   Page Ref: 302

38) The congenital condition of "crossed eyes" is also known as:
   A) hemianopia
   B) strabismus
   C) presbyopia
   D) myopia
   E) hyperopia

Answer: B
Diff: 3   Page Ref: 303

39) The decreased lens elasticity associated with aging that makes it difficult to focus on near objects is known as:
   A) hemianopia
   B) strabismus
   C) presbyopia
   D) myopia
   E) hyperopia
   Answer: C
   Diff: 3   *Page Ref: 304*

40) The only special sense that is NOT fully functional at birth is:
   A) taste
   B) smell
   C) vision
   D) hearing
   E) touch
   Answer: C
   Diff: 3   *Page Ref: 303–304*

True/False

1) The conjunctiva is another name for the sclera.
   Answer: FALSE
   Diff: 2   *Page Ref: 282–283*

2) Tears are secreted from lacrimal glands located on the medial end of each eye.
   Answer: FALSE
   Diff: 2   *Page Ref: 282*

3) The pupil is the circular opening in the iris through which light passes.
   Answer: TRUE
   Diff: 1   *Page Ref: 284*

4) Gross eye movements are produced by five extrinsic eye muscles attached to the outer surface of each eye.
   Answer: FALSE
   Diff: 1   *Page Ref: 282*

5) In close vision and bright light, the pupil will dilate.
   Answer: FALSE
   Diff: 1   *Page Ref: 284*

6) Cones enable vision in dim light.
   Answer: FALSE
   Diff: 1   *Page Ref: 286*

7) The ciliary body is a smooth muscle structure to which the lens is attached.
   Answer: TRUE
   Diff: 1   *Page Ref: 283; 288*

8) There are two varieties of cones; one responds to red light and the other responds to green light.

Answer: FALSE
Diff: 3   *Page Ref: 286; 288*

9) An astigmatism results from unequal curvatures of the cornea or lens.

Answer: TRUE
Diff: 2   *Page Ref: 292*

10) The normal resting eye is generally "set" for distant vision.

Answer: TRUE
Diff: 3   *Page Ref: 290*

11) The pinna, also called the auricle, is what most people call the "ear."

Answer: TRUE
Diff: 1   *Page Ref: 294*

12) The function of the auditory tube is to transmit sound vibrations.

Answer: FALSE
Diff: 2   *Page Ref: 294*

13) The "stirrup" is also referred to as the stapes.

Answer: TRUE
Diff: 1   *Page Ref: 295*

14) The bony labyrinth of the internal ear consists of the cochlea, vestibule, and the semicircular canals.

Answer: TRUE
Diff: 3   *Page Ref: 295*

15) In order to hear sound, vibrations pass from the eardrum to the ossicles, and on to the oval window.

Answer: TRUE
Diff: 3   *Page Ref: 298*

16) Dynamic equilibrium receptors report the position of the head with respect to the pull of gravity when the body is not moving.

Answer: FALSE
Diff: 2   *Page Ref: 296–297*

17) Deafness is defined as hearing loss ranging from slight to total loss.

Answer: TRUE
Diff: 2   *Page Ref: 300*

18) Unlike the taste sensation, it is NOT necessary to have the chemicals associated with smells dissolved in body fluids.

Answer: FALSE
Diff: 1   *Page Ref: 301–302*

19) The olfactory receptors are responsible for the sense of taste.

   Answer: FALSE
   Diff: 1   Page Ref: 301–302

20) There are five basic taste sensations that correspond to one of the five major types of taste buds.

   Answer: TRUE
   Diff: 2   Page Ref: 302

Matching

Match the following descriptions to their appropriate eye structure:

1) "White of the eye"

   Diff: 1   Page Ref: 283

2) Blood–rich tunic that contains dark pigment

   Diff: 1   Page Ref: 283

3) Smooth muscle structures attached to the lens

   Diff: 1   Page Ref: 283

4) Flexible biconvex crystal–like structure

   Diff: 1   Page Ref: 283

5) Circularly and radially arranged pigmented smooth muscle fibers

   Diff: 1   Page Ref: 283

6) Rounded opening through which light passes

   Diff: 1   Page Ref: 284

7) Contains millions of photoreceptors

   Diff: 1   Page Ref: 284

8) Area of greatest visual acuity

   Diff: 1   Page Ref: 286

9) Blind spot

   Diff: 1   Page Ref: 286

A) choroid

B) iris

C) lens

D) optic disk

E) retina

F) extrinsic eye muscles

G) optic disc

H) sclera

I) suspensory ligaments

J) pupil

K) fovea centralis

L) cornea

M) ciliary body

1) H   2) A   3) M   4) C   5) B   6) J
7) E   8) K   9) G

Match the following ear structures to their appropriate descriptions:

10) Pinna

    Diff: 1   Page Ref: 294

11) Tympanic membrane

    Diff: 1   Page Ref: 294

12) Auditory tube

    Diff: 1   Page Ref: 294

13) Malleus

    Diff: 1   Page Ref: 295

14) Incus

    Diff: 1   Page Ref: 295

15) Stapes

    Diff: 1   Page Ref: 295

16) Cochlea

    Diff: 1   Page Ref: 295

17) Spiral organ of Corti

    Diff: 1   Page Ref: 298

18) Semicircular canals

    Diff: 1   Page Ref: 297

19) Vestibule

    Diff: 1   Page Ref: 296

A) eardrum

B) contains the cochlea

C) contains the receptors for static equilibrium

D) wedge

E) saddle horn

F) snail-like subdivision of the osseous labyrinth

G) links the middle ear and the throat

H) stirrup

I) contains the receptors for dynamic equilibrium

J) contains receptors for dynamic equilibrium

K) contains the hair cells

L) outer ear

M) middle ear

N) hammer

O) contains the ossicles

P) links the inner ear and the cochlea

Q) anvil

| 10) L | 11) A | 12) G | 13) N | 14) Q | 15) H |
| 16) F | 17) K | 18) J | 19) C | | |

Match the following taste sensations:

20) Sugar, saccharine
   Diff: 1   *Page Ref: 302*

21) Oranges, tomatoes
   Diff: 1   *Page Ref: 302*

22) Amino acid glutamate
   Diff: 2   *Page Ref: 302*

23) Alkaloids
   Diff: 1   *Page Ref: 302*

24) Metal ions in solution
   Diff: 2   *Page Ref: 302*

25) Hydrogen ions in solution
   Diff: 2   *Page Ref: 302*

A) salty receptors

B) bitter receptors

C) sour receptors

D) umami receptors

E) sweet receptors

20) E   21) C   22) D   23) B   24) A   25) C

Match the following eye disorders with their descriptions:

26) Nearsightedness
   Diff: 1   *Page Ref: 292*

27) Increased pressure within the eye
   Diff: 2   *Page Ref: 289*

28) Blurry images due to unequal curvatures of the cornea or lens
   Diff: 2   *Page Ref: 292*

29) Eyeball is "too short"
   Diff: 1   *Page Ref: 292*

30) Inflammation of the conjunctiva
   Diff: 1   *Page Ref: 282*

31) Prolonged vitamin A deficiency results in deterioration of the neural retina
   Diff: 3   *Page Ref: 286*

A) conjunctivitis

B) hyperopia

C) night blindness

D) presbyopia

E) glaucoma

F) myopia

G) astigmatism

H) cataracts

26) F   27) E   28) G   29) B   30) A   31) C

Essay

1) Describe the pathway of light through the eyeball and the process of light refraction.

Answer: Light travels through the cornea, aqueous humor, lens, and vitreous humor before being focused on the retina during normal vision. Refraction by the cornea and humors is constant, whereas the lens changes its shape to be either more or less convex as needed. The greater the convexity, the more light is bent.

Diff: 3   *Page Ref: 290*

2) Describe the path of the optic fibers from the optic nerve to the occipital lobe of the brain.

Answer: Optic fibers from each eye leave the back of the eyeball through the optic nerve. At the optic chiasma, the medial fibers of each eye cross over to the opposite side. The resultant optic tracts contain fibers from the lateral side of the eye on the same side and the medial side of the opposite eye. The optic fibers synapse with neurons in the thalamus, which then continue on to the occipital lobe of the brain.

Diff: 3   *Page Ref: 291*

3) Describe the role of the lens in vision. Name and explain the disease caused by the hardening of the lens.

Answer: 1.   The lens is the only structure in the eye that can change shape to refract light. The lens becomes more or less convex in order to properly focus light on the retina.
2.   Cataracts are caused when the lens becomes increasingly hard and opaque. Vision becomes hazy and blindness can occur in the affected eye.

Diff: 2   *Page Ref: 288–289*

4) Explain the mechanism of hearing.

Answer: Sound waves enter the pinna and are transmitted down the external auditory canal until they hit the tympanic membrane and cause it to vibrate. Vibration of the tympanic membrane then causes the ossicles of the middle ear to vibrate, which in turn presses on the oval window of the inner ear. Vibration of the oval window sets the fluids of the inner ear in motion. Movement of the cochlear fluids then stimulate the hair cells of the organ of Corti, which in turn transmit impulses along the cochlear nerve to the auditory cortex in the temporal lobe, where interpretation of sound occurs.

Diff: 3   *Page Ref: 298–300*

5) Explain static and dynamic equilibrium and their interrelationships.

Answer: Static equilibrium is regulated by the maculae of the vestibule. The maculae report on the position of the head with respect to the pull of gravity when the body is at rest. Each macula is a patch of receptor cells embedded in the otolithic membrane. The otolithic membrane contains otoliths which roll in response to changes in the pull of gravity. This movement causes the hair cells of the membrane to bend, sending impulses along the vestibular nerve to the cerebellum, relating information regarding the position of the head in space. Dynamic equilibrium is regulated by the semicircular canals. The crista ampullaris of the membranous semicircular canal consists of a tuft of hair cells and their gelatinous cap called the cupula. Movement of the head causes the cupula to move in the opposite direction, stimulating the hair cells, which then transmit impulses up the vestibular nerve to the cerebellum. Static and dynamic equilibrium work together to provide information to the cerebellum to help control balance.

Diff: 3   *Page Ref: 296–298*

6) Explain the meaning of an "odor snapshot" and its relevance to human beings.

   Answer: Olfactory receptor cells transmit impulses to the olfactory cortex of the brain for interpretation. An "odor snapshot" is made, which then becomes part of our long-term memory. The olfactory pathways are closely tied to the limbic system, the emotional–visceral part of the brain. Odors elicit strong emotional responses, both positive and negative. The smell of freshly baked cookies, a certain perfume, or a dentist's office all engender their own unique response.

   Diff: 2   *Page Ref: 301–302*

7) Discuss the age–related disorders presbyopia and presbycusis. Identify the structures each disorder affects.

   Answer: 1.   Presbyopia literally means "old vision" and occurs around age 40 and later. As we age, the lens of the eye becomes less elastic. As a result, we have a difficult time focusing on things close to us, such as reading a newspaper, and we essentially become farsighted.

   2.   Presbycusis is a type of sensorineural deafness that often occurs as we age into our sixties. The deterioration and atrophy of the organ of Corti lead to a loss in the ability to hear high tones and speech sounds. In some cases of presbycusis, the ossicles of the ear fuse leading to difficulty conducting sound in the inner ear.

   Diff: 2   *Page Ref: 304*

Chapter 9 The Endocrine System

Short Answer

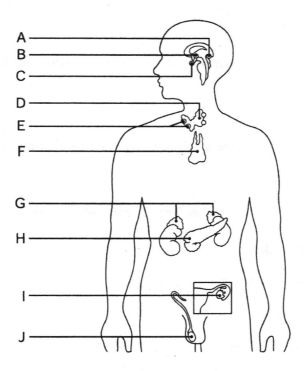

Figure 9.1

Using Figure 9.1, identify the following:

1) The gland that produces thymosin is indicated by letter _____.

   Answer: F
   Diff: 2   Page Ref: 314; 329

2) The gland that produces melatonin is indicated by letter _____.

   Answer: A
   Diff: 2   Page Ref: 314; 329

3) The gland that produces testosterone is indicated by letter _____.

   Answer: J
   Diff: 2   Page Ref: 314; 329

4) The glands that produce steroids and catecholamines are indicated by letter _____.

   Answer: G
   Diff: 2   Page Ref: 314; 322–326

5) The producer of hormones released by the posterior pituitary is indicated by letter _____.

   Answer: B
   Diff: 2   Page Ref: 314; 316–318

6) The gland that produces insulin and glucagon is indicated by letter _____.

Answer: H
Diff: 2   Page Ref: 314; 326

7) The glands that act as antagonists to the thyroid gland are indicated by letter _____.

Answer: E
Diff: 2   Page Ref: 314; 321

8) The gland that has both glandular and nervous tissue associated with it is indicated by letter _____.

Answer: C
Diff: 2   Page Ref: 314

9) The gland that is the major producer of female hormones is indicated by letter _____.

Answer: I
Diff: 2   Page Ref: 314; 329

10) The gland that is primarily responsible for body metabolism is indicated by letter _____.

Answer: D
Diff: 2   Page Ref: 314; 319

11) The thymus gland is indicated by letter _____.

Answer: F
Diff: 1   Page Ref: 314; 329

12) The pancreas is indicated by letter _____.

Answer: H
Diff: 1   Page Ref: 314; 326

13) The pineal gland is indicated by letter _____.

Answer: A
Diff: 1   Page Ref: 314; 329

14) The parathyroid glands are indicated by letter _____.

Answer: E
Diff: 1   Page Ref: 314; 321

Fill in the blank or provide a short answer:

15) Hypersecretion of growth hormone during childhood results in _____.

Answer: gigantism
Diff: 2   Page Ref: 314

16) Adrenocorticotropic hormone stimulates the cortex portion of the _____ gland.

Answer: adrenal
Diff: 2   Page Ref: 315

17) The posterior pituitary gland releases two hormones called _____ and _____.

Answer: oxytocin; antidiuretic hormone
Diff: 2   Page Ref: 318

18) Another name for antidiuretic hormone (ADH) is _____.

Answer: vasopressin
Diff: 2   Page Ref: 318–319

19) An enlargement of the thyroid gland is called a _____.

Answer: goiter
Diff: 1   Page Ref: 319

20) Anteriorly protruding eyes associated with hyperthyroidism is called _____.

Answer: exophthalmos
Diff: 2   Page Ref: 320

21) Calcitonin is made by the _____ of the thyroid gland.

Answer: parafollicular cells
Diff: 3   Page Ref: 320

22) Mineralocorticoids regulate the concentration of _____ and _____ ions in our blood.

Answer: sodium; potassium
Diff: 2   Page Ref: 322–323

23) Cortisone and cortisol and types of _____ produced by the middle cortical layer of the adrenal gland.

Answer: glucocorticoids
Diff: 2   Page Ref: 323

24) The enzyme produced by the kidneys when blood pressure drops, which causes the release of aldosterone, is called _____.

Answer: renin
Diff: 3   Page Ref: 323

25) Male sex hormones produced by the adrenal cortex are called _____.

Answer: androgens
Diff: 1   Page Ref: 324

26) Generalized hyposecretion of all adrenal cortex hormones leads to _____.

Answer: Addison's disease
Diff: 3   Page Ref: 324

27) Hypersecretion of glucocorticoids, often caused by a tumor, results in _____.

Answer: Cushing's syndrome
Diff: 3   Page Ref: 324

28) Another name for epinephrine is _____.

Answer: adrenaline
Diff: 2   Page Ref: 325

29) Insulin and glucagon are both hormones that are produced by _____.

Answer: pancreatic islet cells
Diff: 2   Page Ref: 326

30) Glucagon acts as an antagonist to a hormone called _____.

Answer: insulin
Diff: 1   Page Ref: 326

31) Polyuria, polydipsia, and polyphagia are indicative of a disease called _____.

Answer: diabetes mellitus
Diff: 2   Page Ref: 326

32) A hormone called _____ is believed to play an important role in establishing the body's day–night cycle.

Answer: melatonin
Diff: 3   Page Ref: 329

33) A hormone called _____ plays an important role in incubating a special group of white blood cells.

Answer: thymosin
Diff: 3   Page Ref: 329

34) The _____ cells of the testes produce testosterone.

Answer: interstitial
Diff: 2   Page Ref: 316

35) Home pregnancy tests check for a hormone in the female's urine called _____.

Answer: human chorionic gonadotropin (hCG)
Diff: 3   Page Ref: 332

Multiple Choice

1) Which one of the following is NOT one of the major processes controlled by hormones:
   A) body coordination
   B) mobilizing body defenses against stressors
   C) maintaining electrolyte balance
   D) regulating cellular metabolism
   E) growth and development

Answer: A
Diff: 1   Page Ref: 310

2) The chemical messengers of the endocrine system are known as:
   A) effectors
   B) target cells
   C) hormones
   D) neurons
   E) stimuli

Answer: C
Diff: 1   Page Ref: 310

3) Which one of the following is NOT typical of the changes that follow the binding of a hormone to its target cells:
    A) plasma membrane permeability changes
    B) cellular mutations occur
    C) enzymes are activated or inactivated
    D) mitosis is stimulated
    E) proteins are synthesized in the cell

Answer: B
Diff: 3   Page Ref: 311

4) Prostaglandins are:
    A) amino acid–based hormones
    B) steroid hormones
    C) lipid hormones manufactured in cell plasma membranes
    D) glycerol hormones
    E) target organs

Answer: C
Diff: 3   Page Ref: 311

5) Being lipid soluble, steroids can do all the following EXCEPT:
    A) diffuse through the plasma membranes of target cells
    B) catalyze cyclic AMP
    C) enter the nucleus
    D) bind to receptor proteins within the nucleus
    E) activate genes to transcribe mRNA for protein synthesis

Answer: B
Diff: 3   Page Ref: 311

6) Negative feedback mechanisms regulate:
    A) steroid hormones only
    B) amino acid–based hormones only
    C) prostaglandin hormones only
    D) very few hormones
    E) most hormones

Answer: E
Diff: 3   Page Ref: 311

7) Most endocrine organs are prodded into action by other hormones; this type of stimulus is called:
    A) hormonal stimulus
    B) humoral stimulus
    C) neural stimulus
    D) receptor–mediated stimulus
    E) steroid stimulus

Answer: A
Diff: 2   Page Ref: 311–312

8) Tropic hormones:
    A) stimulate the pineal gland to secrete hormones
    B) stimulate the thymus gland to secrete hormones
    C) stimulate other endocrine glands to secrete hormones
    D) stimulate nervous tissue
    E) stimulate prostaglandins

Answer: C
Diff: 2   Page Ref: 314

9) Growth hormone:
    A) is secreted by the thymus gland
    B) prevents urine production
    C) promotes growth in long bones and skeletal muscles
    D) is produced by the thyroid gland
    E) results in Cushing's disease if produced in excess

Answer: C
Diff: 3   Page Ref: 314

10) Which one of the following is NOT an anterior pituitary hormone:
    A) prolactin
    B) adrenocorticotropic hormone
    C) follicle-stimulating hormone
    D) antidiuretic hormone
    E) luteinizing hormone

Answer: D
Diff: 3   Page Ref: 314–316

11) The hormone that triggers ovulation of an egg from the female ovary is:
    A) luteinizing hormone
    B) prolactin
    C) follicle-stimulating hormone
    D) progesterone
    E) interstitial cell-stimulating hormone

Answer: A
Diff: 3   Page Ref: 316

12) Hypersecretion of growth hormone after long bone growth has ended (as an adult) is called:
    A) pituitary dwarfism
    B) Cushing's disease
    C) acromegaly
    D) myxedema
    E) gigantism

Answer: E
Diff: 2   Page Ref: 314

13) The hypothalamus is most closely associated with the:
    A) pineal gland
    B) pituitary gland
    C) thymus gland
    D) thyroid gland
    E) pancreas

Answer: B
Diff: 2   Page Ref: 316; 318

14) An enlargement of the thyroid gland resulting from a deficiency of dietary iodine is called:
    A) exophthalmos
    B) goiter
    C) cretinism
    D) myxedema
    E) acromegaly

Answer: B
Diff: 1   Page Ref: 319

15) Which one of the following is NOT a function of oxytocin:
    A) stimulation of uterine contractions
    B) stimulation of breast milk ejection
    C) stimulation of menstruation
    D) postpartum bleeding control
    E) labor induction

Answer: C
Diff: 2   Page Ref: 318

16) Diabetes insipidus is caused by hyposecretion of:
    A) antidiuretic hormone (ADH)
    B) growth hormone
    C) glucagon
    D) parathyroid hormone (PTH)
    E) prolactin (PRL)

Answer: A
Diff: 3   Page Ref: 319

17) Which one of the following hormones exerts its primary effects on the reproductive organs:
    A) follicle–stimulating hormone
    B) adrenocorticotropic hormone
    C) prolactin
    D) thyroid–stimulating hormone
    E) growth hormone

Answer: A
Diff: 2   Page Ref: 316

18) Alcohol inhibits the secretion of:
    A) parathyroid hormone (PTH)
    B) antidiuretic hormone (ADH)
    C) glucagon
    D) oxytocin
    E) prolactin (PRL)

Answer: B
Diff: 3   Page Ref: 319

19) The thyroid gland is located:
    A) above the kidneys
    B) below the Adam's apple
    C) within the mediastinum
    D) within the pancreas
    E) within the parathyroid glands

Answer: B
Diff: 1   Page Ref: 319

20) The body's major metabolic hormone is called:
    A) prolactin
    B) growth hormone
    C) adrenaline
    D) thyroid hormone
    E) calcitonin

Answer: D
Diff: 2   Page Ref: 319

21) The element necessary in the diet for proper thyroid function is:
    A) sodium
    B) potassium
    C) calcium
    D) iodine
    E) bromine

Answer: D
Diff: 1   Page Ref: 319

22) Hyposecretion of thyroxine in early childhood leads to:
    A) cretinism
    B) dwarfism
    C) myxedema
    D) exophthalmos
    E) acromegaly

Answer: A
Diff: 3   Page Ref: 319

23) Which of these hormones regulate calcium levels in the body:
   A) T3 and T4
   B) calcitonin and parathyroid hormone
   C) oxytocin and prolactin
   D) insulin and glucagon
   E) melatonin and glucocorticoids

Answer: B
Diff: 2   Page Ref: 320–321

24) Which one of the following is NOT produced by the adrenal cortex:
   A) mineralocorticoids
   B) glucocorticoids
   C) sex hormones
   D) epinephrine
   E) aldosterone

Answer: D
Diff: 2   Page Ref: 322–324

25) Which of these hormones is released by the adrenal medulla:
   A) sex hormones
   B) aldosterone
   C) cortisone
   D) glucocorticoids
   E) epinephrine

Answer: E
Diff: 2   Page Ref: 324–326

26) Rising blood levels of aldosterone cause the kidney tubules to:
   A) reabsorb potassium
   B) reabsorb sodium
   C) reabsorb calcium
   D) reabsorb iodine
   E) reabsorb hydrogen

Answer: B
Diff: 3   Page Ref: 323

27) Tetany resulting from uncontrolled muscle spasms may indicate a malfunction of the:
   A) pineal gland
   B) thymus
   C) parathyroid glands
   D) adrenal cortex
   E) posterior pituitary

Answer: C
Diff: 2   Page Ref: 321

28) The enzyme produced by the kidneys when blood pressure drops, stimulating a release of aldosterone, is called:
   A) cortisone
   B) renin
   C) cortisol
   D) vasopressin
   E) angiotensin

Answer: B
Diff: 2   Page Ref: 323

29) Glucocorticoids do all of the following EXCEPT:
   A) help resist long-term stress
   B) increase blood glucose levels
   C) decrease edema
   D) suppress inflammation
   E) regulate salt content of the blood

Answer: E
Diff: 2   Page Ref: 323

30) Which one of the following is NOT a symptom of Cushing's syndrome:
   A) moon face
   B) bronze skin tones
   C) buffalo hump
   D) high blood pressure
   E) water retention

Answer: B
Diff: 3   Page Ref: 324

31) The "fight-or-flight" response triggers the release of:
   A) ADH
   B) prolactin
   C) growth hormone
   D) epinephrine
   E) melatonin

Answer: D
Diff: 2   Page Ref: 325

32) Which one of the following is NOT an action of the catecholamines:
   A) stimulation of the sympathetic nervous system
   B) dilation of the small passages of the lungs
   C) increased heart rate
   D) decreased blood pressure
   E) increased blood glucose levels

Answer: D
Diff: 2   Page Ref: 325-326

33) Insulin is produced by cells of the pancreatic islets called:
    A) alpha cells
    B) beta cells
    C) delta cells
    D) gamma cells
    E) theta cells

Answer: B
Diff: 2   Page Ref: 326

34) Insulin works as an antagonist to:
    A) testosterone
    B) oxytocin
    C) thyroid hormone
    D) glucagon
    E) thymosin

Answer: D
Diff: 2   Page Ref: 326

35) Insulin causes:
    A) a decrease in the concentration of blood glucose
    B) an increase in the concentration of blood glucose
    C) an increase in blood pressure
    D) an increase in the production of glucagon
    E) a decrease in blood pressure

Answer: A
Diff: 2   Page Ref: 326

36) Which one of the following is NOT a sign of diabetes mellitus:
    A) polyuria
    B) polydipsia
    C) moon face
    D) polyphagia
    E) acidosis

Answer: C
Diff: 2   Page Ref: 326

37) The pineal gland produces
    A) thymosin
    B) melatonin
    C) estrogen
    D) insulin
    E) cortisol

Answer: B
Diff: 1   Page Ref: 329

38) The hormone that appears to help regulate our sleep–awake cycles is:
   A) thymosin
   B) melatonin
   C) progesterone
   D) glucagon
   E) thyroxine

Answer: B
Diff: 1   *Page Ref: 329*

39) The hormone responsible for the maturation of white blood cells known as T lymphocytes is:
   A) thymosin
   B) melatonin
   C) aldosterone
   D) progesterone
   E) thyroxine

Answer: A
Diff: 2   *Page Ref: 329*

40) Estrogens do all of the following EXCEPT:
   A) stimulate the development of secondary sex characteristics in females
   B) stimulate growth of facial hair
   C) stimulate menstruation
   D) help maintain pregnancy
   E) prepare the uterus to receive a fertilized egg

Answer: B
Diff: 3   *Page Ref: 329*

41) Which of these hormones does NOT play a role in reproduction:
   A) antidiuretic hormone
   B) follicle–stimulating hormone
   C) luteinizing hormone
   D) testosterone
   E) estrogen

Answer: A
Diff: 3   *Page Ref: 316; 329*

42) Which one of the following hormones is NOT produced by the anterior lobe of the pituitary gland:
   A) growth hormone
   B) prolactin
   C) oxytocin
   D) luteinizing hormone
   E) thyroid–stimulating hormone

Answer: C
Diff: 2   *Page Ref: 314–316*

43) The cells in the testes that produce testosterone are called:
   A) interstitial cells
   B) alpha cells
   C) beta cells
   D) pancreatic islet cells
   E) gonadotropic cells

Answer: A
Diff: 2   Page Ref: 316

44) The secondary sex characteristics brought about by testosterone secretion do NOT include:
   A) growth of facial hair
   B) development of heavy bones
   C) development of breasts
   D) lowering the voice
   E) development of heavy muscles

Answer: C
Diff: 1   Page Ref: 329

45) Which hormone works with estrogen to bring about the menstual cycle:
   A) human chorionic gonadotropin
   B) progesterone
   C) testosterone
   D) prolactin
   E) oxytocin

Answer: B
Diff: 1   Page Ref: 329

True/False

1) Exocrine glands are considered ductless glands because they release their hormones into the blood or lymph.

Answer: TRUE
Diff: 1   Page Ref: 314

2) The endocrine system is generally faster than the nervous system in coordinating the activities of body cells.

Answer: FALSE
Diff: 1   Page Ref: 310

3) Most hormones are regulated by negative feedback mechanisms.

Answer: TRUE
Diff: 1   Page Ref: 311

4) Releasing and inhibiting hormones produced by the hypothalamus travel to the anterior pituitary through the blood of the portal circulation.

Answer: TRUE
Diff: 2   Page Ref: 316

5) The pituitary gland is found in the brain closely associated with the hypothalamus.

Answer: TRUE
Diff: 1   Page Ref: 314

6) Hypersecretion of growth hormone during childhood leads to pituitary dwarfism.

Answer: FALSE

Diff: 2   Page Ref: 314

7) The target issue of prolactin is the female breast.

Answer: TRUE

Diff: 2   Page Ref: 315

8) Neurosecretory cells transport oxytocin and antidiuretic hormone to the anterior pituitary gland for storage.

Answer: FALSE

Diff: 2   Page Ref: 318

9) The posterior pituitary gland stores the hormones it releases, but does not manufacture them.

Answer: TRUE

Diff: 1   Page Ref: 318

10) Vasopressin is another name for antidiuretic hormone.

Answer: TRUE

Diff: 2   Page Ref: 318–319

11) Hyposecretion of FSH or LH leads to sterility in both males and females.

Answer: TRUE

Diff: 3   Page Ref: 316

12) Alcohol can suppress the production of antidiuretic hormone.

Answer: TRUE

Diff: 2   Page Ref: 319

13) Diabetes insipidus is caused by hyposecretion of insulin.

Answer: FALSE

Diff: 2   Page Ref: 319

14) Thyroid hormone is actually two iodine-containing hormones called T3 and T4.

Answer: TRUE

Diff: 3   Page Ref: 319

15) Hyposecretion of thyroxine in children can result in cretinism.

Answer: TRUE

Diff: 2   Page Ref: 319

16) Myxedema is the result of hyperthyroidism.

Answer: FALSE

Diff: 2   Page Ref: 320

17) Parathyroid hormone is the most important regulator of blood calcium concentration.

Answer: TRUE

Diff: 3   Page Ref: 321

18) Calcitonin is a hormone antagonistic to parathormone in the regulation of blood calcium concentration.

Answer: TRUE
Diff: 1   *Page Ref: 320*

19) Mineralocorticoids help regulate both water and electrolyte balance in body fluids.

Answer: TRUE
Diff: 2   *Page Ref: 322–323*

20) The adrenal glands are similar to the pituitary gland in that they have both glandular and neural tissue.

Answer: TRUE
Diff: 1   *Page Ref: 322*

21) The adrenal cortex is made up of neural tissue.

Answer: FALSE
Diff: 2   *Page Ref: 322*

22) Glucocorticoids, glucagon, and epinephrine are hyperglycemic hormones.

Answer: TRUE
Diff: 3   *Page Ref: 326*

23) The glucocorticoids help the body handle long-term stress primarily by increasing blood glucose levels.

Answer: TRUE
Diff: 2   *Page Ref: 323*

24) Both male and female sex hormones are produced by the adrenal cortex throughout life in relatively small amounts.

Answer: TRUE
Diff: 2   *Page Ref: 324*

25) Hypersecretion of the sex hormones may lead to masculinization in both men and women.

Answer: TRUE
Diff: 2   *Page Ref: 324*

26) The adrenal medulla and posterior pituitary are both composed of nervous tissue.

Answer: TRUE
Diff: 2   *Page Ref: 324*

27) Adrenaline is also known as epinephrine.

Answer: TRUE
Diff: 1   *Page Ref: 325*

28) The pancreas produces both glucagon and glucocorticoids.

Answer: FALSE
Diff: 2   *Page Ref: 323; 326*

29) Melatonin production peaks during the night to help regulate the body's day-night cycle.

Answer: TRUE
Diff: 2   *Page Ref: 329*

30) The thymus gland is located in the neck wrapped around the trachea.

Answer: FALSE
Diff: 1   *Page Ref: 329*

31) The pancreas has both endocrine and exocrine functions.

Answer: TRUE
Diff: 1   *Page Ref: 329*

32) The placenta is a temporary organ formed in the uterus of pregnant women.

Answer: TRUE
Diff: 1   *Page Ref: 332*

Matching

Match the following hormones with their endocrine gland:

1) Growth hormone
   Diff: 2   Page Ref: 314

2) Prolactin
   Diff: 2   Page Ref: 315

3) Adrenocorticotropic hormone
   Diff: 2   Page Ref: 315

4) Thyroid-stimulating hormone
   Diff: 2   Page Ref: 315

5) Luteinizing hormone
   Diff: 2   Page Ref: 316

6) Oxytocin
   Diff: 2   Page Ref: 318

7) Antidiuretic hormone
   Diff: 2   Page Ref: 318

8) Follicle-stimulating hormone
   Diff: 2   Page Ref: 316

9) Thyroxine
   Diff: 2   Page Ref: 319

10) Calcitonin
   Diff: 2   Page Ref: 320

11) Parathormone
   Diff: 2   Page Ref: 321

12) Aldosterone
   Diff: 2   Page Ref: 322

13) Cortisone
   Diff: 2   Page Ref: 323

14) Catecholamines
   Diff: 2   Page Ref: 325

15) Glucocorticoids
   Diff: 2   Page Ref: 323

16) Insulin
   Diff: 2   Page Ref: 326

A) thyroid
B) testes
C) pancreatic islets
D) posterior pituitary
E) ovaries
F) anterior pituitary
G) adrenal cortex
H) thymus
I) placenta
J) adrenal medulla
K) corpus luteum
L) alpha cells of pancreatic islets
M) pineal
N) beta cells of pancreatic islets
O) parathyroids
P) uterus

17) Glucagon

Diff: 2 *Page Ref: 326*

18) Melatonin

Diff: 2 *Page Ref: 329*

19) Thymosin

Diff: 2 *Page Ref: 329*

20) Human chorionic
gonadotropin

Diff: 2 *Page Ref: 332*

1) F	2) F	3) F	4) F	5) F	6) D
7) D	8) F	9) A	10) A	11) O	12) G
13) G	14) J	15) G	16) N	17) L	18) M
19) H	20) I				

Match the following actions with the appropriate hormone:

21) Stimulates milk production

Diff: 3 *Page Ref: 315*

22) Promotes water retention by
the kidneys

Diff: 3 *Page Ref: 318*

23) Stimulates growth of bone
and muscles

Diff: 3 *Page Ref: 314*

24) Reduces blood glucose levels

Diff: 3 *Page Ref: 326*

25) Raises blood calcium levels

Diff: 3 *Page Ref: 321*

26) Promotes growth of uterine
lining

Diff: 3 *Page Ref: 329*

27) Stimulates contraction of the
uterus

Diff: 3 *Page Ref: 318*

28) Programs T lymphocytes

Diff: 3 *Page Ref: 329*

A) progesterone

B) calcitonin

C) oxytocin

D) antidiuretic hormone

E) insulin

F) glucagon

G) thymosin

H) epinephrine

I) parathyroid hormone

J) estrogen

K) growth hormone

L) prolactin

M) thyroid hormone

N) glucocorticoids

21) L	22) D	23) K	24) E	25) I	26) A
27) C	28) G				

Essay

1) Explain the two major chemical classifications of hormones.

   Answer: The amino acid-based molecules include proteins, peptides, and amines. The steroid hormones include the sex hormones made by the gonads and the hormones produced by the adrenal cortex.

   Diff: 2   *Page Ref: 310*

2) Describe the three types of stimuli that activate the endocrine organs.

   Answer: The most common stimulus is hormonal. In hormonal stimulus, endocrine organs are prodded into action by other hormones, known as tropic hormones. Another type of stimulus is humoral, in which changing blood levels of certain ions and nutrients stimulate hormone release. The third type of stimulus is neural, in which nerve fibers stimulate hormone release.

   Diff: 2   *Page Ref: 311-312*

3) Explain the pituitary-hypothalamus relationship.

   Answer: Hormones from the anterior pituitary are released in response to releasing and inhibiting hormones produced by the hypothalamus. The hypothalamus releases these hormones into the blood of the portal circulation, which connects the blood supply of the hypothalamus with that of the anterior pituitary. Hormones from the posterior pituitary are made in the hypothalamus by hypothalamic neurons. Those hormones are then stored in the posterior pituitary until their release is necessary.

   Diff: 3   *Page Ref: 316; 318*

4) Explain the negative feedback interaction between calcitonin and parathormone.

   Answer: Calcitonin, released by the thyroid gland, decreases blood calcium levels by causing calcium to be deposited in the bones. Parathormone, released by the parathyroids in response to low blood calcium levels, stimulates bone destruction by osteoclasts, causing release of calcium into the blood. PTH is, therefore, a hypercalcemic hormone, whereas calcitonin is a hypocalcemic hormone. PTH is the most important regulator of calcium ion homeostasis of the blood.

   Diff: 3   *Page Ref: 320-322*

5) Explain the causes and effects of menopause.

   Answer: The onset of menopause, commonly called "change of life," is brought about by decline and atrophy of the ovaries. The decreased production of estrogen and other female hormones results in the inability to bear children, arteriosclerosis, osteoporosis, decreased skin elasticity, and sympathetic nervous system changes. These changes in the sympathetic nervous system bring about what are commonly called "hot flashes." Other symptoms include fatigue, nervousness, and mood changes.

   Diff: 1   *Page Ref: 332*

6) Four-year-old Tim is extremely small for his age, and he shows signs of mental retardation. His hair is thinning and his skin is dry. His parents have read about cretinism and pituitary dwarfism as possible diagnoses for their son and have taken him to the pediatrician for tests to be run. Which diagnosis do you think is correct? Explain why.

Answer: The likely diagnosis is cretinism. Hyposecretion of the thyroid hormone in early childhood leads to cretinism. Cretinism results in dwarfism and mental retardation. Cretinism also causes hair to be scanty and the dry skin. It is unlikely Tim suffers from pituitary dwarfism. Pituitary dwarfism results from hyposecretion of growth hormone in children but does not cause the other symptoms listed.

Diff: 3   Page Ref: 314; 319–320

7) Jamie is dehydrated from playing a rough game of football on a hot summer afternoon. Explain why beer is not a good choice of beverage considering what you know about antidiuretic hormone.

Answer: Antidiuretic hormone prevents urine production and promotes water retention by the kidneys. However, alcoholic beverages inhibit ADH secretion and result in a large output of urine. Jamie is already dehydrated and alcohol will only further that situation.

Diff: 3   Page Ref: 318–319

8) Explain how insulin and glucagon work as antagonists to one another.

Answer: Hormones that perform opposite actions are called antagonists. Insulin lowers blood glucose levels by increasing the ability of cells to transport glucose across their plasma membranes. Glucagon targets the liver to break down stored glycogen into glucose. The glucose is then released into the bloodstream to increase blood glucose levels.

Diff: 2   Page Ref: 326; 328

9) Compare the effects of hypersecretion and hyposecretion of growth hormone on a child.

Answer: Hyposecretion of growth hormone in a child leads to pituitary dwarfism. Body proportions are normal, but the person does not exceed 4 feet in height. Hypersecretion of growth hormone in a child leads to gigantism. Although body proportions are normal, the person can reach 8 to 9 feet in height.

Diff: 2   Page Ref: 314–315

Short Answer

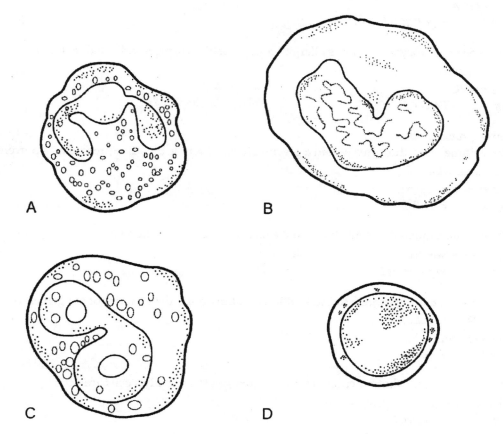

Figure 10.1

Using Figure 10.1, identify the following:

    1) The neutrophil is indicated by letter _____.

        Answer: A
        Diff: 1   *Page Ref: 345–347*

    2) The eosinophil is indicated by letter _____.

        Answer: C
        Diff: 1   *Page Ref: 345–347*

    3) The monocyte is indicated by letter _____.

        Answer: B
        Diff: 1   *Page Ref: 345–347*

    4) The lymphocyte is indicated by letter _____.

        Answer: D
        Diff: 1   *Page Ref: 345–347*

5) The granulocytes are indicated by letters _____ and _____.

Answer: A; C
Diff: 2   Page Ref: 345–347

6) The most common type of leukocyte is indicated by letter _____.

Answer: A
Diff: 2   Page Ref: 345–347

7) The type of leukocyte that fights allergies and parasitic worms is indicated by letter
_____.

Answer: C
Diff: 2   Page Ref: 345–347

Fill in the blank or provide a short answer:

8) The volume of erythrocytes within a given volume of whole blood, expressed as a percentage,
is _____.

Answer: hematocrit
Diff: 1   Page Ref: 340

9) The plasma protein that contributes to the osmotic pressure of blood is _____.

Answer: albumin
Diff: 2   Page Ref: 342

10) The iron–containing protein found in RBCs that transports the majority of oxygen carried in the
blood is _____.

Answer: hemoglobin
Diff: 2   Page Ref: 342

11) The anucleate cells that function to transport oxygen to the body's cells are called _____.

Answer: erthrocytes (RBCs)
Diff: 1   Page Ref: 342

12) A decrease in the blood's ability to transport oxygen is called _____.

Answer: anemia
Diff: 1   Page Ref: 343

13) The red blood cell disorder caused by life at a high altitude is called _____.

Answer: polycythemia
Diff: 2   Page Ref: 344

14) White blood cells are also called _____.

Answer: leukocytes
Diff: 1   Page Ref: 344

15) The movement of WBCs to areas of inflammation in response to chemical mediators is called
_____.

Answer: positive chemotaxis
Diff: 2   Page Ref: 345

16) An abnormal elevation of WBCs above the normal count of 11,000 cells/mm^3 is called
_____.

Answer: leukocytosis
Diff: 2   Page Ref: 345

17) The process by which WBCs are able to easily slip in and out of blood vessels is called
_____.

Answer: diapedesis
Diff: 2   Page Ref: 344

18) The process of blood cell formation within the red marrow of bones is called _____.

Answer: hematopoiesis
Diff: 3   Page Ref: 347

19) The process by which bleeding is stopped is called _____.

Answer: hemostasis
Diff: 1   Page Ref: 349

20) A thrombus that has broken away from a vessel wall and is freely floating in the bloodstream is
called an _____.

Answer: embolus
Diff: 2   Page Ref: 350

21) An insufficiency of circulating platelets is called _____.

Answer: thrombocytopenia
Diff: 2   Page Ref: 351

22) Hereditary bleeding disorders that result from lack of clotting factors are referred to as
_____.

Answer: hemophilia
Diff: 1   Page Ref: 351

23) Substances that the body recognizes as foreign are called _____.

Answer: antigens
Diff: 2   Page Ref: 351

24) The rarest blood type in the United States is type _____.

Answer: AB
Diff: 2   Page Ref: 353

25) Blood type A carries the _____ antigen.

Answer: A
Diff: 1   Page Ref: 353

26) The blood type referred to as the universal donor is called type _____.

Answer: O
Diff: 2   Page Ref: 353

27) A person with type B blood can receive blood from blood type(s) _____.

Answer: B; O
Diff: 3   Page Ref: 353

28) If you carry the Rh antigen, you are referred to as Rh _____.

Answer: positive
Diff: 2   Page Ref: 353

29) The condition in which maternal antibodies cross the placenta and destroy the baby's RBCs is called _____.

Answer: hemolytic disease of the newborn
Diff: 3   Page Ref: 354

30) The condition in which fetal RBCs are destroyed faster than the infant liver can rid the body of the breakdown products of hemoglobin is called _____.

Answer: physiologic jaundice
Diff: 2   Page Ref: 356

Multiple Choice

1) The matrix of blood is called:
   A) buffy coat
   B) plasma
   C) erythrocytes
   D) lymphocytes
   E) formed elements

Answer: B
Diff: 1   Page Ref: 340

2) In a centrifuged blood sample, the buffy coat between the formed elements and the plasma contains:
   A) leukocytes and erythrocytes
   B) platelets and erythrocytes
   C) leukocytes and platelets
   D) eythrocytes only
   E) leukocytes only

Answer: C
Diff: 3   Page Ref: 340

3) Which one of the following is NOT a physical characteristic of blood:
   A) sticky
   B) opaque
   C) sweet tasting
   D) heavier than water
   E) alkaline

Answer: C
Diff: 2   Page Ref: 340

4) Which one of the following does NOT describe blood plasma:
    A) it contains plasma proteins
    B) it contains metal ions (salts)
    C) its pH is 7.35 to 7.45
    D) it contains hormones
    E) it is the color of red wine
Answer: E
Diff: 2   Page Ref: 340; 342

5) Which one of the following formed elements is the most abundant:
    A) erythrocytes
    B) eosinophils
    C) platelets
    D) basophils
    E) lymphocytes
Answer: A
Diff: 1   Page Ref: 340; 343

6) Erythrocytes:
    A) have lobed nuclei and cytoplasmic granules
    B) are anucleate
    C) number 4000 to 11,000 per cubic millimeter of blood
    D) can travel by diapedesis
    E) clot blood
Answer: B
Diff: 3   Page Ref: 342–343

7) Normal whole blood contains _____ g of hemoglobin per 100 mL.
    A) 4–8
    B) 12–18
    C) 15–20
    D) 30–35
    E) 42–48
Answer: B
Diff: 3   Page Ref: 343

8) Which of the following is not a type of red blood cell disorder?
    A) aplastic anemia
    B) sickle cell anemia
    C) pernicious anemia
    D) polycythemia
    E) leukemia
Answer: E
Diff: 3   Page Ref: 343–344

9) Excessive erythrocytes result in:
   A) sickle cell anemia
   B) leukocytosis
   C) polycythemia
   D) leukopenia
   E) pernicious anemia

Answer: C
Diff: 2   Page Ref: 344

10) There are an average of _____ WBCs per cubic millimeter of whole blood.
   A) 100–1000
   B) 4000–11,000
   C) 10,000–20,000
   D) 50,000–100,000
   E) 1 million–3 million

Answer: B
Diff: 3   Page Ref: 344

11) Which one of the following is NOT true of WBCs:
   A) they use diapedesis to move in and out of blood vessels
   B) they locate areas of tissue damage through chemotaxis
   C) they move by ameboid motion
   D) they account for less than 1 percent of total blood volume
   E) they initiate the clotting process

Answer: E
Diff: 1   Page Ref: 344–345

12) Which one of the following groups consist of granulocytes:
   A) neutrophils, eosinophils, and basophils
   B) lymphocytes and monocytes
   C) eosinophils and monocytes
   D) basophils and eosinophils
   E) neutrophils, lymphocytes, and eosinophils

Answer: A
Diff: 2   Page Ref: 345

13) The type of leukocytes that would increase rapidly during allergy attacks and infections of parasitic worms are:
   A) eosinophils
   B) basophils
   C) neutrophils
   D) lymphocytes
   E) monocytes

Answer: A
Diff: 3   Page Ref: 345

14) The most numerous white blood cells are the:
   A) lymphocytes
   B) neutrophils
   C) eosinophils
   D) monocytes
   E) basophils

Answer: B
Diff: 2   Page Ref: 345

15) Which type of leukocyte contains heparin, an anticoagulant:
   A) neutrophil
   B) monocyte
   C) lymphocyte
   D) basophil
   E) eosinophil

Answer: D
Diff: 3   Page Ref: 346

16) The type of leukocytes that become macrophages in the tissues are:
   A) neutrophils
   B) eosinophils
   C) basophils
   D) lymphocytes
   E) monocytes

Answer: E
Diff: 3   Page Ref: 345-346

17) Platelets are fragments of multinucleate cells called:
   A) erythrocytes
   B) eosinophils
   C) basophils
   D) megakaryocytes
   E) macrophages

Answer: D
Diff: 1   Page Ref: 347

18) Blood cell formation in adults occurs in all of the following EXCEPT the:
   A) flat bones of the skull
   B) flat bones of the pelvis
   C) shaft of the femur
   D) proximal epiphyses of the humerus and femur
   E) the epiphyseal plates

Answer: C
Diff: 2   Page Ref: 347

19) Blood cell formation is called _____ and occurs in red bone marrow.
   A) hematopoiesis
   B) hemostasis
   C) agglutination
   D) coagulation
   E) hemolysis

Answer: A
Diff: 2   *Page Ref: 347*

20) The average functional lifespan of an RBC is:
   A) 20–30 days
   B) 50–75 days
   C) 100–120 days
   D) one year
   E) the body's lifetime

Answer: C
Diff: 1   *Page Ref: 347*

21) An immature RBC is called a:
   A) megakaryocyte
   B) hemocytoblast
   C) reticulocyte
   D) agranulocyte
   E) granulocyte

Answer: C
Diff: 3   *Page Ref: 347*

22) The hormone that regulates the rate of erythrocyte production is called:
   A) renin
   B) leukopoietin
   C) vasopressin
   D) erythropoietin
   E) thrombopoietin

Answer: D
Diff: 3   *Page Ref: 348*

23) Megakaryocytes pinch off anucleate fragments called:
   A) granulocytes
   B) platelets
   C) agranulocytes
   D) erythrocytes
   E) neutrophils

Answer: B
Diff: 3   *Page Ref: 347*

24) The series of reactions that stop blood flow following a cut is called:
    A) homeostasis
    B) coagulation
    C) hemostasis
    D) erythropoiesis
    E) agglutination

Answer: C
Diff: 1   Page Ref: 349

25) Which one of the following represents the proper sequence of hemostasis:
    A) platelet plug formation, coagulation, vascular spasm
    B) vascular spasm, coagulation, platelet plug formation
    C) coagulation, vascular spasm, platelet plug formation
    D) vascular spasm, platelet plug formation, coagulation
    E) coagulation, platelet plug formation, vascular spasm

Answer: D
Diff: 3   Page Ref: 349

26) Which chemical is released to bring about vasoconstriction during the vascular spasm phase of hemostasis:
    A) renin
    B) erythropoietin
    C) serotonin
    D) thrombopoietin
    E) interleukin

Answer: C
Diff: 3   Page Ref: 349

27) Blood normally clots in approximately:
    A) 1 minute
    B) 3 to 6 minutes
    C) 5 to 10 minutes
    D) 15 minutes
    E) 30 minutes

Answer: B
Diff: 1   Page Ref: 350

28) Prothrombin activator coverts prothrombin to:
    A) prothrombin activator
    B) thrombin
    C) fibrinogen
    D) fibrin activator
    E) serotonin

Answer: B
Diff: 3   Page Ref: 350

29) A _____ clot is formed during the process of hemostasis.
   A) fibrinogen
   B) fibrin
   C) prothrombin
   D) thrombin
   E) thromboplastin

Answer: B
Diff: 3   Page Ref: 350

30) A clot that breaks away from a vessel wall and circulates freely within the bloodstream is called a(n):
   A) embolus
   B) fibrin
   C) thromboplastin
   D) thrombus
   E) clotting cascade

Answer: A
Diff: 2   Page Ref: 350

31) Which of the following is a blood clotting disorder:
   A) polycythemia
   B) hemophilia
   C) leukocytosis
   D) leukopenia
   E) anemia

Answer: B
Diff: 2   Page Ref: 351

32) Bleeding disorders often result from a lack of which one of the following vitamins:
   A) vitamin B12
   B) vitamin A
   C) vitamin C
   D) vitamin D
   E) vitamin K

Answer: E
Diff: 2   Page Ref: 351

33) The ion essential for blood clotting is:
   A) sodium
   B) calcium
   C) iodine
   D) potassium
   E) hydrogen

Answer: B
Diff: 2   Page Ref: 349–350

34) The organ largely responsible for the synthesis of clotting factors is the:
   A) pancreas
   B) thyroid
   C) liver
   D) spleen
   E) kidneys

Answer: C
Diff: 2   Page Ref: 351

35) Treatment of hemophilia often involves:
   A) transfusion of plasma and vitamin K supplements
   B) injections of missing clotting factors and B12 injections
   C) vitamin K supplements only
   D) transfusion of plasma or injections of missing clotting factor
   E) vitamin K supplements and B12 injections

Answer: D
Diff: 3   Page Ref: 351

36) Severe shock occurs with blood loss of:
   A) over 5 percent
   B) over 10 percent
   C) over 20 percent
   D) over 30 percent
   E) over 50 percent

Answer: D
Diff: 3   Page Ref: 351

37) A substance that stimulates the immune system to release antibodies:
   A) antigen
   B) antibody
   C) interleukin
   D) fibrinogen
   E) prothrombin activator

Answer: A
Diff: 1   Page Ref: 351

38) The process whereby the binding of antibodies to antigens causes RBCs to clump is called:
   A) hemostasis
   B) coagulation
   C) agglutination
   D) clotting cascade
   E) hemolysis

Answer: C
Diff: 2   Page Ref: 351

39) Which antigen(s) does type AB blood contain:
   A) A antigen
   B) B antigen
   C) A and B antigens
   D) sometimes A antigens, other times B antigens
   E) no antigens

Answer: C
Diff: 3   *Page Ref: 353*

40) The most common type of blood in the U.S. population is:
   A) A
   B) B
   C) AB
   D) O
   E) AO

Answer: D
Diff: 1   *Page Ref: 353*

41) The universal recipient has blood type:
   A) A
   B) B
   C) AB
   D) O
   E) ABO

Answer: C
Diff: 2   *Page Ref: 353*

42) ABO blood groups are based on the presence of:
   A) A antigens
   B) B antigens
   C) O antigens
   D) A and B antigens
   E) A, B, and O antigens

Answer: D
Diff: 2   *Page Ref: 353*

43) Which blood type(s) can a person with blood type O receive:
   A) blood type A
   B) blood type B
   C) blood type AB
   D) blood type O
   E) blood types A, B, AB, or O

Answer: D
Diff: 2   *Page Ref: 353*

44) The immune serum used to prevent maternal sensitization to Rh antigens is:
    A) serotonin
    B) interleukin
    C) agglutinin
    D) RhoGAM
    E) HepBIg

Answer: D
Diff: 2   *Page Ref: 354*

45) Which of these blood types carries no antigens:
    A) blood type A
    B) blood type B
    C) blood type AB
    D) blood types A, B, and AB
    E) blood type O

Answer: E
Diff: 3   *Page Ref: 353*

46) Compatibility testing for agglutination of donor RBCs by the recipients' serum is called:
    A) blood typing
    B) transfusion reaction
    C) cross matching
    D) hemolysis
    E) hemodialysis

Answer: C
Diff: 3   *Page Ref: 354*

47) Anemias appearing in old age result from all of the following EXCEPT:
    A) nutritional deficiencies
    B) drug therapy
    C) leukemia
    D) erythrocyte mutations
    E) vitamin deficiencies

Answer: D
Diff: 3   *Page Ref: 343-344*

True/False

1) Normal pH of blood is between 7.35 and 7.45.

Answer: TRUE
Diff: 2   *Page Ref: 340*

2) Blood plasma is largely water.

Answer: TRUE
Diff: 1   *Page Ref: 340*

3) The temperature of blood is slightly lower than body temperature.

Answer: FALSE
Diff: 1   *Page Ref: 340*

4) Leukocytes are more numerous in blood than erythrocytes.

Answer: FALSE

Diff: 2   Page Ref: 340

5) The process by which white blood cells move in and out of blood vessels is called phagocytosis.

Answer: FALSE

Diff: 3   Page Ref: 344

6) An abnormally low WBC count is called leukopenia.

Answer: TRUE

Diff: 2   Page Ref: 345

7) Basophils are the most numerous type of leukocyte.

Answer: FALSE

Diff: 2   Page Ref: 345

8) All formed elements arise from a common type of stem cell called a hemocytoblast.

Answer: TRUE

Diff: 3   Page Ref: 347

9) Normal blood volume in healthy males is 5–6 liters.

Answer: TRUE

Diff: 1   Page Ref: 340

10) Erythropoeitin is released to stimulate platelet production in response to inadequate amounts of oxygen in the blood.

Answer: FALSE

Diff: 3   Page Ref: 348

11) Hemophilia is commonly called "bleeder's disease."

Answer: TRUE

Diff: 1   Page Ref: 351

12) A phlebotomist collects and processes blood samples for laboratory analysis.

Answer: TRUE

Diff: 1   Page Ref: 352

13) Blood type A will respond to a blood transfusion of blood type B with anti–B antibodies.

Answer: TRUE

Diff: 3   Page Ref: 353

14) Rh–related problems occur in pregnant Rh⁻ women carrying an Rh⁺ baby.

Answer: TRUE

Diff: 2   Page Ref: 354

15) Universal donors can receive blood groups A, B, AB, and O.

Answer: FALSE

Diff: 1   Page Ref: 353

Matching

Match the following function with its blood cell:

1) Transports oxygen bound to hemoglobin

   Diff: 1   *Page Ref: 342*

2) Active phagocytes that increase rapidly during acute infection

   Diff: 2   *Page Ref: 345*

3) Kill parasitic worms

   Diff: 2   *Page Ref: 345*

4) Transport carbon dioxide

   Diff: 1   *Page Ref: 342*

5) Active phagocytes that become macrophages

   Diff: 2   *Page Ref: 345*

6) Form B and T lymphocytes

   Diff: 2   *Page Ref: 345*

7) Contain histamine

   Diff: 2   *Page Ref: 345*

8) Increase during allergy attacks

   Diff: 2   *Page Ref: 345*

9) Produce antibodies

   Diff: 2   *Page Ref: 345*

10) Long-term "clean-up team"

    Diff: 2   *Page Ref: 345*

A) neutrophils

B) lymphocytes

C) basophils

D) monocytes

E) erythrocytes

F) leukocytes

G) eosinophils

| 1) E | 2) A | 3) G | 4) E | 5) D | 6) B |
| 7) C | 8) G | 9) B | 10) D | | |

Match the following blood types:

11) The blood type that has no antigens

   Diff: 2   *Page Ref: 353*

12) The blood type that possesses the A antigen only

   Diff: 2   *Page Ref: 353*

13) The blood type that can receive blood types B and O only

   Diff: 2   *Page Ref: 353*

14) The blood type that forms anti–A and anti–B antibodies

   Diff: 2   *Page Ref: 353*

15) The blood type known as the univeral donor

   Diff: 1   *Page Ref: 353*

16) The blood type known as the universal recipient

   Diff: 1   *Page Ref: 353*

A) Blood type O

B) Blood type A

C) Blood type B

D) Blood type AB

11) A   12) B   13) C   14) A   15) A   16) D

Essay

1) Scott's blood test shows that he has excess red blood cells. Identify and describe two causes of this disorder.

   Answer: Scott's disorder is polycythemia, which results from excess numbers of erythrocytes in the blood.
   This disorder may result from:
   1. Bone marrow cancer (called polycythemia vera)
   2. Life at a high altitude where the air is thinner and less oxygen is available (called secondary polycythemia)
   Increased sluggishness of the blood results from polycythemia.

   Diff: 2   *Page Ref: 344*

2) Joanna has learned that she has leukocytosis. Explain this disorder to her.

   Answer: Leukocytosis is a white blood cell disorder. It results when the total WBC count is above 11,000 cells per cubic millimeter of blood. Leukocytosis generally indicates a bacterial or viral infection in the body.

   Diff: 2   *Page Ref: 345*

3) List and describe the structure of the two major classifications of leukocytes.

Answer: The two major groups are the granulocytes and the agranulocytes.
1. The granulocytes have lobed nuclei and granules in the cytoplasm.
2. The agranulocytes lack cytoplasmic granules. Their nuclei are more normal in shape (either spherical, oval, or kidney–shaped).

Diff: 1   *Page Ref: 345*

4) Describe the three phases of the normal blood–clotting process.

Answer: Hemostasis involves three major phases. The first phase is platelet plug formation, in which platelets become "sticky" and cling to the site of injury. The second phase is the vascular spasm phase, in which serotonin released by the platelets causes the blood vessels to spasm and constrict, thus decreasing blood loss. The third phase is coagulation wherein thromboplastin interacts with PF3 and calcium, as well as other blood proteins, to form prothrombin activator. Prothrombin activator converts prothrombin to thrombin, which then joins with fibrinogen to form fibrin, the basis of the clot.

Diff: 3   *Page Ref: 349–350*

5) Explain the cause, effect, and treatment of hemophilia.

Answer: Hemophilia refers to several different hereditary bleeding disorders that can result from a lack of any of the factors needed for clotting. Hemophilia causes uncontrolled bleeding. Treatment involves transfusion of either fresh blood plasma or the specific purified clotting factor that the individual is missing.

Diff: 3   *Page Ref: 351*

6) Describe ABO and Rh blood groups.

Answer: The blood groups are based on the presence or absence of specific surface antigens. Blood group A has type A antigens on their RBCs, blood group B has type B antigens on their RBCs, blood group AB has both type A and type B antigens on their RBCs, and blood group O lacks either type A or type B antigens. The Rh^+ blood group indicates the presence of the Rh antigens on their RBCs. Individuals belong to blood groups A, B, AB, or O, and they are also classified as either Rh^+ or Rh^-.

Diff: 2   *Page Ref: 351; 353–354*

7) Explain the antigen–antibody response as it relates to blood groups.

Answer: Antigens are surface proteins found on all cells including blood cells. In the case of blood groups, an individual's blood type reflects the presence or absence of specific antigens. An antigen–antibody response is initiated if the individual receives a transfusion of blood containing antigens that it identifies as being "foreign." Antibodies found in a person's blood bind to the foreign antigen, causing agglutination, or clumping. The antigen–antibody complexes clog the small blood vessels, and the foreign RBCs are lysed, releasing hemoglobin into the bloodstream. The most serious complication of a transfusion reaction is kidney failure due to blockage of the kidney tubules by the hemoglobin molecules.

Diff: 3   *Page Ref: 351; 353*

8) Discuss hemolytic disease of the newborn (erythroblastosis fetalis).

Answer: Erythroblastosis fetalis results from Rh incompatibility between an Rh⁻ woman and her Rh⁺ baby. With delivery of the first such infant, the mother's blood becomes sensitized by the Rh⁺ antigens of the infant and she begins forming anti–Rh⁺ antibodies. With the second and subsequent pregnancies, in which the woman carries Rh⁺ infants, the mother's antibodies cross the placenta and destroy the baby's RBCs. The baby becomes anemic and hypoxic, and brain damage and death may result unless fetal transfusions are performed. Prevention of problems in future pregnancies involves treatment of the Rh⁻ woman with RhoGAM upon the birth of her first child to prevent sensitization and anti–Rh antibody formation.

Diff: 3   *Page Ref: 354*

Chapter 11 The Cardiovascular System

Short Answer

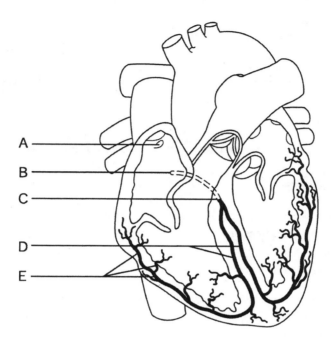

Figure 11.1

Using Figure 11.1, identify the following:

 1) The Purkinje fibers are indicated by label _____.

 Answer: E
 Diff: 1   Page Ref: 368–369

 2) The sinoatrial (SA) node is indicated by letter _____.

 Answer: A
 Diff: 1   Page Ref: 368–369

 3) The specific chamber of the heart that is indicated by letter A is called the _____.

 Answer: right atrium
 Diff: 1   Page Ref: 364

 4) The atrioventricular (AV) node is indicated by letter _____.

 Answer: B
 Diff: 1   Page Ref: 368–369

 5) The bundle branches are indicated by letter _____.

 Answer: D
 Diff: 1   Page Ref: 368–369

6) The layer of the heart wall that receives the stimulus from letter E is called the _____.

Answer: myocardium

Diff: 1   *Page Ref: 368–369*

7) The partition where the bundle branches are located is called the _____.

Answer: interventricular septum

Diff: 1   *Page Ref: 365; 368*

Fill in the blank or provide a short answer:

8) Crushing chest pain caused by oxygen deprivation of the myocardium is called _____.

Answer: angina pectoris

Diff: 1   *Page Ref: 368*

9) The visceral layer of the serous pericardium is actually the same layer as the _____.

Answer: epicardium

Diff: 3   *Page Ref: 363*

10) The two superior receiving chambers of the heart are known as the _____, while the two inferior discharging chambers of the heart are known as the _____.

Answer: atria; ventricles

Diff: 2   *Page Ref: 365*

11) The valves located between the atria and ventricles are known as the _____ valves.

Answer: atrioventricular (or AV)

Diff: 2   *Page Ref: 366*

12) The pointed tip of the heart that is directed toward the left hip is called the _____.

Answer: apex

Diff: 1   *Page Ref: 362*

13) Lack of adequate blood supply to the heart is called _____.

Answer: ischemia

Diff: 1   *Page Ref: 369*

14) The tiny white cords that anchor the cusps or flaps of endocardium to the walls of the ventricles are called the _____.

Answer: chordae tendineae

Diff: 1   *Page Ref: 366*

15) A decrease in the elasticity of blood vessels (i.e., increase in rigidity) causes arterial blood pressure to _____.

Answer: increase

Diff: 2   *Page Ref: 388*

16) The circulation from the heart to the lungs and back is known as _____ circulation.

Answer: pulmonary

Diff: 2   *Page Ref: 365*

17) The bicuspid valve is also referred to as the _____ valve.

Answer: mitral

Diff: 1   *Page Ref: 366*

18) When ventricles _____, the AV valves are closed.

Answer: contract
Diff: 2   Page Ref: 366

19) The coronary veins empty blood from the myocardium into a large vein on the posterior side of the heart known as the _____.

Answer: coronary sinus
Diff: 3   Page Ref: 367–368

20) The sinoatrial node, located in the right atrium of the heart, is often called the _____.

Answer: pacemaker
Diff: 1   Page Ref: 368

21) _____ are abnormal heart sounds that are fairly common in young children with healthy hearts because their heart walls are relatively thin and vibrate with rushing blood.

Answer: Heart murmurs
Diff: 1   Page Ref: 371–372

22) The electrocardiogram (ECG) wave that results from depolarization of the atria is the

_____.

Answer: P wave
Diff: 2   Page Ref: 370

23) A heart rate over 100 beats per minute is referred to as _____.

Answer: tachycardia
Diff: 2   Page Ref: 369

24) The term that means heart contraction is _____.

Answer: systole
Diff: 1   Page Ref: 369

25) During diastole, the pressure in the heart is _____.

Answer: low
Diff: 2   Page Ref: 371

26) The average heart beats about _____ times per minute.

Answer: 75
Diff: 1   Page Ref: 369

27) Cardiac output is the product of _____ and _____.

Answer: heart rate (HR); stroke volume (SR)
Diff: 2   Page Ref: 372

28) The hormones epinephrine and thyroxine will cause the heart rate to _____.

Answer: increase
Diff: 2   Page Ref: 373

29) Larger blood vessels that carry blood away from the heart are called _____.

Answer: arteries
Diff: 1   Page Ref: 374

30) The smallest blood vessels known as _____ connect arterioles and venules.

Answer: capillaries
Diff: 2   *Page Ref: 374; 377*

31) The innermost blood vessel wall that lines the lumen and consists of cells that fit closely together to form a slick surface that decreases friction and allows blood to flow smoothly is the _____.

Answer: tunica intima
Diff: 1   *Page Ref: 374*

32) The amount of blood being pumped out of the heart at any time is called _____.

Answer: cardiac output
Diff: 2   *Page Ref: 372*

33) Larger veins have _____ to prevent the backflow of blood.

Answer: valves
Diff: 2   *Page Ref: 376*

34) The flow of blood through a capillary bed is called _____.

Answer: microcirculation
Diff: 1   *Page Ref: 377*

35) Inflammation of varicose veins can result in a clot in that vessel; this condition is referred to as _____.

Answer: thrombophlebitis
Diff: 3   *Page Ref: 377*

36) The blood vessel that is the immediate inferior continuation of the external iliac artery is the _____.

Answer: femoral artery
Diff: 2   *Page Ref: 378*

37) The vessel that drains blood from all body regions below the diaphragm muscle before emptying into the right atrium is the _____.

Answer: inferior vena cava
Diff: 1   *Page Ref: 380*

38) The _____ veins join to form the superior vena cava before emptying into the right atrium.

Answer: brachiocephalic
Diff: 1   *Page Ref: 380*

39) The single vessel that drains blood from the digestive tract organs to the liver is the _____.

Answer: hepatic portal vein
Diff: 2   *Page Ref: 380*

40) The complete circle of connecting vessels in the brain is called the _____.

Answer: circle of Willis or cerebral arterial circle
Diff: 1   *Page Ref: 383*

41) The umbilical cord contains an umbilical _____ that transports oxygen and nutrient–rich blood to the fetus.

Answer: vein
Diff: 3   Page Ref: 383–384

42) The flaplike opening in the interatrial septum of the fetus through which blood is shunted directly from the right atrium to the left atrium is the _____.

Answer: foramen ovale
Diff: 1   Page Ref: 384–385

43) The pressure blood exerts against the inner walls of the blood vessels is known as _____.

Answer: blood pressure
Diff: 1   Page Ref: 387

44) The amount of friction blood encounters as it flows through the blood vessels is known as

_____.

Answer: peripheral resistance
Diff: 2   Page Ref: 388

45) The narrowing of blood vessels is known as _____.

Answer: vasoconstriction
Diff: 2   Page Ref: 389

46) A systolic blood pressure reading below 100 mm HG is called _____.

Answer: hypotension
Diff: 2   Page Ref: 391

47) Fluid tends to be forced out of a capillary bed by _____ while _____ tends to draw fluid into the capillary bed.

Answer: blood pressure; osmotic pressure
Diff: 3   Page Ref: 394

Multiple Choice

1) The thick layer of the heart wall that contains contractile cardiac muscle tissue is the:
   A) visceral pericardium
   B) parietal pericardium
   C) endocardium
   D) epicardium
   E) myocardium

Answer: E
Diff: 1   Page Ref: 363–364

2) The layer of the heart wall synonymous with the visceral layer of the serous pericardium is:
   A) myocardium
   B) endocardium
   C) epicardium
   D) parietal layer of the serous pericardium
   E) either endocardium or epicardium

Answer: C
Diff: 1   Page Ref: 363

3) Which area of the heart receives blood from the systemic veins:
    A) right ventricle
    B) left ventricle
    C) aorta
    D) right atrium
    E) left atrium

Answer: D
Diff: 2   Page Ref: 365

4) The right AV valve is known as the:
    A) aortic semilunar valve
    B) tricuspid valve
    C) mitral valve
    D) pulmonary semilunar valve
    E) bicuspid valve

Answer: B
Diff: 1   Page Ref: 366

5) Pulmonary veins:
    A) transport oxygenated blood to the lungs
    B) transport blood rich in carbon dioxide to the lungs
    C) transport oxygenated blood to the heart
    D) split off the pulmonary trunk
    E) return blood to the right atrium of the heart

Answer: C
Diff: 3   Page Ref: 365

6) What structure divides the left from the right ventricle:
    A) interventricular septum
    B) interatrial septum
    C) bicuspid valve
    D) tricuspid valve
    E) chordae tendineae

Answer: A
Diff: 1   Page Ref: 365

7) When the ventricles contract, the bicuspid (mitral) valve prevents blood from flowing from the:
    A) right ventricle to the right atrium
    B) left ventricle to the left atrium
    C) left atrium to the right atrium
    D) right atrium to the left atrium
    E) left ventricle to the right ventricle

Answer: B
Diff: 2   Page Ref: 366

8) The tricuspid valve is located between the:
    A) right atrium and left atrium
    B) right atrium and right ventricle
    C) left ventricle and pulmonary artery
    D) left ventricle and aorta
    E) right ventricle and the pulmonary trunk

Answer: B
Diff: 2   *Page Ref: 366*

9) The superior vena cava empties:
    A) oxygenated blood into the left atrium
    B) oxygenated blood into the left ventricle
    C) deoxygenated blood into the right atrium
    D) deoxygenated blood into the right ventricle
    E) deoxygenated blood into the left atrium

Answer: C
Diff: 2   *Page Ref: 365*

10) Which one of the following blood vessels carries oxygenated blood:
    A) superior vena cava
    B) inferior vena cava
    C) coronary sinus
    D) pulmonary artery
    E) pulmonary vein

Answer: E
Diff: 2   *Page Ref: 365*

11) The aortic semilunar valve is composed of:
    A) two cusps and opens when the left ventricle contracts
    B) three cusps and opens when the left ventricle contracts
    C) two cusps and opens when the right atrium contracts
    D) three cusps and opens when the right atrium contracts
    E) two cusps and closes when blood is filling the pulmonary circuit

Answer: B
Diff: 3   *Page Ref: 366*

12) Which one of the following are direct branches of the left coronary artery:
    A) circumflex and marginal arteries
    B) anterior and posterior interventricular arteries
    C) anterior interventricular and marginal arteries
    D) anterior interventricular and circumflex arteries
    E) posterior interventricular and marginal arteries

Answer: D
Diff: 3   *Page Ref: 367*

13) The sinoatrial node is located in the:
  A) aorta
  B) right atrium
  C) left atrium
  D) right ventricle
  E) interventricular septum

Answer: B
Diff: 1   Page Ref: 368

14) Which one of the following represents the correct path for the transmission of an impulse in the intrinsic conduction system of the heart:
  A) atrioventricular (AV) node, sinoatrial (SA) node, atrioventricular (AV) bundle, right and left bundle branches, Purkinje fibers
  B) atrioventricular (AV) node, atrioventricular (AV) bundle, sinoatrial (SA) node, Purkinje fibers, right and left bundle branches
  C) sinoatrial (SA) node, atrioventricular (AV) bundle, atrioventricular (AV) node, Purkinje fibers, right and left bundle branches
  D) sinoatrial (SA) node, atrioventricular (AV) bundle, atrioventricular (AV) node, right and left bundle branches, Purkinje fibers
  E) sinoatrial (SA) node, atrioventricular (AV) node, atrioventricular (AV) bundle, right and left bundle branches, Purkinje fibers

Answer: E
Diff: 3   Page Ref: 368

15) A heart rate of over 100 beats per minute is called:
  A) bradycardia
  B) tachycardia
  C) ischemia
  D) diastole
  E) heart block

Answer: B
Diff: 1   Page Ref: 369

16) Which one of the following vessels receives blood during right ventricular systole:
  A) pulmonary veins
  B) pumonary trunk
  C) aorta
  D) superior vena cava
  E) coronary arteries

Answer: B
Diff: 2   Page Ref: 365; 370–371

17) The mitral valve is normally closed:
  A) when the ventricle is in diastole
  B) when the ventricle is in systole
  C) when the atrium is contracting
  D) by the movement of blood from the atrium to the ventricle
  E) when the ventricle is contracting

Answer: B
Diff: 2   Page Ref: 368; 370–371

18) A person with a heart rate of 75 beats per minute and a stroke volume of 60 mL per beat has a cardiac output of:
  A) 4500 mL/minute
  B) 1.25 mL/minute
  C) 0.8 mL/minute
  D) 6000 mL/minute
  E) 120 mL/minute

Answer: A
Diff: 3 *Page Ref: 372*

19) Which one of the following is true concerning the lub-dup sounds of the heart:
  A) the first sound is longer and louder and is caused by closure of the tricuspid valve; the second sound is shorter and sharper and is caused by closure of the mitral valve
  B) the first sound is shorter and sharper and is caused by closure of the tricuspid valve; the second sound is longer and louder and is caused by closure of the mitral valve
  C) they are caused by contraction of the ventricles, followed by contraction of the atria
  D) the first sound is longer and louder and is caused by closure of the AV valves; the second sound is shorter and sharper and is caused by closure of the semilunar valves
  E) the first sound is shorter and sharper and is caused by closure of the semilunar valves; the second sound is longer and louder and is caused by closure of the AV valves

Answer: D
Diff: 3 *Page Ref: 371*

20) The volume of blood pumped out by each ventricle with each beat of the heart is called the:
  A) cardiac output
  B) cardiac cycle
  C) stroke volume
  D) heart rate
  E) diastolic pressure

Answer: C
Diff: 1 *Page Ref: 372*

21) The path of blood flow within the systemic vascular system is:
  A) arterioles, arteries, capillary beds, venules, veins
  B) arterioles, arteries, capillary beds, veins, venules
  C) arterioles, arteries, venules, veins, capillary beds
  D) arteries, arterioles, capillary beds, veins, venules
  E) arteries, arterioles, capillary beds, venules, veins

Answer: E
Diff: 1 *Page Ref: 374*

22) An increase in parasympathetic activity (primarily by the vagus nerves) causes:
  A) a decrease in both heart rate and cardiac output
  B) a decrease in heart rate and an increase in cardiac output
  C) an increase in both heart rate and cardiac output
  D) an increase in heart rate and a decrease in cardiac output
  E) no change in both heart rate and cardiac output

Answer: A
Diff: 2 *Page Ref: 372*

23) Which of the following reduces heart rate:
   A) exercise
   B) epinephrine
   C) thyroxine
   D) increased body temperature
   E) high blood pressure

   Answer: E
   Diff: 3   Page Ref: 372–373

24) Veins:
   A) carry blood away from the heart
   B) branch into smaller vessels called arterioles
   C) transport oxygen–rich blood
   D) operate under high pressure
   E) often have valves to prevent the backflow of blood

   Answer: E
   Diff: 2   Page Ref: 374; 376

25) Which one of the following is caused by a decrease in venous return to the heart:
   A) a decrease in stroke volume and cardiac output
   B) a decrease in stroke volume and an increase in cardiac output
   C) an increase in stroke volume and cardiac output
   D) an increase in stroke volume and a decrease in cardiac output
   E) no change in stroke volume and cardiac output

   Answer: A
   Diff: 3   Page Ref: 372–373

26) Which one is the correct sequence going from the outermost to the innermost layer of a blood vessel wall:
   A) tunica media, tunica intima, tunica externa
   B) tunica media, tunica externa, tunica intima
   C) tunica externa, tunica media, tunica intima
   D) tunica externa, tunica intima, tunica media
   E) tunica intima, tunica media, tunica externa

   Answer: C
   Diff: 1   Page Ref: 374–376

27) Which of the following blood vessels is a direct branch of the ascending aorta:
   A) right subclavian artery
   B) carotid artery
   C) right coronary artery
   D) left coronary artery
   E) both the right and left coronary arteries

   Answer: E
   Diff: 2   Page Ref: 378

28) Which one of the following does NOT receive blood directly from the aortic arch:
    A) brachiocephalic artery
    B) left subclavian artery
    C) left common carotid artery
    D) right common carotid artery
    E) thoracic aorta

Answer: D
Diff: 3   Page Ref: 378

29) Which of these arteries is NOT a branch of the abdominal aorta:
    A) renal arteries
    B) left common carotid artery
    C) inferior mesenteric artery
    D) common iliac arteries
    E) gonadal arteries

Answer: B
Diff: 3   Page Ref: 378

30) Which of these pathways correctly traces blood as it travels from the aortic arch to the left arm:
    A) aortic arch, brachiocephalic trunk, right common carotid artery
    B) aortic arch, left common carotid artery, left internal carotid artery
    C) aortic arch, left subclavian artery, left axillary artery, left brachial artery
    D) ascending aorta, right coronary arteries
    E) abdominal aorta, celiac trunk, left gastric artery

Answer: C
Diff: 3   Page Ref: 378

31) The carotid artery is located in the:
    A) armpit
    B) groin
    C) neck
    D) abdomen
    E) leg

Answer: C
Diff: 1   Page Ref: 378–379

32) Blood travels to the stomach by way of the branch of the celiac trunk called the:
    A) left gastric atery
    B) splenic artery
    C) common hepatic artery
    D) superior mesenteric artery
    E) inferior mesenteric artery

Answer: A
Diff: 2   Page Ref: 378

33) The right and left renal veins empty blood from the:
    A) kidneys
    B) common iliac vein
    C) inferior vena cava
    D) hepatic portal vein
    E) vertebral vein

Answer: C
Diff: 2   Page Ref: 380

34) The external iliac vein receives blood from all of the following EXCEPT:
    A) anterior tibial vein
    B) fibular vein
    C) popliteal vein
    D) femoral vein
    E) vertebral vein

Answer: E
Diff: 3   Page Ref: 380

35) The brachial vein:
    A) drains blood from the radial and ulnar veins, then empties that blood into the axillary
       vein
    B) drains blood from the internal jugular vein, then empties that blood into the superior
       vena cava
    C) drains blood from the popliteal vein, then empties that blood into the external iliac vein
    D) drains blood from the axillary vein, then empties that blood into the superior vena cava
    E) drains blood from the popliteal vein, then empties that blood into the femoral vein

Answer: A
Diff: 2   Page Ref: 380

36) The umbilical vein carries:
    A) metabolic wastes and carbon dioxide from the fetus to the placenta
    B) metabolic wastes and carbon dioxide from the placenta to the fetus
    C) oxygen and nutrients from the fetus to the placenta
    D) oxygen and nutrients from the placenta to the fetus
    E) blood from the navel into the inferior vena cava

Answer: D
Diff: 3   Page Ref: 383–384

37) Which one of the following blood vessels in the fetus has the highest concentration of oxygen:
    A) umbilical arteries
    B) inferior vena cava
    C) ductus venosus
    D) ductus arteriosus
    E) left atrium

Answer: C
Diff: 3   Page Ref: 383–385

38) Which one of the following areas is NOT a pressure point:
   A) renal artery
   B) radial artery
   C) facial artery
   D) dorsalis pedis artery
   E) posterior tibial artery

Answer: A
Diff: 2   Page Ref: 387

39) In which one of the following blood vessels is blood pressure the highest:
   A) veins
   B) capillaries
   C) vena cava
   D) arteries
   E) arterioles

Answer: D
Diff: 2   Page Ref: 387

40) The friction blood encounters as it flows through the vessels is called:
   A) cardiac output
   B) stroke volume
   C) peripheral resistance
   D) blood pressure
   E) diastolic pressure

Answer: C
Diff: 2   Page Ref: 388

41) Generalized vasoconstriction occurs as a result of:
   A) an increase in parasympathetic nervous system firing
   B) a decrease in parasympathetic nervous system firing
   C) an increase in sympathetic nervous system firing
   D) a decrease in sympathetic nervous system firing
   E) an increase in blood pressure

Answer: C
Diff: 2   Page Ref: 389

42) Which one of the following is the main function of renin and aldosterone:
   A) they are produced whenever blood pressure rises and ultimately cause an increase in
      blood volume and blood pressure
   B) they are produced whenever blood pressure rises and ultimately cause a decrease in
      blood volume and blood pressure
   C) they are produced when blood pressure rises and have no long–term effect on blood
      volume and blood pressure
   D) they are produced whenever blood pressure falls and ultimately cause an increase in
      blood volume and blood pressure
   E) they are produced whenever blood pressure falls and ultimately cause a decrease in
      blood volume and blood pressure

Answer: D
Diff: 3   Page Ref: 390–391

43) Which one of the following are the main functions of renin and angiotensin II:
   A) blood pressure rises—this causes vasoconstriction and further increases blood pressure
   B) blood pressure rises—this causes vasoconstriction and a decrease in blood pressure
   C) blood pressure rises—this causes vasodilation and a decrease in blood pressure
   D) blood pressure falls—this causes vasoconstriction and an increase in blood pressure
   E) blood pressure falls—this causes vasodilation and an increase in blood pressure

Answer: D
Diff: 3   Page Ref: 390–391

44) Substances tend to leave the bloodstream at the arterial end of the capillary because:
   A) the osmotic pressure of the blood is higher at the arterial end of the capillary
   B) the osmotic pressure of the blood is higher at the venular end of the capillary
   C) blood pressure is higher at the arterial end of the capillary
   D) blood pressure is higher at the venular end of the capillary
   E) interstitial pressure is higher at the arterial end of the capillary

Answer: C
Diff: 2   Page Ref: 394–395

45) Varicose veins are caused by:
   A) a loss of elasticity in blood vessels
   B) the accumulation of fatty substances within blood vessels
   C) excessive production of the enzyme renin
   D) incompetent venous valves
   E) orthostatic hypotension

Answer: D
Diff: 1   Page Ref: 397

True/False

1) Cardiac muscle is enclosed by a double sac of serous membrane known as the peritoneum.

Answer: FALSE
Diff: 1   Page Ref: 362

2) The pulmonary arteries carry deoxygenated blood to the lungs.

Answer: TRUE
Diff: 2   Page Ref: 365

3) The chordae tendineae anchor the semilunar valves to the walls of the ventricles.

Answer: FALSE
Diff: 2   Page Ref: 366

4) The tricuspid valve is located on the right side of the heart between the right atrium and right ventricle.

Answer: TRUE
Diff: 1   Page Ref: 366

5) The semilunar valves prevent the backflow of blood into the atria when the ventricles are contracting.

Answer: FALSE
Diff: 3   Page Ref: 366

6) Arteries always carry blood away from the heart.

Answer: TRUE
Diff: 1   *Page Ref: 374*

7) The coronary sinus on the backside of the heart drains deoxygenated blood from the wall of the heart into the left atrium.

Answer: FALSE
Diff: 3   *Page Ref: 367–368*

8) The coronary sulcus is also known as the atrioventricular groove.

Answer: TRUE
Diff: 1   *Page Ref: 367*

9) The part of the intrinsic conduction system of the heart that directly supplies the walls of the ventricles is the Purkinje fibers.

Answer: TRUE
Diff: 3   *Page Ref: 368*

10) The pacemaker of the heart under normal circumstances is called the sinoatrial (SA) node.

Answer: TRUE
Diff: 1   *Page Ref: 368*

11) Systole means contraction of the ventricles.

Answer: TRUE
Diff: 1   *Page Ref: 369*

12) During ventricular diastole, the bicuspid and tricuspid valves are closed.

Answer: FALSE
Diff: 3   *Page Ref: 371*

13) Cardiac output is calculated by multiplying the stroke volume times the systolic blood pressure.

Answer: FALSE
Diff: 1   *Page Ref: 372*

14) Reductions in venous return cause reductions in both stroke volume and cardiac output.

Answer: TRUE
Diff: 3   *Page Ref: 372*

15) An increased firing of the parasympathetic nervous system causes increased cardiac output.

Answer: FALSE
Diff: 3   *Page Ref: 372*

16) Smooth muscle and elastic tissue in a blood vessel wall is found primarily in the tunica media.

Answer: TRUE
Diff: 2   *Page Ref: 376*

17) The larger arteries contain valves to prevent the backflow of blood.

Answer: FALSE
Diff: 2   *Page Ref: 376*

18) Exchanges between blood and tissue cells occur in capillary beds.

Answer: TRUE
Diff: 2   Page Ref: 376

19) When precapillary sphincters are closed, blood flows through the shunts and bypasses the tissue cells.

Answer: TRUE
Diff: 3   Page Ref: 377

20) The portion of the aorta in the abdominopelvic cavity is known as the thoracic aorta.

Answer: FALSE
Diff: 2   Page Ref: 378

21) The three branches of the aortic arch are the brachiocephalic trunk, left common carotid artery, and the left subclavian artery.

Answer: TRUE
Diff: 2   Page Ref: 378

22) The superior and inferior mesenteric arteries drain blood from the intestines.

Answer: FALSE
Diff: 2   Page Ref: 378

23) The common iliac vein drains blood into the inferior vena cava.

Answer: TRUE
Diff: 1   Page Ref: 380

24) Veins draining the head and arms empty into the inferior vena cava.

Answer: FALSE
Diff: 2   Page Ref: 380

25) The great saphenous vein, the longest vein in the body, drains deoxygenated blood from the dorsal venous arch in the foot which then empties into the femoral vein.

Answer: TRUE
Diff: 3   Page Ref: 380

26) The circle of Willis involves blood flow through the liver.

Answer: FALSE
Diff: 1   Page Ref: 383

27) The major vessels involved in hepatic portal circulation are the inferior and superior mesenteric arteries, the splenic artery, and the left gastric artery.

Answer: FALSE
Diff: 3   Page Ref: 385–386

28) The umbilical vein carries blood rich in nutrients and oxygen to the fetus.

Answer: TRUE
Diff: 2   Page Ref: 383–384

29) In fetal circulation, blood travels directly from the right atrium to the left atrium through the foramen ovale.

Answer: TRUE
Diff: 2   Page Ref: 384–385

30) Diastolic blood pressure is the pressure in the arteries at the peak of ventricular contraction.

Answer: FALSE
Diff: 2   Page Ref: 388

31) An increase in blood vessel diameter causes arterial blood pressure to decrease.

Answer: TRUE
Diff: 2   Page Ref: 388–390

32) Hypotension is diastolic blood pressure below 100 mm Hg.

Answer: FALSE
Diff: 1   Page Ref: 391

33) Cold temperatures have a vasoconstricting effect on blood vessels.

Answer: TRUE
Diff: 2   Page Ref: 391

Matching

Match the following:

1) Heart chamber with the
   thickest wall

   Diff: 1   Page Ref: 365–366

2) Superior discharging chamber
   on the left side of the heart

   Diff: 1   Page Ref: 365–366

3) Heart chamber that pumps
   blood to the pulmonary trunk

   Diff: 1   Page Ref: 365–366

4) Heart chamber that contains
   the sinoatrial node

   Diff: 1   Page Ref: 368

5) Roof of this chamber contains
   the bicuspid valve

   Diff: 1   Page Ref: 366

6) The coronary sinus empties
   blood from cardiac circulation
   into this chamber

   Diff: 2   Page Ref: 367–368

7) The four pulmonary veins
   return oxygenated blood to
   this chamber

   Diff: 2   Page Ref: 365

8) This chamber sends blood
   into the aorta

   Diff: 2   Page Ref: 365

A) right ventricle

B) left ventricle

C) left atrium

D) right atrium

E) right atrium

1) B   2) B   3) A   4) E   5) B   6) D
7) C   8) B

Match the following:

9) Part of the cardiac cycle when the coronary system is emptying of blood

Diff: 2   Page Ref: 371

A) ventricular systole

B) ventricular diastole

10) Part of the cardiac cycle when the bicuspid and tricuspid valves are open

Diff: 2   Page Ref: 371

11) Part of the cardiac cycle when both of the semilunar valves are closed

Diff: 2   Page Ref: 371

9) A   10) B   11) B

Match the following:

12) Epinephrine and thyroxine
   cause both heart rate and
   cardiac output to

   Diff: 2   Page Ref: 373; 391

13) An increase in vagus nerve
   firing causes heart rate to

   Diff: 2   Page Ref: 372

14) An increase in sympathetic
   nervous system firing causes
   cardiac output to

   Diff: 2   Page Ref: 372

15) A decrease in peripheral
   resistance causes arterial
   blood pressure to

   Diff: 2   Page Ref: 388

16) Aldosterone causes blood
   volume to

   Diff: 2   Page Ref: 390–391

17) An increase in the deposition
   of saturated fats in the lining
   of blood vessels causes
   arterial blood pressure to

   Diff: 2   Page Ref: 391

18) Salt causes both blood volume
   and arterial blood pressure to

   Diff: 2   Page Ref: 391

A) decrease

B) increase

12) B   13) A   14) B   15) A   16) B   17) B
18) B

Match the following:

19) These vessels carry blood
   away from the heart

   Diff: 1   Page Ref: 374

20) These vessels return blood to
   the heart

   Diff: 1   Page Ref: 374

21) Superior and inferior vena
   cava are classified as these
   types of vessels

   Diff: 1   Page Ref: 380

A) veins

B) arteries

C) capillaries

22) The aorta is classified as one
    of these vessels
    Diff: 1   *Page Ref: 378*

23) These vessesls have thicker
    walls and a heavier tunica
    media
    Diff: 1   *Page Ref: 376*

24) Nutrient and gas exchange
    occur in these vessels
    Diff: 1   *Page Ref: 376*

25) Blood pressure in these
    vessels is low
    Diff: 2   *Page Ref: 376*

26) These vessels have thinner
    walls and transport
    oxygen–poor blood
    Diff: 1   *Page Ref: 376*

27) Some of these larger vessels
    have valves to prevent
    backflow
    Diff: 2   *Page Ref: 376*

28) Venules drain these tiny
    vessels
    Diff: 2   *Page Ref: 374*

| 19) B | 20) A | 21) A | 22) B | 23) B | 24) C |
| 25) A | 26) A | 27) A | 28) C | | |

Essay

1) Trace the path of a drop of blood, starting at the right atrium and returning to the right atrium, through the pulmonary and systemic circuits of the cardiovascular system. Identify the chambers, valves, and vessels (except specific systemic blood vessels that are not directly associated with the heart), and indicate whether the blood is oxygenated or deoxygenated in each area.

   Answer: Deoxygenated blood in the right atrium, deoxygenated blood through the pulmonary tricuspid valve, deoxygenated blood in the right ventricle, deoxygenated blood through the pulmonary semilunar valve, deoxygenated blood in the pulmonary trunk, deoxygenated blood in the right and left pulmonary arteries, deoxygenated blood in the pulmonary capillaries in the lungs, oxygenated blood in the pulmonary veins, oxygenated blood in the left atrium, oxygenated blood through the bicuspid (mitral) valve, oxygenated blood in the left ventricle, oxygenated blood through the aortic semilunar valve, oxygenated blood in the aorta, oxygenated blood in the systemic arteries, oxygenated blood in the systemic arterioles, oxygenated blood in the systemic capillaries, deoxygenated blood in the systemic venules, deoxygenated blood in the systemic veins, deoxygenated blood in the superior and inferior vena cava, deoxygenated blood in the right atrium.

   Diff: 2   *Page Ref: 365–366*

2) Identify the five major parts of the intrinsic conduction system of the heart in their normal order, beginning with the pacemaker.

   Answer: Sinoatrial (SA) node in the right atrium, atrioventricular (AV) node at the junction of the atria and ventricles, atrioventricular (AV) bundle or bundle of His in the interventricular septum, right and left bundle branches in the interventricular septum, Purkinje fibers in the muscle of the ventricle walls.

   Diff: 2   *Page Ref: 368*

3) Discuss the events that are taking place in the cardiac cycle during the left ventricular systole. Indicate whether the other heart chambers are in systole or diastole and whether they are filling or emptying of blood. If they are emptying, state where the blood is going. If they are filling with blood, state where the blood is coming from. Include an explanation of which valves are open and which valves are closed, in addition to whether the coronary system is filling or emptying of blood.

   Answer: When the left ventricle is in systole, oxygenated blood is leaving the left ventricle and entering the aorta. At that time, the aortic semilunar valve is open and the bicuspid valve is closed. The right ventricle is also in systole and deoxygenated blood is leaving the right ventricle and entering the pulmonary trunk. At that time, the pulmonary semilunar valve is open and the tricuspid valve is closed. When the ventricles are in systole, both the right and left atria are in diastole. The right atrium is filling with deoxygenated blood, which is returning to this chamber via the coronary sinus and the superior and inferior vena cava. The left atrium is filling with oxygenated blood that is returning to the heart from the lungs via the pulmonary veins. Finally, during ventricular systole, blood is leaving the coronary system and entering the right side of the heart via the coronary sinus.

   Diff: 3   *Page Ref: 369; 371*

4) Define *peripheral resistance*. Explain several factors that cause it to increase and its effect on arterial blood pressure.

Answer: Peripheral resistance is the amount of friction encountered by blood as it flows through the blood vessels. Probably the most important factor that increases peripheral resistance is the narrowing of the diameter of a blood vessel (mainly by arterioles), which is called vasoconstriction. Vasoconstriction occurs normally due to an increase in sympathetic nervous system firing. It can also occur abnormally in atherosclerosis. Another factor that causes an increase in peripheral resistance is increased volume of blood in the vascular system or increased viscosity (thickness) of the blood. Regardless of the cause of this increase in peripheral resistance, the result is an increase in arterial blood pressure.

Diff: 3   Page Ref: 388

5) Explain the role of valves in heart functioning.

Answer: Valves allow blood to flow in one direction through the heart chambers (from atria to ventricles) and out the two arteries leaving the heart.
There are two types of valves found in the heart:
1.   The atrioventricular, or AV, valves are located between the atrium and ventricle on each side of the heart. These valves prevent the backflow of blood into the atria when the heart contracts. In summary, these AV valves are open during heart relaxation and closed during heart contraction.
2.   The semilunar valves guard the base of the two large arteries, aorta and pulmonary trunk, leaving the heart via the two ventricles. These valves close after blood has passed through the arteries on its way out of the heart. They prevent the backflow of blood into the ventricles from the arteries. In summary, these valves are closed during heart relaxation and open during heart contraction.

Diff: 2   Page Ref: 366

6) Explain how pulmonary circulation differs from systemic circulation.

Answer: 1.   The right side of the heart deals with pulmonary circulation. The right atrium receives oxygen-poor blood from systemic veins and sends it to the right ventricle. The right ventricle sends this blood out through the pulmonary trunk. The pulmonary trunk branches into pulmonary arteries, which carry blood to the lungs. In the lungs, oxygen is loaded into the bloodstream while carbon dioxide is unloaded. The oxygen-rich blood returns to the left atrium of the heart via the pulmonary veins, completing pulmonary circulation.
2.   The left ventricle sends oxygenated blood out to the body via the aorta to begin systemic circulation. This blood travels in arteries, which branch into arterioles. Arterioles feed the capillary beds where nutrient and gas exchange occurs. The oxygen-poor blood drains into the venules, which empty blood into the veins. Veins finally empty into the superior vena cava and inferior vena cava, which return blood into the right atrium of the heart from systemic circulation.

Diff: 2   Page Ref: 365-366; 374

7) Trace a drop of blood from the aorta to the stomach.

Answer: Blood leaves the aorta (the aorta becomes the aortic arch, thoracic aorta, then the abdominal aorta). It travels to the celiac trunk, the first branch of the abdominal aorta. The blood travels via the left gastric artery to the stomach.

Diff: 1   Page Ref: 378

Short Answer

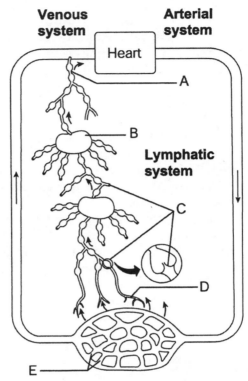

Figure 12.1

Using Figure 12.1, identify the following:

      1) A lymph capillary is indicated by letter _____.

        Answer: D
        Diff: 2   Page Ref: 404

      2) A lymph node is indicated by letter _____.

        Answer: B
        Diff: 2   Page Ref: 404

      3) The lymph duct is indicated by lettter _____.

        Answer: A
        Diff: 2   Page Ref: 404

      4) Blood capillaries are indicated by letter _____.

        Answer: E
        Diff: 2   Page Ref: 404

      5) Lymphatic collecting vessels are indicated by letter _____.

        Answer: C
        Diff: 2   Page Ref: 404

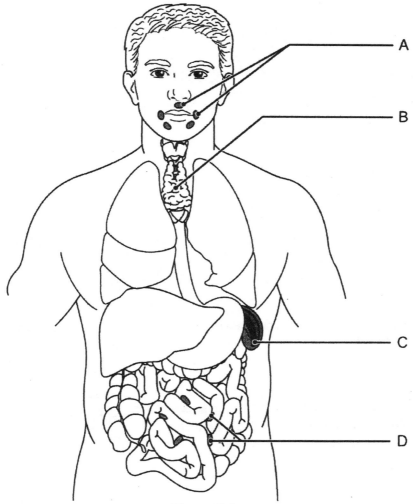

Figure 12.2

Using Figure 12.2, identify the following:

6) The spleen is indicated by letter _____.

Answer: C
Diff: 1   Page Ref: 407

7) The tonsils are indicated by letter _____.

Answer: A
Diff: 1   Page Ref: 407

8) The thymus gland is indicated by letter _____.

Answer: B
Diff: 1   Page Ref: 407

9) The Peyer's patches are indicated by letter _____.

Answer: D
Diff: 1   Page Ref: 407

10) The lymphoid organ that destroys worn–out blood cells is indicated by letter _____.

Answer: C
Diff: 2   Page Ref: 407

11) The lymphoid tissues that trap and remove bacteria that enter the throat are indicated by letter _____.

Answer: A
Diff: 2   Page Ref: 407–408

Fill in the blank or provide a short answer:

12) Lymph fluid and some plasma proteins originate (escape) from the _____.

Answer: blood plasma
Diff: 2   Page Ref: 403–404

13) Excess accumulations of fluid, which impair the exchange of materials within the tissues, is called _____.

Answer: edema
Diff: 2   Page Ref: 403

14) The fibrous capsule of lymph nodes contains strands called _____ that divide the node into compartments.

Answer: trabeculae
Diff: 3   Page Ref: 406

15) Lymph exits the lymph node via the _____ vessels.

Answer: efferent lymphatic
Diff: 2   Page Ref: 406

16) The role of the _____ in the lymphatic system is to remove worn–out blood cells and return some of the products to the liver.

Answer: spleen
Diff: 2   Page Ref: 407

17) Peyer's patches and the tonsils are part of the collection of small lymphoid tissues that protect the upper respiratory and digestive tracts from infection and are referred to as _____.

Answer: MALT (mucosa–associated lymphatic tissue)
Diff: 3   Page Ref: 408

18) Harmful or disease–causing microorganisms from which nonspecific defenses protect the body are called _____.

Answer: pathogens
Diff: 1   Page Ref: 409

19) The process by which WBCs and phagocytes migrate to an area experiencing acute inflammation is called _____.

Answer: chemotaxis
Diff: 3   Page Ref: 411

20) The process by which neutrophils squeeze through capillary walls is called _____.

Answer: diapedesis
Diff: 2   Page Ref: 412

21) The binding of complement proteins to certain sugar or proteins on a foreign cell's surface is called _____.

Answer: complement fixation
Diff: 3   Page Ref: 413

22) One effect of complement fixation that causes the cell membranes of foreign cells to become sticky so that they are easier to phagocytize is called _____.

Answer: opsonization
Diff: 3   Page Ref: 413

23) Cells studded with protein molecules found on our own cells that do not trigger an immune response within us (but may within others) are called _____.

Answer: self-antigens (autoantigens)
Diff: 1   Page Ref: 416

24) Troublesome small molecules or incomplete antigens that may mount an attack that is harmful rather than protective are called _____.

Answer: haptens
Diff: 3   Page Ref: 416

25) When an antigen binds to B cell surface receptors, it becomes sensitized (activated) and undergoes _____.

Answer: clonal selection
Diff: 3   Page Ref: 418

26) When B cells encounter antigens and produce antibodies against them, we exhibit _____.

Answer: active immunity
Diff: 2   Page Ref: 420

27) Antibodies constitute an important part of blood proteins and are also referred to as _____.

Answer: immunoglobulins
Diff: 2   Page Ref: 421

28) The five major immunoglobulin classes are _____.

Answer: IgM, IgA, IdD, IgG, IgE
Diff: 1   Page Ref: 422

29) The binding of antibodies to specific sites on bacterial exotoxins or viruses is called _____.

Answer: neutralization
Diff: 2   Page Ref: 424

30) The clumping of foreign cells, a type of antigen-antibody reaction, is called _____.

Answer: agglutination
Diff: 2   Page Ref: 424

31) Killer T cells, which kill virus-invaded body cells, are also called _____.

Answer: cytotoxic T cells
Diff: 3   Page Ref: 425

32) Antigens that produce abnormally vigorous immune responses whereby the immune system causes tissue damage as it fights off a perceived threat that would otherwise be harmless are called _____.

Answer: allergens or hypersensitivities
Diff: 2   Page Ref: 430

33) Systemic (bodywide) acute allergic response caused by allergens that directly enter the blood, as with certain bee stings or spider bites, is called _____.

Answer: anaphylactic shock
Diff: 2   Page Ref: 430

34) AIDS cripples the immune system by interfering with the activity of cells called _____.

Answer: helper T cells
Diff: 2   Page Ref: 431

35) A tropical disease that results when parasitic worms clog the lymphatic vessels is called _____.

Answer: elephantiasis
Diff: 2   Page Ref: 431

Multiple Choice

1) The fluid that is forced out of the capillary beds by hydrostatic and osmotic pressures and into the tissue spaces is called:
   A) arterial blood
   B) venous blood
   C) plasma
   D) interstitial fluid
   E) lymph

Answer: E
Diff: 1   Page Ref: 403–404

2) Lymph flows:
   A) in a circular pattern within the tissues
   B) away from the heart only
   C) toward the heart only
   D) both toward and away from the heart
   E) into the capillaries

Answer: C
Diff: 1   Page Ref: 404

3) Lymph from the left arm would return to the heart through the:
   A) inferior vena cava
   B) thoracic duct
   C) right lymphatic duct
   D) left subclavian artery
   E) aorta

Answer: B
Diff: 3   Page Ref: 404; 406

4) Which one of the following is NOT a mechanism that aids lymph return:
　　A) milking action of skeletal muscles
　　B) pressure changes within the thorax
　　C) the pumping action of the heart
　　D) smooth muscle contractions within the lymphatic vessels
　　E) presence of valves within the larger lymph vessels

Answer: C
Diff: 1　　*Page Ref: 404*

5) Which one of the following is NOT true of lymph nodes:
　　A) they remove foreign materials from the lymph fluid
　　B) they have valves similar to those found in veins
　　C) they contain lymphocytes
　　D) they act as filters along the lymphatic vessels
　　E) they contain macrophages

Answer: B
Diff: 2　　*Page Ref: 405–406*

6) Which lymphatic organ's major job is to destroy worn-out red blood cells and return some of the products to the liver:
　　A) tonsils
　　B) spleen
　　C) thymus gland
　　D) tonsils
　　E) Peyer's patches

Answer: B
Diff: 2　　*Page Ref: 407*

7) Which lymphoid tissues trap and remove bacteria entering the throat:
　　A) axillary lymph nodes
　　B) cervical lymph nodes
　　C) tonsils
　　D) Peyer's patches
　　E) thymus gland

Answer: C
Diff: 2　　*Page Ref: 408*

8) Which one of the following is NOT a type of lymphoid organ:
　　A) spleen
　　B) thymus gland
　　C) tonsils
　　D) appendix
　　E) Peyer's patches

Answer: D
Diff: 2　　*Page Ref: 407–408*

9) The lymph organ that programs T cells and functions at peak levels only during youth is the:
   A) thymus
   B) spleen
   C) appendix
   D) tonsils
   E) Peyer's patches

   Answer: A
   Diff: 2   Page Ref: 408

10) The lymph tissues found within the walls of the small intestine are called:
    A) tonsils
    B) appendix
    C) Peyer's patches
    D) thymus tissues
    E) intestinal nodes

    Answer: C
    Diff: 2   Page Ref: 408

11) Which of these lymphoid organs is found along the left side of the abdominal cavity:
    A) spleen
    B) Peyer's patches
    C) thymus gland
    D) tonsils
    E) axillary lymph nodes

    Answer: A
    Diff: 1   Page Ref: 407

12) Musoca-associated lymphatic tissue (MALT) includes:
    A) spleen
    B) thymus gland
    C) tonsils only
    D) tonsils and Peyer's patches
    E) tonsils and spleen

    Answer: D
    Diff: 3   Page Ref: 408

13) The body's first line of defense against the invasion of disease-causing microorganisms is:
    A) phagocytes
    B) natural killer cells
    C) skin and mucous membranes
    D) inflammatory response
    E) fever

    Answer: C
    Diff: 2   Page Ref: 409

14) Compared to the nonspecific chemicals that cover body surfaces and mucous membranes, the specific body defense system is:
   A) faster
   B) slower
   C) the same speed
   D) sometimes faster and sometimes slower
   E) not comparable in speed

Answer: B
Diff: 2   Page Ref: 409

15) Which one of the following is NOT one of the nonspecific body defenses:
   A) intact skin
   B) antibody production
   C) the inflammatory response
   D) fever
   E) natural killer cells

Answer: B
Diff: 2   Page Ref: 409–415

16) The process by which neutrophils are squeezed through the capillary walls during the inflammatory process is called:
   A) agglutination
   B) chemotaxis
   C) diapedesis
   D) coagulation
   E) antibody production

Answer: C
Diff: 2   Page Ref: 412

17) Which one of the following is NOT one of the four most common indicators of the inflammatory response:
   A) redness
   B) heat
   C) swelling
   D) fever
   E) pain

Answer: D
Diff: 1   Page Ref: 410–412

18) The migration of phagocytes and white blood cells to an inflamed area along a chemical gradient is called:
   A) diapedesis
   B) chemotaxis
   C) immunity
   D) perforins
   E) complement fixation

Answer: B
Diff: 2   Page Ref: 411

19) The inflammatory process begins with release of chemicals, which do all of the following EXCEPT:
    A) dilate blood vessels
    B) attract phagocytes to the area
    C) stimulate release of lysozyme
    D) cause capillaries to become leaky
    E) activate pain receptors

Answer: C
Diff: 2   Page Ref: 411–412

20) Tissues invaded by viruses, which attempt to replicate themselves by taking over cellular machinery, secrete small proteins called _____ to protect nearby cells and hinder further multiplication of the viruses.
    A) histamine
    B) interferon
    C) kinins
    D) interleukins
    E) pyrogens

Answer: B
Diff: 2   Page Ref: 413; 415

21) The body's temperature-regulating "thermostat" that can be reset upward in response to pyrogens is located in the:
    A) hypothalamus
    B) thalamus
    C) pineal gland
    D) cerebellum
    E) medulla oblongata

Answer: A
Diff: 1   Page Ref: 415

22) Fever has the effect of doing all of the following EXCEPT:
    A) denaturing (scrambling) proteins
    B) stimulating the liver and spleen to gather up iron and zinc
    C) increasing metabolic rate of tissue cells
    D) stimulating complement fixation
    E) speeding up repair processes

Answer: D
Diff: 3   Page Ref: 415

23) The study of immunity is called:
    A) histology
    B) anatomy
    C) pathology
    D) immunology
    E) microbiology

Answer: D
Diff: 1   Page Ref: 415

24) Which of the following substances is NOT typically perceived as an antigen:
   A) pollen grains
   B) bacteria
   C) self-antigens
   D) fungi
   E) virus particles

Answer: C
Diff: 2   Page Ref: 416

25) Which one of the following CANNOT be said about the history of immunity:
   A) the ancient Greeks knew something existed within the body to protect it from infectious disease
   B) scientists of the 1800s discovered "factors" now called antibodies
   C) scientists of the 1800s demonstrated that immune serum could protect another animal from disease
   D) scientists of the mid-1900s discovered the viral origin of AIDS
   E) scientists of the mid-1900s discovered that injection of serum containing antibodies did NOT always protect a recipient from disease

Answer: D
Diff: 2   Page Ref: 415

26) Regardless of whether it matures into a B cell or a T cell, a lymphocyte that is capable of responding to a specific antigen by binding to it is said to be:
   A) clonal
   B) incompetent
   C) immune
   D) immunocompetent
   E) complemented

Answer: D
Diff: 3   Page Ref: 416

27) The specific foreign substances that an individual's immune system has the ability to recognize and resist is determined by:
   A) individual exposure to the specific foreign substance
   B) individual genetic makeup
   C) the total number of lymphocytes present at a given time
   D) the total number of macrophages at a given time
   E) the total number of self-antigens at a given time

Answer: B
Diff: 3   Page Ref: 417

28) Which one of the following is NOT true of macrophages:
   A) they are considered the "big eaters" of the immune system
   B) they engulf foreign particles
   C) they circulate continuously throughout the body
   D) they act as antigen presenters
   E) they secrete monokines

Answer: C
Diff: 2   Page Ref: 418

29) B cells develop immunocompetence in the:
A) thymus gland
B) bone marrow
C) spleen
D) thyroid gland
E) lymph nodes

Answer: B
Diff: 2   Page Ref: 417

30) The specific type of acquired immunity that a fetus obtains from maternal antibodies that cross the placenta is called:
A) naturally acquired active immunity
B) naturally acquired passive immunity
C) artificially acquired active immunity
D) artificially acquired passive immunity
E) artificially acquired natural immunity

Answer: B
Diff: 1   Page Ref: 420

31) What specific type of acquired immunity do vaccines provide:
A) naturally acquired active immunity
B) naturally acquired passive immunity
C) artificially acquired active immunity
D) artificially acquired passive immunity
E) naturally acquired artificial immunity

Answer: C
Diff: 1   Page Ref: 420

32) Vaccines are NOT for:
A) pneumonia
B) tetanus
C) measles
D) snake bites
E) polio

Answer: D
Diff: 2   Page Ref: 420

33) Immune sera are used for all of the following EXCEPT:
A) tuberculosis
B) rabies
C) snake bites
D) botulism
E) tetanus

Answer: A
Diff: 2   Page Ref: 421

34) Which one of the following is NOT true of basic antibody structure:
   A) they consist of four amino acid chains
   B) they are linked together by disulfide bonds
   C) the heavy chains are identical
   D) the heavy chains are about 400 amino acids long
   E) the light chains are often of differing lengths

Answer: E
Diff: 3   Page Ref: 421–422

35) Which one of the following is NOT true of the constant (C) regions of antibodies:
   A) they are the same or nearly the same
   B) they form the "stem" of an antibody
   C) they determine the specific type of antibody class formed
   D) they form an antigen-binding site
   E) they determine how an antibody class will carry out its immune role

Answer: D
Diff: 3   Page Ref: 422

36) Which one of the following is NOT one of the antibody classes:
   A) IgA
   B) IgB
   C) IgD
   D) IgG
   E) IgE

Answer: B
Diff: 1   Page Ref: 422

37) IgA:
   A) is mainly found in mucus and secretions such as tears and saliva
   B) is passed from mother to fetus during pregnancy
   C) is the most abundant antibody in blood plasma
   D) can fix complement
   E) is involved in allergies

Answer: A
Diff: 3   Page Ref: 423

38) Which one of the following is NOT a method by which antibodies inactivate antigens:
   A) agglutination
   B) chemotaxis
   C) complement fixation
   D) neutralization
   E) precipitation

Answer: B
Diff: 2   Page Ref: 423–424

39) The specific antibody class that has the ability to cross the placental barrier and provide immunity to the fetus is:
   A) IgM
   B) IgA
   C) IgD
   D) IgG
   E) IgE
   Answer: D
   Diff: 2   Page Ref: 422–423

40) The process by which antibodies bind to specific sites on bacterial exotoxins (toxic chemicals secreted by bacteria) to block their harmful effects is called:
   A) agglutination
   B) chemotaxis
   C) complement fixation
   D) neutralization
   E) precipitation
   Answer: D
   Diff: 2   Page Ref: 424

41) Antigen presentation is essential for the activation and clonal selection of:
   A) T cells
   B) B cells
   C) plasma cell
   D) antigen–presenting cells
   E) antibodies
   Answer: A
   Diff: 2   Page Ref: 425

42) An isograft is a tissue graft donated by:
   A) an unrelated person
   B) a parent
   C) a different animal species
   D) the same person
   E) an identical twin
   Answer: E
   Diff: 2   Page Ref: 427

43) Which one of the following is NOT a type of immunosuppressive therapy given after surgery to prevent rejection of a graft:
   A) corticosteroids
   B) radiation
   C) antiproliferative drugs
   D) gamma globulin
   E) immunosuppressive drugs
   Answer: D
   Diff: 2   Page Ref: 429

44) With immediate hypersensitivy, the antibody class that binds to mast cells and basophils that trigger the release of histamine and other chemicals is:
A) IgM
B) IgA
C) IgD
D) IgG
E) IgE
Answer: E
Diff: 2   Page Ref: 422–423

45) Allergic contact dermatitis following skin contact with poison ivy would normally lead to:
A) immediate hypersensitivity
B) acute hypersensitivity
C) delayed hypersensitivity
D) anaphylactic shock
E) immunodeficiency
Answer: C
Diff: 2   Page Ref: 431

46) The relatively common autoimmune disease in which the thyroid gland produces excessive amounts of thyroxine is called:
A) multiple sclerosis
B) Graves' disease
C) myasthenia gravis
D) glomerulonephritis
E) systemic lupus erythematosis
Answer: B
Diff: 2   Page Ref: 429

47) Which one of the following is NOT an autoimmune disease:
A) AIDS
B) multiple sclerosis
C) Graves' disease
D) type I diabetes mellitus
E) rheumatoid arthritis
Answer: A
Diff: 2   Page Ref: 429

True/False

1) The flaplike minivalves of the lymph capillaries act like one-way swinging doors that allow lymph fluid to enter the lymph capillaries but not exit.
Answer: TRUE
Diff: 2   Page Ref: 404

2) The daughter cells of B cells, called plasma cells, release antibodies.
Answer: TRUE
Diff: 2   Page Ref: 418

3) Lymph in the right arm is returned to the heart via the right lymphatic duct.

Answer: TRUE
Diff: 2   Page Ref: 404

4) The thymus gland, found around the trachea, programs certain lymphocytes.

Answer: FALSE
Diff: 2   Page Ref: 408

5) The tonsils, spleen, thymus gland, and Peyer's patches are referred to as mucosa–associated lymphatic tissue (MALT).

Answer: FALSE
Diff: 2   Page Ref: 408

6) Natural killers are unique phagocytic defense cells that can kill cancer cells and virus–infected body cells well before the immune system is activated.

Answer: FALSE
Diff: 2   Page Ref: 410

7) Some pathologists consider limitation of joint movement to be an additional fifth cardinal sign of inflammation.

Answer: TRUE
Diff: 1   Page Ref: 412

8) The final disposal of cell debris as inflammation subsides is performed by neutrophils.

Answer: FALSE
Diff: 3   Page Ref: 412

9) The nonspecific defense by which complement proteins attach to sugars or proteins on the surface of foreign cells is called *complement fixation.*

Answer: TRUE
Diff: 1   Page Ref: 413

10) Chemicals secreted by white blood cells and macrophages exposed to foreign substances that can increase body temperature are called *pyrogens.*

Answer: TRUE
Diff: 1   Page Ref: 415

11) Fever is a systemic response triggered by pyrogens.

Answer: TRUE
Diff: 2   Page Ref: 415

12) Like all blood cells, lymphocytes originate from hemocytoblasts contained within red bone marrow.

Answer: TRUE
Diff: 3   Page Ref: 416

13) Macrophages arise from monoctyes formed within the bone marrow.

Answer: TRUE
Diff: 2   Page Ref: 418

14) Extremely weakened pathogens that are still alive are attenuated.

Answer: TRUE
Diff: 2   Page Ref: 420

15) Artificially acquired passive immunity is conferred when one receives immune serum for poisonous snake bites.

Answer: TRUE
Diff: 3   Page Ref: 421

16) Antibodies are also referred to as immunoglobulins.

Answer: TRUE
Diff: 1   Page Ref: 421

17) There are three major immunoglobulin classes: IgM, IgA, and IgD.

Answer: FALSE
Diff: 2   Page Ref: 422

18) The antibody a mother passes to her fetus is IgM.

Answer: FALSE
Diff: 3   Page Ref: 422–423

19) The process that occurs when antibodies clump foreign cells is called agglutination.

Answer: TRUE
Diff: 2   Page Ref: 424

20) Memory cells are descendants of an activated B or T cell.

Answer: TRUE
Diff: 3   Page Ref: 427

21) An antibody is a substance capable of provoking an immune response.

Answer: FALSE
Diff: 2   Page Ref: 416

22) Tissue grafts harvested from an unrelated person are called *xenografts*.

Answer: FALSE
Diff: 1   Page Ref: 427

23) Allografts are tissue grafts taken from an unrelated person.

Answer: TRUE
Diff: 2   Page Ref: 427

24) Allergies, or hypersensitivities, are normal immune responses.

Answer: FALSE
Diff: 2   Page Ref: 430

25) Autoimmune diseases occur when the immune system loses its ability to tolerate self-antigens while still recognizing and attaching foreign antigens.

Answer: TRUE
Diff: 3   Page Ref: 429

26) Our immune system can be affected by severe stress.

Answer: TRUE

Diff: 1   Page Ref: 435

Matching

Match the following descriptions with the appropriate lymphoid organ or tissue:

1) Located on the left side of the abdominal cavity

   Diff: 1   Page Ref: 407

2) Trap and remove bacteria and pathogens entering the throat

   Diff: 2   Page Ref: 408

3) Located overlying the heart

   Diff: 1   Page Ref: 408

4) Filters and cleanses the blood of bacteria, viruses, and other debris

   Diff: 2   Page Ref: 407–408

5) Located in the wall of the small intestines

   Diff: 1   Page Ref: 408

6) Located in the pharynx (throat)

   Diff: 1   Page Ref: 408

A) thymus gland

B) spleen

C) Peyer's patches

D) tonsils

1) B   2) D   3) A   4) B   5) C   6) D

Match the following protective mechanism with its associated element:

7) Traps microorganisms in
respiratory and digestive
tracts
Diff: 1   Page Ref: 409

8) Inhibits growth of bacteria
and fungi in female
reproductive tract
Diff: 1   Page Ref: 409

9) Contains lysozyme
Diff: 2   Page Ref: 409

10) Provides resistance against
acids, alkalis, and bacterial
enzymes
Diff: 1   Page Ref: 409

11) Filters and traps
microorganisms within
inhaled air
Diff: 1   Page Ref: 409

12) Contains concentrated
hydrochloric acid and
protein–digested enzymes
that destroy pathogens within
the stomach
Diff: 1   Page Ref: 409

13) Propels debris–laden mucus
away from lower respiratory
passages
Diff: 1   Page Ref: 409

A) keratin

B) nasal hairs

C) acid mantle

D) mucus

E) cilia

F) gastric juice

G) lacrimal secretions

7) D   8) C   9) G   10) A   11) B   12) F
13) E

Match the following biological function with its antibody class:

14) Believed to be cell surface receptor of immunocompetent B cell

    Diff: 3   Page Ref: 422–423

A) IgA

B) IgE

C) IgD

D) IgG

E) IgM

15) First immunoglobulin class released to plasma by plasma cells during primary response

    Diff: 3   Page Ref: 422–423

16) Main antibody of primary and secondary responses

    Diff: 3   Page Ref: 422–423

17) Bathes and protects mucosal surfaces from attachment of pathogens

    Diff: 3   Page Ref: 422–423

18) Triggers the release of histamine

    Diff: 3   Page Ref: 422–423

19) Potent agglutinating agent

    Diff: 3   Page Ref: 422–423

20) Crosses placenta and provides passive immunity to fetus

    Diff: 3   Page Ref: 422–423

14) C   15) E   16) D   17) A   18) B   19) E
20) D

Essay

1) Explain the origin and pathway of lymph.

    Answer: Lymph fluid arises from blood plasma that has been forced out of the capillary beds by osmotic and hydrostatic pressures. The fluid left behind is called interstitial fluid. The interstitial fluid is then picked up by lymph capillaries, after which it is called *lymph*. Lymph is routed up the lymphatic vessels until it is finally returned to the venous system through either the right lymphatic duct or the thoracic duct.

    Diff: 2   Page Ref: 403–404

2) Describe the methods the body uses to help return lymph to the heart.

    Answer: The return of lymph to the heart is aided by: 1. the milking action of the skeletal muscles, 2. pressure changes in the thorax during breathing, 3. smooth muscles in the walls of the larger lymphatics contract rhythmically.

    Diff: 1   Page Ref: 404–405

3) Describe several of the protective chemicals produced by the skin and mucous membranes.

   Answer: Skin produces acid secretions that inhibit bacterial growth, and sebum contains chemicals that are toxic to bacteria. Vaginal secretions are highly acidic. The stomach mucosa secretes hydrochloric acid and protein-digesting enzymes, both of which can kill pathogens. Saliva and tears contain lysozyme, an enzyme that destroys bacteria. Mucus is a sticky mucous membrane secretion that traps microorganisms.
   Diff: 2   *Page Ref: 409*

4) Identify the four most common indicators and major symptoms of an acute inflammatory response and explain their origins.

   Answer: The four most common indicators of the inflammatory response are redness, heat, swelling, and pain. Redness and heat are a result of dilation of blood vessels that increase blood flow to the injured area. Swelling occurs when increased permeability of the capillaries allows plasma to leak from the bloodstream into the tissue spaces. The excess fluid, or edema, triggers the activation of pain receptors in the area, accounting for the pain associated with an injury.
   Diff: 2   *Page Ref: 410-412*

5) List and describe the cells and chemicals the body uses as its second line of defense.

   Answer: 1.   Phagocytes, such as neutrophils or macrophages, engulf foreign particles. These cells are in nearly every body organ and confront pathogens that make it through the surface membrane barriers.
   2.   Natural killer cells, found in blood and lymph, are lymphocytes. They can lyse and kill cancer cells and virus-infected body cells.
   3.   The inflammatory response is a nonspecific response that occurs when body tissues are injured.
   Diff: 2   *Page Ref: 409-411*

6) Describe the four major types of transplant grafts.

   Answer: Autografts are tissue grafts transplanted from one site to another within the same person. Isografts are tissue grafts harvested from a genetically identical person (identical twin). Allografts are tissue grafts harvested from an unrelated person. Xenografts are tissue grafts harvested from different animal species.
   Diff: 2   *Page Ref: 427*

7) Explain three current theories that attempt to explain why self-tolerance breaks down in autoimmune disorders.

   Answer: Inefficient lymphocyte programming is one theory that suggests self-reactive B or T cells escape to the rest of the body. Another theory is that self-proteins appear within the circulation that were not previously exposed to the immune system, thus initiating an immune response. These "hidden" antigens are found in sperm cells, the eye lens, and thyroid proteins. Another theory is that antibodies produced against foreign antigens cross-react with self-antigens such as when streptococcal bacteria cross-react with heart antigens causing rheumatic fever.
   Diff: 3   *Page Ref: 429*

Chapter 13 The Respiratory System

Short Answer

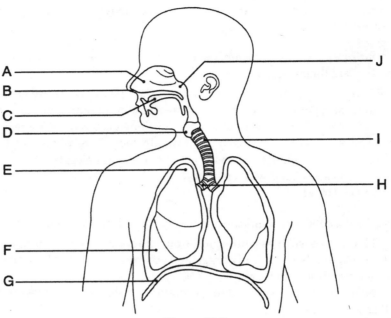

Figure 13.1

Using Figure 13.1, identify the following:

1) The nasal cavity is indicated by the letter _____.

   Answer: A
   Diff: 1   Page Ref: 442

2) The right primary bronchus is indicated by letter _____.

   Answer: H
   Diff: 1   Page Ref: 442

3) The trachea is indicated by letter _____.

   Answer: I
   Diff: 1   Page Ref: 442

4) The diaphragm muscle is indicated by letter _____.

   Answer: G
   Diff: 1   Page Ref: 442

5) The oral cavity is indicated by letter _____.

   Answer: C
   Diff: 1   Page Ref: 442

6) The base of the right lung is indicated by letter _____.

   Answer: F
   Diff: 1   Page Ref: 442

7) The nostrils are indicated by letter _____.

Answer: B
Diff: 1   Page Ref: 442

8) The apex of the right lung is indicated by letter _____.

Answer: E
Diff: 1   Page Ref: 446

9) The larynx is indicated by letter _____.

Answer: D
Diff: 1   Page Ref: 442

10) The pharynx is indicated by letter _____.

Answer: J
Diff: 1   Page Ref: 442

Fill in the blank or provide a short answer:

11) The three mucosa-covered projections into the nasal cavity that greatly increase surface area of mucosa exposed to air are called _____.

Answer: conchae
Diff: 3   Page Ref: 442

12) The anterior portion of the palate that is supported by bone is called the _____.

Answer: hard palate
Diff: 1   Page Ref: 442

13) The throat is also known as the _____.

Answer: pharynx
Diff: 1   Page Ref: 443

14) Inflammation of the sinuses that can cause marked changes in voice quality is called _____.

Answer: sinusitis
Diff: 1   Page Ref: 443

15) The large shield-shaped thyroid cartilage that protrudes anteriorly is commonly called the _____.

Answer: Adam's apple
Diff: 1   Page Ref: 444

16) The mucosa-lined windpipe that extends from the larynx to the level of the fifth thoracic vertebra is called the _____.

Answer: trachea
Diff: 1   Page Ref: 444

17) The tonsils found in the nasopharynx are called _____ or _____.

Answer: pharyngeal tonsils; adenoids
Diff: 2   Page Ref: 444

18) The opening between the vocal folds is called the _____.

Answer: glottis

Diff: 1   Page Ref: 444

19) The C-shaped rings that reinforce the trachea are constructed of _____ cartilage.

Answer: hyaline

Diff: 2   Page Ref: 444

20) The flap of elastic cartilage that protects the opening of the larynx is called the _____.

Answer: epiglottis

Diff: 1   Page Ref: 444

21) A procedure in which air within the lungs is used to forcibly expel an obstructing piece of food to avoid suffocation is called the _____.

Answer: Heimlich maneuver

Diff: 1   Page Ref: 444

22) The central area between the two lungs that houses the heart, great blood vessels, bronchi, and esophagus is called the _____.

Answer: mediastinum

Diff: 2   Page Ref: 445

23) The smallest conducting passageways of the lungs are called _____.

Answer: bronchioles

Diff: 1   Page Ref: 447

24) "Dust cells" that wander in and out of the alveoli, picking up bacteria, carbon particles, and other debris, are actually _____.

Answer: macrophages

Diff: 3   Page Ref: 447

25) The air sacs of the lungs are called _____.

Answer: alveoli

Diff: 1   Page Ref: 447

26) The process of moving air into and out of the lungs is commonly called breathing or _____.

Answer: pulmonary ventilation

Diff: 2   Page Ref: 448

27) Gas exchange between the blood and tissue cells is called _____.

Answer: internal respiration

Diff: 2   Page Ref: 449

28) The inspiratory muscles that contract so we can inspire air are the _____ and _____.

Answer: diaphragm; external intercostals

Diff: 2   Page Ref: 451

29) The presence of air in the intrapleural space is known as _____.

Answer: pneumothorax

Diff: 2   Page Ref: 451–452

30) Normal quiet breathing moves about _____ mL of air into and out of the lungs with each breath.

Answer: 500
Diff: 2   Page Ref: 452

31) A mechanism that clears the upper respiratory passages, which is similar to a cough except that the expelled air is directed through the nasal cavities instead of the oral cavity, is called a

_____.

Answer: sneeze
Diff: 1   Page Ref: 452

32) Air that remains in the conducting zone passageways and never reaches the alveoli is called the

_____.

Answer: dead space volume
Diff: 3   Page Ref: 453

33) Respiratory capacities are measured with a _____.

Answer: spirometer
Diff: 2   Page Ref: 453

34) An abnormal bubbling sound caused by diseased respiratory tissue, mucus, or pus is called

_____.

Answer: crackle
Diff: 2   Page Ref: 453

35) Oxygen bound to hemoglobin molecules on RBCs is called _____.

Answer: oxyhemoglobin
Diff: 1   Page Ref: 454

36) Most carbon dioxide is dissolved in blood plasma and transported as _____.

Answer: bicarbonate ion
Diff: 2   Page Ref: 454

37) Inadequate oxygen delivery to body tissues is called _____.

Answer: hypoxia
Diff: 1   Page Ref: 455

38) During internal respiration, the blood gas _____ is loaded into the bloodstream.

Answer: carbon dioxide
Diff: 2   Page Ref: 455–456

39) A normal respiratory rate of about 12–15 breaths per minute is called _____.

Answer: eupnea
Diff: 3   Page Ref: 456

40) The most important stimulus for breathing in a healthy person is the body's need to rid itself of the blood gas called _____.

Answer: carbon dioxide
Diff: 3   Page Ref: 457; 460

41) Enlargement of the alveoli and chronic inflammation of the lungs are characteristics of a respiratory disease called _____.

Answer: emphysema
Diff: 3   Page Ref: 461

42) Chronically inflamed, hypersensitive bronchial passages that can be irritated by dust mite and cockroach droppings are indicative of _____.

Answer: asthma
Diff: 2   Page Ref: 464

Multiple Choice

1) The conducting passageways of the respiratory system include all of the following structures EXCEPT:
   A) nose
   B) pharynx
   C) larynx
   D) trachea
   E) alveoli

Answer: E
Diff: 1   Page Ref: 441

2) The respiratory conducting passageways perform all of the following functions EXCEPT:
   A) allow air to reach the lungs
   B) purify air
   C) humidify air
   D) exchange gases
   E) warm incoming air

Answer: D
Diff: 1   Page Ref: 441

3) Which one of the following terms does not apply to the nose:
   A) external nares
   B) nasopharynx
   C) nostrils
   D) nasal cavity
   E) nasal septum

Answer: B
Diff: 1   Page Ref: 441–442

4) What is the role of mucus in the nasal cavity:
   A) increase the air turbulence in the nasal cavity
   B) separate the oral from the nasal cavity
   C) lighten the skull
   D) act as a resonance chamber for speech
   E) trap incoming bacteria and other foreign debris

Answer: E
Diff: 2   Page Ref: 442

5) The nasal cavity is separated from the oral cavity by:
   A) the hard palate
   B) the nasal conchae
   C) the soft palate
   D) both the hard and soft palate
   E) both the nasal conchae and hard palate

   Answer: D
   Diff: 2   Page Ref: 442

6) Which one of the following bones does NOT contain paranasal sinuses:
   A) frontal
   B) sphenoid
   C) mandible
   D) ethmoid
   E) maxilla

   Answer: C
   Diff: 2   Page Ref: 442

7) Which one of the following is NOT a function of the paranasal sinuses:
   A) they lighten the skull
   B) they act as resonance chambers for speech
   C) they produce mucus
   D) they are olfactory receptors for smell
   E) they help to moisten air

   Answer: D
   Diff: 2   Page Ref: 443

8) Air from the nasal cavity enters the superior portion of the pharynx called the:
   A) nasopharynx
   B) oropharynx
   C) palatopharynx
   D) laryngopharynx
   E) tracheopharynx

   Answer: A
   Diff: 1   Page Ref: 443

9) The pharynogotympanic tubes, which drain the middle ear, open into the:
   A) nasopharynx
   B) oropharynx
   C) palatopharynx
   D) laryngopharynx
   E) tracheopharynx

   Answer: A
   Diff: 1   Page Ref: 444

10) Tonsils that lie at the base of the tongue are called:
   A) adenoids
   B) pharyngeal tonsils
   C) palatine tonsils
   D) lingual tonsils
   E) pharyngotympanic tonsils

Answer: D
Diff: 2   Page Ref: 444

11) Following the removal of the larynx, a person would be unable to:
   A) speak
   B) sneeze
   C) eat
   D) hear
   E) breathe

Answer: A
Diff: 3   Page Ref: 444

12) The opening between the vocal cords is called the:
   A) epiglottis
   B) glottis
   C) larynx
   D) thyroid cartilage
   E) esophagus

Answer: B
Diff: 2   Page Ref: 444

13) The flap of elastic cartilage that protects food from entering the larynx when swallowing is the:
   A) glottis
   B) thyroid cartilage
   C) Adam's apple
   D) epiglottis
   E) trachea

Answer: D
Diff: 2   Page Ref: 444

14) Vibration due to exhaled air that results in speech is a function of the:
   A) complete voice box
   B) true vocal cords
   C) false vocal cords
   D) glottis
   E) epiglottis

Answer: B
Diff: 1   Page Ref: 444

15) Cilia of the trachea that beat continually propel contaminated mucus:
   A) toward the throat to be swallowed or spat out
   B) toward the nose to be sneezed out
   C) toward the epiglottis to be coughed out
   D) toward the lungs to be encapsulated
   E) toward the glottis to be hiccupped out

Answer: A
Diff: 2   Page Ref: 444–445

16) The serous membrane covering the surface of the lungs is called the:
   A) mediastinum
   B) visceral pleura
   C) parietal pleura
   D) main (primary) bronchi
   E) pleurisy

Answer: B
Diff: 2   Page Ref: 447

17) Which one of the following is NOT true of the lungs:
   A) the narrower portion of each lung is called the apex
   B) the bases rest on the diaphragm
   C) the left lung has two lobes
   D) the right lung has three lobes
   E) both lungs have two lobes

Answer: E
Diff: 1   Page Ref: 445; 447

18) When oxygen enters the respiratory system, what is the next structure to which it travels immediately upon leaving the trachea:
   A) bronchioles
   B) alveoli
   C) pleura
   D) main (primary) bronchi
   E) tertiary bronchi

Answer: D
Diff: 3   Page Ref: 445

19) Which one of the following structures is NOT part of the respiratory zone:
   A) respiratory bronchioles
   B) alveolar ducts
   C) alveolar sacs
   D) alveoli
   E) primary bronchi

Answer: E
Diff: 2   Page Ref: 447

20) The walls of the alveoli are composed largely of:
    A) simple squamous epithelium
    B) stratified squamous epithelium
    C) simple cuboidal epithelium
    D) stratified cuboidal epithelium
    E) pseudostratified epithelium

Answer: A
Diff: 1   Page Ref: 447

21) Exchange of both oxygen and carbon dioxide through the respiratory membrane occurs by:
    A) osmosis
    B) simple diffusion
    C) facilitated diffusion
    D) active transport
    E) passive transport

Answer: B
Diff: 1   Page Ref: 447

22) The lipid molecule critical to lung function that coats the gas–exposed alveolar surfaces is called:
    A) surfactant
    B) interferon
    C) kinin
    D) renin
    E) lecithin

Answer: A
Diff: 2   Page Ref: 447

23) Air moving in and out of the lungs is called:
    A) internal respiration
    B) inspiration
    C) external respiration
    D) expiration
    E) pulmonary ventilation

Answer: E
Diff: 1   Page Ref: 448

24) Which one of the following is NOT true of inspiration:
    A) contraction of the diaphragm muscle helps increase the size of the thoracic cavity
    B) relaxation of the external intercostal muscles helps increase the size of the thoracic cavity
    C) increased intrapulmonary volume causes inhaled gases to spread out
    D) the decreased gas pressure produces a partial vacuum that forcibly sucks air in
    E) air continues to move into the lungs until intrapulmonary pressure equals atmospheric pressure

Answer: B
Diff: 3   Page Ref: 451

25) The gas exchange that occurs between blood and tissue cells at systemic capillaries is called:
   A) pulmonary ventilation
   B) expiration
   C) internal respiration
   D) external respiration
   E) respiratory gas transport

Answer: C
Diff: 2   *Page Ref: 449*

26) In order to inspire:
   A) gas pressure in the lungs must increase
   B) the intrapulmonary volume must increase
   C) the diaphragm relaxes
   D) the intrapulmonary volume must decrease
   E) the external intercostal muscles relax

Answer: B
Diff: 2   *Page Ref: 451*

27) An emotionally–induced response during which air movement is similar to crying is:
   A) coughing
   B) sneezing
   C) laughing
   D) hiccupping
   E) yawning

Answer: C
Diff: 1   *Page Ref: 452*

28) A very deep inspiration that ventilates all alveoli is:
   A) coughing
   B) sneezing
   C) crying
   D) hiccupping
   E) yawning

Answer: E
Diff: 1   *Page Ref: 452*

29) The respiratory movement representing the total amount of exchangeable air is the:
   A) tidal volume
   B) inspiratory reserve volume
   C) expiratory reserve volume
   D) vital capacity
   E) dead space volume

Answer: D
Diff: 2   *Page Ref: 452*

30) The amount of air that can be forcibly exhaled after a tidal expiration is about:
     A) 500 mL
     B) 1200 mL
     C) 2100 mL
     D) 4800 mL
     E) 6000 mL

Answer: B
Diff: 2   Page Ref: 452

31) The amount of air exchanged during normal quiet breathing is about:
     A) 500 mL
     B) 1200 mL
     C) 2100 mL
     D) 4800 mL
     E) 6000 mL

Answer: A
Diff: 2   Page Ref: 452

32) Most carbon dioxide is transported within blood plasma as:
     A) carbohemoglobin
     B) bicarbonate ion
     C) oxyhemoglobin
     D) hydrogen ion
     E) carbonic acid

Answer: B
Diff: 3   Page Ref: 454

33) Oxygen binds with hemoglobin in the blood to form:
     A) bicarbonate ion
     B) oxyhemoglobin
     C) carbonic acid
     D) carbon dioxide
     E) plasma

Answer: B
Diff: 1   Page Ref: 454

34) The bluish cast that results from inadequate oxygenation of the skin and mucosa is called:
     A) cyanosis
     B) xanthosis
     C) melanosis
     D) albinism
     E) erythema

Answer: A
Diff: 1   Page Ref: 455

35) Which one of the following is NOT a factor influencing respiratory rate and depth:
   A) physical exercise
   B) volition
   C) emotional factors
   D) enzymatic factors
   E) levels of oxygen and carbon dioxide

Answer: D
Diff: 1   Page Ref: 456–457

36) Cessation of breathing is called:
   A) apnea
   B) dyspnea
   C) eupnea
   D) hyperpnea
   E) tachypnea

Answer: A
Diff: 1   Page Ref: 460

37) Hypoventilation dramatically increases carbonic acid concentration and involves:
   A) extremely deep breathing
   B) extremely fast breathing
   C) extremely slow breathing
   D) intermittent breathing
   E) irregular breathing

Answer: C
Diff: 1   Page Ref: 460

38) Hyperventilation leads to all of the following EXCEPT:
   A) brief periods of apnea
   B) cyanosis
   C) dizziness
   D) fainting
   E) buildup of carbon dioxide in the blood

Answer: E
Diff: 2   Page Ref: 460

39) The most important chemical stimuli leading to increased rate and depth of breathing is:
   A) decreased oxygen level in the blood
   B) increased blood pH
   C) increased carbon dioxide in the blood
   D) increased hydrogen ion in the blood
   E) decreased carbon dioxide in the blood

Answer: C
Diff: 2   Page Ref: 457; 460

40) Which one of the following is NOT a feature of COPD:
    A) most patients have a genetic predisposition to COPD
    B) dyspnea becomes progressively more severe
    C) frequent pulmonary infections are common
    D) most COPD victims are hypoxic
    E) most patients have a history of smoking

Answer: A
Diff: 2   Page Ref: 460–461

41) Emphysema results in all of the following EXCEPT:
    A) enlarged alveoli
    B) lung fibrosis
    C) expanded barrel chest
    D) decreased lung elasticity
    E) moon face

Answer: E
Diff: 2   Page Ref: 461

42) The molecule that prevents lung collapse by lowering the surface tension of the water film lining each alveolar sac is called:
    A) resorbin
    B) renin
    C) lecithin
    D) surfactant
    E) fibrosin

Answer: D
Diff: 2   Page Ref: 461

43) Surfactant is usually present in fetal lungs in adequate quantities by:
    A) 20–22 weeks of pregnancy
    B) 22–24 weeks of pregnancy
    C) 24–26 weeks of pregnancy
    D) 26–28 weeks of pregnancy
    E) 28–30 weeks of pregnancy

Answer: E
Diff: 2   Page Ref: 461

44) The abbreviation IRDS stands for:
    A) infant respiratory disease state
    B) intermittent respiratory distress state
    C) infant respiratory distress syndrome
    D) intermittent respiratory disease syndrome
    E) infant respiratory disease syndrome

Answer: C
Diff: 2   Page Ref: 461

45) Which one of the following is NOT true of cystic fibrosis:
    A) it is the most common lethal genetic disease in the U.S.
    B) it causes oversecretion of thick mucus that clogs the respiratory passages
    C) it impairs food digestion
    D) it causes sweat glands to produce an extremely salty perspiration
    E) it is rarely fatal

Answer: E
Diff: 2   *Page Ref: 461; 464*

46) The respiratory rate in adults is:
    A) 5–10 respirations per minute
    B) 12–18 respirations per minute
    C) 20–25 respirations per minute
    D) 30 respirations per minute
    E) over 40 respirations per minute

Answer: B
Diff: 2   *Page Ref: 464*

47) The homeostatic imbalance associated with the death of many full–term newborn infants is called:
    A) CF
    B) SIDS
    C) CTRL
    D) COPD
    E) IRDS

Answer: B
Diff: 1   *Page Ref: 464*

48) Obstruction of the trachea by a piece of food can lead to:
    A) hemothorax
    B) pleurisy
    C) aspiration pneumonia
    D) pneumothorax
    E) pulmonary tamponade

Answer: C
Diff: 2   *Page Ref: 464*

49) Which of the following are currently the most damaging and disabling respiratory diseases in the U.S.:
    A) tuberculosis and COPD
    B) COPD and lung cancer
    C) lung cancer and asthma
    D) asthma and tuberculosis
    E) tuberculosis and pneumonia

Answer: B
Diff: 2   *Page Ref: 464*

50) Which one of the following is NOT true of lung cancer:
   A) it accounts for one-third of all cancer deaths in the U.S.
   B) its incidence is currently increasing
   C) it is generally more prevalent in males than females
   D) most types of lung cancer are very aggressive
   E) lung cancers often metastasize rapidly and widely

Answer: C
Diff: 2   Page Ref: 458–459

True/False

1) The ciliated cells of the nasal mucosa propel contaminated mucus posteriorly toward the pharynx.

Answer: TRUE
Diff: 1   Page Ref: 442

2) The nasal cavity is separated from the oral cavity by the nasal conchae.

Answer: FALSE
Diff: 1   Page Ref: 442

3) There are only three paranasal sinuses located in the frontal, sphenoid, and parietal bones.

Answer: FALSE
Diff: 2   Page Ref: 442

4) Inflammation of the nasal mucosa by cold viruses and various antigens is called rhinitis.

Answer: TRUE
Diff: 1   Page Ref: 443

5) The larynx serves as a passageway for both food and air.

Answer: FALSE
Diff: 1   Page Ref: 443

6) The larynx routes air and food into their proper channel and plays an important role in speech production.

Answer: TRUE
Diff: 1   Page Ref: 444

7) The "guardian of the airways" that prevents food from entering the superior opening of the larynx is the thyroid cartilage.

Answer: FALSE
Diff: 2   Page Ref: 444

8) The pharyngeal tonsils are also known as the adenoids.

Answer: TRUE
Diff: 1   Page Ref: 444

9) The emergency surgical opening of the trachea is called a tracheostomy.

Answer: TRUE
Diff: 1   Page Ref: 444

10) The C-shaped rings of cartilage that reinforce the trachea are made of elastic cartilage.
Answer: FALSE
Diff: 3   Page Ref: 444

11) The superior portion of the lung is called the base.
Answer: FALSE
Diff: 2   Page Ref: 445; 447

12) The bronchioles are the smallest of the conducting passageways in the lungs.
Answer: TRUE
Diff: 1   Page Ref: 447

13) Inflammation of the pleura is often caused by decreased secretion of pleural fluid called pleurisy.
Answer: TRUE
Diff: 1   Page Ref: 447

14) The respiratory membrane is the air–blood barrier, where gases are exchanged.
Answer: TRUE
Diff: 2   Page Ref: 447

15) The respiratory zone includes the respiratory bronchioles, alveolar ducts, alveolar sacs, and alveoli.
Answer: TRUE
Diff: 2   Page Ref: 447

16) The process of breathing is known as pulmonary ventilation.
Answer: TRUE
Diff: 2   Page Ref: 448

17) Inspiration results when the diaphragm and external intercostal muscles relax.
Answer: FALSE
Diff: 3   Page Ref: 451

18) Expiration occurs when the thoracic and intrapulmonary volumes decrease and the intrapulmonary pressure increases.
Answer: TRUE
Diff: 3   Page Ref: 451

19) The amount of air that can be forcibly inhaled over the tidal volume is about 2100 to 3200 mL.
Answer: TRUE
Diff: 2   Page Ref: 452

20) The total amount of exchangeable air in a healthy young male is typically around 4800 mL.
Answer: TRUE
Diff: 2   Page Ref: 452

21) Sudden inspirations resulting from spasms of the diaphragm are hiccups.
Answer: TRUE
Diff: 1   Page Ref: 452

22) The amount of air that can be forcibly exhaled after a normal tidal expiration is the residual volume.

Answer: FALSE
Diff: 3   *Page Ref: 452*

23) Wheezing is a whistling sound associated with diseased respiratory tissue, mucus, or pus.

Answer: TRUE
Diff: 1   *Page Ref: 453*

24) According to the laws of diffusion, movement of a respiratory gas occurs toward the area of higher concentration of that particular respiratory gas.

Answer: FALSE
Diff: 1   *Page Ref: 454*

25) The general term for inadequate oxygen delivery to body tissues regardless of the cause is called hypoxia.

Answer: TRUE
Diff: 1   *Page Ref: 455*

26) Venous blood in systemic circulation is poorer in oxygen and richer in carbon dioxide.

Answer: TRUE
Diff: 2   *Page Ref: 456*

27) Inspiration by the diaphragm muscle is regulated by the phrenic nerves.

Answer: TRUE
Diff: 2   *Page Ref: 456*

28) The lungs of the fetus are filled with air late in pregnancy.

Answer: FALSE
Diff: 1   *Page Ref: 461*

29) The faulty gene associated with cystic fibrosis codes for the CFTR protein, which controls the flow of chloride in and out of cells.

Answer: TRUE
Diff: 2   *Page Ref: 461; 464*

Matching

Match the following structure with its description:

1) Throat
   Diff: 1   Page Ref: 443

2) Windpipe
   Diff: 1   Page Ref: 444

3) Voice box
   Diff: 1   Page Ref: 444

4) Opening to the larynx
   Diff: 2   Page Ref: 444

5) The trachea branches into
   these tubes
   Diff: 2   Page Ref: 445

6) Tube posterior to the trachea
   Diff: 1   Page Ref: 444

7) Smallest conducting
   passageways in the lungs
   Diff: 1   Page Ref: 447

8) Air sacs within the lungs
   Diff: 1   Page Ref: 447

A) pharynx

B) glottis

C) alveoli

D) trachea

E) esophagus

F) main (primary) bronchi

G) larynx

H) bronchioles

1) A   2) D   3) G   4) B   5) F   6) E
7) H   8) C

Match the following mechanism with its associated nonrespiratory movement:

9) Involves using the uvula to close the oral cavity off from the pharynx in order to clear the upper respiratory passages

   Diff: 2   Page Ref: 452

10) An emotionally induced response that produces air movements similar to crying

   Diff: 2   Page Ref: 452

11) A very deep inspiration formerly believed to be triggered by low oxygen

   Diff: 2   Page Ref: 452

12) Primarily an emotionally induced mechanism that involves release of air in a number of short breaths, similar to laughing

   Diff: 2   Page Ref: 452

13) Blast of upward rushing air that clears the lower respiratory passageways

   Diff: 2   Page Ref: 452

14) Sudden inspirations resulting from spasms of the diaphragm

   Diff: 2   Page Ref: 452

A) coughing

B) laughing

C) yawning

D) sneezing

E) throat–clearing

F) crying

G) hiccupping

9) D   10) B   11) C   12) F   13) A   14) G

Match the following definitions with their associated respiratory volume or capacity:

15) Amount of air that can be forcibly exhaled after a normal tidal expiration

Diff: 2   Page Ref: 452

16) Normal, quiet breathing which moves approximately 500 mL of air per breath

Diff: 2   Page Ref: 452

17) Air that enters the respiratory tract and remains within the conducting zone passageways

Diff: 2   Page Ref: 453

18) Amount of air that can be inhaled forcibly over the tidal volume

Diff: 2   Page Ref: 452

19) Total amount of exchangeable air

Diff: 2   Page Ref: 452

20) Air that remains in the lungs even after the most strenuous expiration

Diff: 2   Page Ref: 452

21) Sum total of tidal volume, inspiratory reserve volume, and expiratory reserve volume

Diff: 2   Page Ref: 452

A) residual volume

B) expiratory reserve volume

C) inspiratory reserve volume

D) conducting zone volume

E) total lung capacity

F) vital capacity

G) dead space volume

H) tidal volume

15) B   16) H   17) G   18) C   19) F   20) A
21) F

Essay

1) Explain the roles of mucus and cilia in the respiratory system.

Answer: Respiratory mucosa lines the nasal cavity which produces sticky mucus. This mucus moistens the air and traps incoming bacteria and other foreign debris entering the nasal cavity. The ciliated cells of the nasal mucosa move this contaminated mucus posteriorly toward the pharynx where it can be swallowed. The trachea is also lined with ciliated mucosa. These cilia move contaminated mucus toward the throat where it either can be swallowed or spat out.

Diff: 2   Page Ref: 442; 444–445

2) List the three regions of the pharynx and identify their relative superior and inferior endpoints in the respiratory passageway.

Answer: The three portions of the pharynx are the nasopharynx, the oropharynx, and the laryngopharynx. The nasopharynx is the superior portion that extends from the nasal cavity to the soft palate. The oropharynx is the central portion that lies between the soft palate and the upper epiglottis. The laryngopharynx is the most inferior portion and is the connecting point to the larynx below.

Diff: 2   Page Ref: 443–444

3) Explain the role of the epiglottis in the respiratory system.

Answer: The epiglottis is a part of the larynx. This structure is made of elastic cartilage. The epiglottis protects the superior opening (glottis) of the trachea. When we swallow foods or fluids, the larynx is pulled upward and the epiglottis tips to form a lid over the opening of the larynx. Food and fluids are then forced into the posterior tube called the esophagus.

Diff: 2   Page Ref: 444

4) Identify the two pleural membranes and describe them under normal and disease conditions.

Answer: The pleural membranes, the visceral pleura and the parietal pleura, produce a slippery serous secretion that allows the lungs to glide easily over the thorax wall during breathing. This serous fluid causes the two pleural layers to cling together. They can slide easily from side to side across one another, but they cannot easily be pulled apart. As surface tension of water holds them tightly to each other, the lungs are held tightly to the thorax wall. The pleural space is more of a potential space than an actual space, and it is only during illness or injury that this space becomes apparent, such as with a pneumothorax that can lead to atelectasis.

Diff: 2   Page Ref: 447

5) Explain the structure and function of the respiratory membrane.

Answer: The respiratory membrane, also known as the air–blood barrier, is comprised of the fused basement membranes of the alveolar and capillary walls. It has gas flowing past on one side and blood flowing past on the other. Gas exchanges occur by simple diffusion through the respiratory membrane. Oxygen passes from the alveolar air into the capillary blood and carbon dioxide leaves the blood to enter the gas–filled alveoli.

Diff: 3   Page Ref: 447

6) Identify and describe the four distinct events that are collectively called respiration.

Answer: Pulmonary ventilation is commonly called *breathing* and involves the movement of air into and out of the lungs. External respiration is the exchange of gases between the pulmonary blood and the alveoli. Respiratory gas transport is the transport of oxygen and carbon dioxide to and from the lungs and tissue cells of the body via the bloodstream. Internal respiration is the exchange of gases between the blood and tissue cells.

Diff: 3   Page Ref: 448–449

7) Describe how oxygen and carbon dioxide are transported in the blood.

Answer: Oxygen is transported in two ways:
1.   Most oxygen attaches to hemoglobin molecules on the RBCs to form oxyhemoglobin.
2.   A small amount of oxygen dissolves in the plasma for transport.
Carbon dioxide is also transported in two ways:
1.   Most carbon dioxide dissolves in the plasma as the bicarbonate ion.
2.   A small amount of carbon dioxide is carried inside the RBCs bound to hemoglobin (bound to a different site from oxygen).

Diff: 3   *Page Ref: 454–455*

8) Describe some of the major and minor effects of smoking on the human body.

Answer: Answers will vary depending on what effects were discussed in class, since smoking has numerous effects on the body. Respiratory effects include airway obstruction, dyspnea, coughing, frequent infections, breakdown of elastin in the connective tissue in the lungs, continual bronchial irritation and inflammation, hypoxia, respiratory acidosis, and respiratory failure. Other effects include clubbing of the fingers due to hypoxia, impotence, and impairment of the immune system.

Diff: 2   *Page Ref: 458–460*

Chapter 14 The Digestive System and Body Metabolism

Short Answer

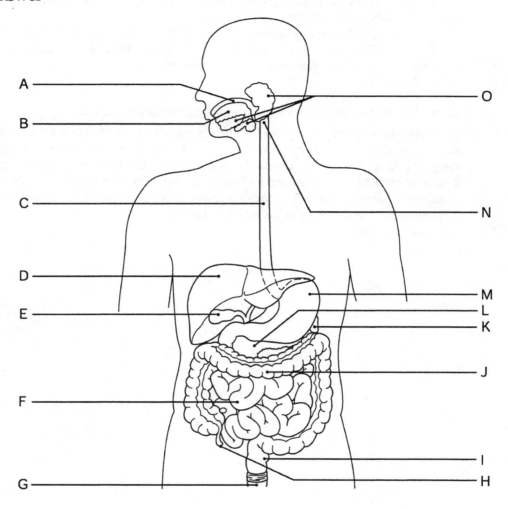

Figure 14.1

Using Figure 14.1, identify the following:

1) The mouth (oral cavity) is indicated by letter _____.

Answer: A
Diff: 2   Page Ref: 470

2) The large intestine is indicated by letter _____.

Answer: J
Diff: 2   Page Ref: 470

3) The salivary glands are indicated by letter _____.

Answer: O
Diff: 2   Page Ref: 470

4) The small intestine is indicated by letter _____.

Answer: F
Diff: 2   *Page Ref: 470*

5) The liver is indicated by letter _____.

Answer: D
Diff: 2   *Page Ref: 470*

6) The tongue is indicated by letter _____.

Answer: B
Diff: 2   *Page Ref: 470*

7) The stomach is indicated by letter _____.

Answer: M
Diff: 2   *Page Ref: 470*

8) The esophagus is indicated by letter _____.

Answer: C
Diff: 2   *Page Ref: 470*

9) The rectum is indicated by letter _____.

Answer: I
Diff: 2   *Page Ref: 470*

10) The spleen is indicated by letter _____.

Answer: K
Diff: 2   *Page Ref: 470*

11) The pharynx is indicated by letter _____.

Answer: N
Diff: 2   *Page Ref: 470*

12) The anus is indicated by letter _____.

Answer: G
Diff: 2   *Page Ref: 470*

13) The appendix is indicated by letter _____.

Answer: H
Diff: 2   *Page Ref: 470*

14) The pancreas is indicated by letter _____.

Answer: L
Diff: 2   *Page Ref: 470*

15) The gallbladder is indicated by letter _____.

Answer: E
Diff: 2   *Page Ref: 470*

Fill in the blank or provide a short answer:

16) The opening on the terminal end of the large intestine is called the _____.

Answer: anus
Diff: 1   Page Ref: 471; 478

17) The organ that connects the pharynx to the stomach is the _____.

Answer: esophagus
Diff: 1   Page Ref: 472

18) The innermost layer of the alimentary canal is referred to as the _____.

Answer: mucosa
Diff: 2   Page Ref: 472

19) The serosal membrane lining the abdominopelvic cavity by way of the mesentery is called the

_____.

Answer: parietal peritoneum
Diff: 2   Page Ref: 472

20) The upper, expanded part of the stomach lateral to the cardiac region is called the _____.

Answer: fundus
Diff: 1   Page Ref: 472–473

21) Large wrinklelike folds in the stomach lining, present when the stomach is empty, that allow
for expansion when the stomach is filling are called _____.

Answer: rugae
Diff: 1   Page Ref: 473

22) Food that resembles heavy cream after being processed in the stomach is called _____.

Answer: chyme
Diff: 2   Page Ref: 475

23) The last subdivision of the small intestine is called the _____.

Answer: ileum
Diff: 2   Page Ref: 476

24) The sphincter that prevents food from leaving the stomach is the _____ sphincter.

Answer: pyloric
Diff: 2   Page Ref: 473; 476

25) Bile is formed by the _____.

Answer: liver
Diff: 2   Page Ref: 481

26) The rich capillary bed and modified lymphatic capillary found within each villus is called a

_____.

Answer: lacteal
Diff: 2   Page Ref: 477

27) Cells abundant within the large intestine that produce large amounts of lubricating mucus to aid in the passage of feces to the end of the digestive tract are called _____.

Answer: goblet cells
Diff: 1   Page Ref: 478

28) Milk teeth that begin to erupt at around six months are also called the _____.

Answer: deciduous teeth
Diff: 2   Page Ref: 479

29) The enamel-covered crown of the tooth is exposed just above the _____.

Answer: gingiva (or gum)
Diff: 1   Page Ref: 480

30) The material on the outermost surface of the root that attaches a tooth to the periodontal membrane (ligament) is called _____.

Answer: cementum
Diff: 1   Page Ref: 480

31) Bile breaks large fat globules into smaller ones to provide more surface area for fat–digesting enzymes to operate in a process known as _____.

Answer: emulsification
Diff: 2   Page Ref: 481

32) Segmentation is a type of mechanical digestion that occurs only in the _____.

Answer: small intestine
Diff: 2   Page Ref: 482

33) The voluntary process of placing food into the mouth is referred to as _____.

Answer: ingestion
Diff: 1   Page Ref: 481

34) The process of eliminating indigestible residues from the GI tract is called _____.

Answer: defecation
Diff: 2   Page Ref: 483

35) The sphincter found at the distal end of the esophagus is the _____ sphincter.

Answer: cardioesophageal
Diff: 2   Page Ref: 472; 485

36) The hormone responsible for promoting the release of pepsinogens, mucus, and hydrochloric acid in the stomach is called _____.

Answer: gastrin
Diff: 3   Page Ref: 485

37) Two items absorbed through the stomach walls are _____ and _____.

Answer: alcohol; aspirin
Diff: 2   Page Ref: 487

38) The emetic (vomiting) center in the brain is called the _____.

Answer: medulla
Diff: 1   Page Ref: 487

39) The chemical responsible for about half of protein digestion and all of fat digestion is

_____.

Answer: pancreatic juice
Diff: 3   *Page Ref: 489–490*

40) When feces are forced into the rectum by mass movements and the wall of the rectum becomes stretched, the _____ is initiated.

Answer: defecation reflex
Diff: 2   *Page Ref: 492*

41) The energy value of foods is measured in units called _____.

Answer: kilocalories (kcal)
Diff: 1   *Page Ref: 493*

42) Amino acids that cannot be made by human body cells and therefore must be ingested in the diet are said to be _____.

Answer: essential
Diff: 1   *Page Ref: 495*

43) A chemical reaction in which substances are broken down into simpler substances is referred to as _____.

Answer: catabolism
Diff: 2   *Page Ref: 495*

44) The major fuel for making ATP in most cells of the body is a type of carbohydrate known as

_____.

Answer: glucose
Diff: 1   *Page Ref: 496*

45) The specific metabolic pathway of cellular respiration in which virtually all carbon dioxide is made is the _____.

Answer: Krebs cycle
Diff: 2   *Page Ref: 496*

46) In order for fats to be used for ATP synthesis, they must be broken down to form _____.

Answer: acetic acid
Diff: 2   *Page Ref: 498*

47) The polysaccharide, glycogen, is formed from the combination of thousands of glucose molecules during a process called _____.

Answer: glycogenesis
Diff: 3   *Page Ref: 500*

48) The lipoprotein that transports cholesterol and other lipids to body cells is called _____.

Answer: low–density lipoprotein (LDL)
Diff: 2   *Page Ref: 502*

49) The total amount of kilocalories the body must consume to fuel all ongoing activities, which increases dramatically during physical exertion, is called the _____.

Answer: total metabolic rate
Diff: 1   *Page Ref: 503*

50) Chemical substances released by macrophages and white blood cells that cause an upward resetting of the body's thermostat are called _____.

Answer: pyrogens
Diff: 3   Page Ref: 506

Multiple Choice

1) Which one of the following is NOT an organ of the alimentary canal:
   A) mouth
   B) teeth
   C) pharynx
   D) esophagus
   E) stomach

Answer: B
Diff: 1   Page Ref: 470–471

2) Which one of the following represents the correct order through which food passes in the alimentary canal:
   A) mouth, pharynx, esophagus, stomach, large intestine, small intestine
   B) mouth, esophagus, pharynx, stomach, small intestine, large intestine
   C) pharynx, mouth, esophagus, stomach, large intestine, small intestine
   D) mouth, pharynx, esophagus, stomach, small intestine, large intestine
   E) mouth, pharynx, esophagus, small intestine, stomach, large intestine

Answer: D
Diff: 1   Page Ref: 470–471

3) The structure that forms the anterior roof of the mouth is the:
   A) uvula
   B) soft palate
   C) cheek
   D) teeth
   E) hard palate

Answer: E
Diff: 2   Page Ref: 471

4) The fold of mucous membrane that secures the tongue to the floor of the mouth and limits its posterior movements is called the:
   A) lingual frenulum
   B) hyoid bone
   C) palatal frenulum
   D) styloid bone
   E) mandibular frenulum

Answer: A
Diff: 2   Page Ref: 471

5) Which one of the following is continuous with the esophagus:
    A) nasopharynx
    B) oropharynx
    C) linguopharynx
    D) laryngopharynx
    E) esophagopharynx

Answer: D
Diff: 1   *Page Ref: 472*

6) Which one of the following is NOT a layer of the alimentary canal:
    A) mucosa
    B) submucosa
    C) muscularis interna
    D) muscularis externa
    E) serosa

Answer: C
Diff: 2   *Page Ref: 472*

7) The submucosal and myenteric nerve plexuses that help regulate the mobility and secretory activity of the GI tract organs are both part of the:
    A) somatic nervous system
    B) autonomic nervous system
    C) sympathetic nervous system
    D) fight–or–flight mechanism
    E) central nervous system

Answer: B
Diff: 3   *Page Ref: 472*

8) When full, the average adult stomach can hold approximately:
    A) 1 liter of food
    B) 2 liters of food
    C) 3 liters of food
    D) 4 liters of food
    E) 2 gallons of food

Answer: D
Diff: 1   *Page Ref: 473*

9) The release of food from the stomach into the small intestine is regulated by the:
    A) cardioesophageal sphincter
    B) pyloric sphincter (valve)
    C) ileocecal valve
    D) internal anal sphincter
    E) hepatopancreatic ampulla

Answer: B
Diff: 2   *Page Ref: 476*

10) Protein digestion begins in the:
   A) mouth
   B) esophagus
   C) stomach
   D) small intestine
   E) large intestine

Answer: C
Diff: 2   Page Ref: 473

11) Intrinsic factor in digestion is a stomach secretion needed for absorption of _____ from the small intestine.
   A) vitamin A
   B) vitamin B12
   C) vitamin C
   D) vitamin D
   E) vitamin K

Answer: B
Diff: 3   Page Ref: 475

12) The small intestine extends from the:
   A) cardioesophageal sphincter to the pyloric sphincter
   B) pyloric sphincter to the ileocecal valve
   C) ileocecal valve to the appendix
   D) appendix to the sigmoid colon
   E) cardioesophageal sphincter to ileocecal valve

Answer: B
Diff: 2   Page Ref: 475-476

13) Which one of the following is the middle section of the small intestine:
   A) duodenum
   B) ascending colon
   C) jejunum
   D) descending colon
   E) ileum

Answer: C
Diff: 1   Page Ref: 476

14) Enzymes and bile are carried by the pancreatic duct and bile duct into the:
   A) duodenum
   B) jejunum
   C) ileocecal valve
   D) ileum
   E) large intestine

Answer: A
Diff: 3   Page Ref: 476

15) The primary function of the small intestine is:
   A) absorption of nutrients
   B) absorption of water
   C) waste secretion
   D) vitamin conversion
   E) mineral secretion
   Answer: A
   Diff: 1   Page Ref: 476

16) Which one of the following is NOT a modification (which is designed to increase surface area for absorption) within the small intestine:
   A) microvilli
   B) villi
   C) Peyer's patches
   D) circular folds
   E) plicae circulares
   Answer: C
   Diff: 2   Page Ref: 475–477

17) Which one of the following is NOT a subdivision of the large intestine:
   A) cecum
   B) appendix
   C) duodenum
   D) colon
   E) rectum
   Answer: C
   Diff: 1   Page Ref: 477

18) The organ responsible for drying out indigestible food residue through water absorption and the elimination of feces is the:
   A) stomach
   B) large intestine
   C) small intestine
   D) pancreas
   E) lever
   Answer: B
   Diff: 2   Page Ref: 477

19) The opening of the large intestine is called the:
   A) cecum
   B) sigmoid colon
   C) rectum
   D) anus
   E) ileum
   Answer: D
   Diff: 1   Page Ref: 478

20) Amylase is an enzyme that is only able to digest:
    A) protein
    B) starch
    C) fat
    D) vitamins
    E) minerals
Answer: B
Diff: 2   Page Ref: 485; 490

21) The number of permanent teeth within a full set of adult teeth is:
    A) 20
    B) 24
    C) 28
    D) 32
    E) 36
Answer: D
Diff: 1   Page Ref: 479

22) The anterior chisel-shaped teeth that are adapted for cutting are called:
    A) incisors
    B) canines
    C) premolars
    D) molars
    E) wisdom teeth
Answer: A
Diff: 1   Page Ref: 479

23) The accesory digestive organ that produces enzymes that break down all food groups is the:
    A) liver
    B) gallbladder
    C) salivary glands
    D) pancreas
    E) liver and gallbladder
Answer: D
Diff: 3   Page Ref: 480

24) Bile is produced by the _____ but stored in the _____.
    A) liver; pancreas
    B) gallbladder; liver
    C) liver; gallbladder
    D) small intestine; pancreas
    E) gallbladder; pancreas
Answer: C
Diff: 3   Page Ref: 481

25) Buildup of bile within the liver leading to bile pigments circulating through the body could cause tissues to turn yellow and a condition called:
   A) cyanosis
   B) erythematosis
   C) jaundice
   D) hepatitis
   E) cirrhosis
   Answer: C
   Diff: 1   Page Ref: 481

26) The sequence of steps by which large food molecules are broken down into their respective building blocks by catalytic enzymes within hydrolysis reactions is called:
   A) ingestion
   B) propulsion
   C) mechanical digestion
   D) chemical digestion
   E) absorption
   Answer: D
   Diff: 1   Page Ref: 483

27) The propulsive process that moves food from one organ to the next is called:
   A) ingestion
   B) peristalsis
   C) chemical digestion
   D) mastication
   E) absorption
   Answer: B
   Diff: 2   Page Ref: 481–482

28) The process by which food within the small intestine is mixed with digestive juices by backward and forward movement across the internal wall of the organ is called:
   A) peristalsis
   B) segmentation
   C) defecation
   D) chemical digestion
   E) absorption
   Answer: B
   Diff: 1   Page Ref: 482

29) Which one of the following is NOT one of the carbohydrates that the human digestive system is able to break down to simple sugars:
   A) cellulose
   B) sucrose
   C) lactose
   D) maltose
   E) starch
   Answer: A
   Diff: 2   Page Ref: 483

30) Proteins are digested to their building blocks which are called:
   A) peptides
   B) amino acids
   C) polypeptides
   D) fatty acids
   E) glycerol

Answer: B
Diff: 1   *Page Ref: 483*

31) Transport of digested end products from the lumen GI tract into the bloodstream or lymphatic fluid is called:
   A) ingestion
   B) propulsion
   C) digestion
   D) absorption
   E) defecation

Answer: D
Diff: 2   *Page Ref: 483*

32) Digestion is primarily controlled by the:
   A) sympathetic division of the autonomic nervous system
   B) medulla oblongata
   C) somatic nervous system
   D) enterogastric reflex
   E) parasympathetic division of the autonomic nervous system

Answer: E
Diff: 1   *Page Ref: 483*

33) Which one of the following is NOT true of the sensors involved in digestive reflexes:
   A) they activate or inhibit lacteal absorption
   B) they respond to stretch of the organ by the volume of food within its lumen
   C) they start reflexes that either activate or inhibit digestive glands
   D) they respond to the relative pH content within that particular digestive organ
   E) they respond to the presence of breakdown products of digestion

Answer: A
Diff: 3   *Page Ref: 483*

34) The first nutrient to be chemically digested is:
   A) starch
   B) protein
   C) fat
   D) minerals
   E) vitamins

Answer: A
Diff: 2   *Page Ref: 485*

35) The process of swallowing is also known as:
   A) mastication
   B) segmentation
   C) deglutition
   D) defecation
   E) absorption

   Answer: C
   Diff: 1   Page Ref: 485

36) Which one of the following alimentary segments has no digestive function:
   A) stomach
   B) ascending colon
   C) ileum
   D) esophagus
   E) duodenum

   Answer: D
   Diff: 1   Page Ref: 485

37) Which one of the following is NOT involved in the swallowing reflex:
   A) tongue
   B) soft palate
   C) larynx
   D) pharynx
   E) esophagus

   Answer: C
   Diff: 2   Page Ref: 485

38) The amount of gastric juice produced every day by an average-sized adult is:
   A) 1–2 liters
   B) 2–3 liters
   C) 3–4 liters
   D) 1–2 gallons
   E) 2–3 gallons

   Answer: B
   Diff: 2   Page Ref: 485

39) The hormone responsible for causing the stomach to release pepsinogens, mucus, and hydrochloric acid is:
   A) rennin
   B) bile
   C) gastrin
   D) pepsin
   E) amylase

   Answer: C
   Diff: 3   Page Ref: 485

40) The enzyme responsible for converting milk protein in the stomach to a substance that looks
   like sour milk in infants is:
   A) pepsin
   B) salivary amylase
   C) pancreatic amylase
   D) bile
   E) rennin

   Answer: E
   Diff: 2   Page Ref: 486

41) The journey of chyme through the small intestine takes:
   A) 2–4 hours
   B) 3–6 hours
   C) 6–8 hours
   D) 8–10 hours
   E) 10–12 hours

   Answer: B
   Diff: 1   Page Ref: 487

42) Enzyme–rich pancreatic juice contains all the following EXCEPT:
   A) amylase
   B) trypsin
   C) nuclease
   D) pancreatase
   E) lipase

   Answer: D
   Diff: 2   Page Ref: 490

43) Which of the following influence the release of pancreatic juice and bile:
   A) rennin and cholecystokinin
   B) gastrin and rennin
   C) cholecystokinin and gastrin
   D) secretin and gastrin
   E) cholecystokinin and secretin

   Answer: E
   Diff: 3   Page Ref: 491

44) Which one of the following is NOT absorbed by the human large intestine:
   A) water
   B) vitamin K
   C) some of the B vitamins
   D) ions
   E) protein

   Answer: E
   Diff: 1   Page Ref: 492

45) The energy value of foods commonly counted by dieters is measured in units called:
   A) ATP
   B) calories
   C) kilocalories
   D) coenzymes
   E) carb units

   Answer: C
   Diff: 1   *Page Ref: 493*

46) Inorganic substances necessary to body functioning that must be ingested through the diet are:
   A) vitamins
   B) coenzymes
   C) carbon
   D) minerals
   E) complete proteins

   Answer: D
   Diff: 2   *Page Ref: 495*

47) The process by which larger molecules or structures are built up from smaller ones is called:
   A) anabolism
   B) catabolism
   C) metabolism
   D) carbolysis
   E) glycolysis

   Answer: A
   Diff: 1   *Page Ref: 495*

48) Adenosine triphosphate (ATP) is produced in greatest quantity during:
   A) glycolysis
   B) the Krebs cycle
   C) protein metabolism
   D) the electron transport chain
   E) fat metabolism

   Answer: D
   Diff: 2   *Page Ref: 496*

49) The liver metabolizes fats for all of the following reasons EXCEPT:
   A) ATP production
   B) synthesis of lipoproteins
   C) synthesis of thromboplastin
   D) synthesis of vitamin K
   E) synthesis of cholesterol

   Answer: D
   Diff: 3   *Page Ref: 500–502*

50) Acidosis (ketoacidosis) occurs when _____ is digested.
 A) fat
 B) glycogen
 C) glucose
 D) protein
 E) glycogen or glucose

Answer: A
Diff: 3   Page Ref: 498

51) Which one of the following is NOT a main role of the liver:
 A) to detoxify drugs and alcohol
 B) to degrade hormones
 C) to make cholesterol
 D) to process nutrients during digestion
 E) to add ammonia to the blood

Answer: E
Diff: 1   Page Ref: 500-502

52) Nutrients detour through the liver via the:
 A) circle of Willis
 B) hepatic portal circulation
 C) Bowman's capsule
 D) electron transport chain
 E) glycogenesis

Answer: B
Diff: 1   Page Ref: 500

53) Which one of the following is NOT true of cholesterol:
 A) it provides energy fuel for muscle contraction
 B) it serves as the structural basis of steroid hormones
 C) it serves as the structural basis of vitamin D
 D) it is a major building block of plasma membranes
 E) only about 15 percent comes from the diet

Answer: A
Diff: 3   Page Ref: 501-502

54) The hereditary inability of tissue cells to metabolize the amino acid phenylalanine, which can result in brain damage and retardation unless a special diet low in phenylalanine is followed, is called:
 A) cystic fibrosis
 B) cleft lip
 C) cleft palate
 D) phenylketonuria
 E) tracheoesophageal fistula

Answer: D
Diff: 2   Page Ref: 506-507

55) The reflex that helps an infant hold on to the nipple and swallow is called the:
  A) rooting reflex
  B) nursing reflex
  C) sucking reflex
  D) peristaltic reflex
  E) fetal reflex
Answer: C
Diff: 1   Page Ref: 507

True/False

1) Another name for the alimentary canal is the gastrointestinal (GI) tract.
Answer: TRUE
Diff: 1   Page Ref: 470

2) The rhythmic, wavelike propelling mechanism of the alimentary canal is called peristalsis.
Answer: TRUE
Diff: 1   Page Ref: 472

3) The process of mastication is simply known as chewing.
Answer: TRUE
Diff: 1   Page Ref: 472

4) The innermost layer of the serosa is called the parietal peritoneum.
Answer: FALSE
Diff: 2   Page Ref: 472

5) The lacy apron of the peritoneum that covers the abdominal organs is called the lesser omentum.
Answer: FALSE
Diff: 2   Page Ref: 473

6) The chief cells produce hydrochloric acid, which activates stomach enzymes.
Answer: FALSE
Diff: 2   Page Ref: 475

7) The small intestine runs from the pyloric sphincter to the ileocecal valve.
Answer: TRUE
Diff: 2   Page Ref: 475–476

8) The first portion of the small intestine is the jejunum.
Answer: FALSE
Diff: 1   Page Ref: 476

9) Bile enters the duodenum of the small intestine through the pancreatic duct.
Answer: FALSE
Diff: 3   Page Ref: 476

10) Villi are projections of the mucosa of the stomach.
Answer: FALSE
Diff: 2   Page Ref: 476–477

11) The ascending colon is found on the left side of the abdominal cavity.

Answer: FALSE
Diff: 2   *Page Ref: 478*

12) The segment of the colon to which the appendix is attached is the cecum.

Answer: TRUE
Diff: 1   *Page Ref: 477-478*

13) The anal canal has a voluntary sphincter formed by smooth muscle only.

Answer: FALSE
Diff: 1   *Page Ref: 478*

14) Small pocketlike sacs within the large intestine that most often are partially contracted are called haustra.

Answer: TRUE
Diff: 2   *Page Ref: 479*

15) The enamel found on teeth is heavily mineralized with calcium salts and comprises the hardest substance within the entire body.

Answer: TRUE
Diff: 2   *Page Ref: 480*

16) The bicuspids are also called wisdom teeth.

Answer: FALSE
Diff: 1   *Page Ref: 479*

17) Pancreatic enzymes are released into the stomach to break down all categories of digestible foods.

Answer: FALSE
Diff: 2   *Page Ref: 480*

18) Bile is produced by the liver but stored in the gallbladder.

Answer: TRUE
Diff: 2   *Page Ref: 481*

19) Food within the lumen of the alimentary canal is considered to be outside the body.

Answer: TRUE
Diff: 2   *Page Ref: 483*

20) The involuntary phase of swallowing is called the buccal phase.

Answer: FALSE
Diff: 2   *Page Ref: 485*

21) Diverticulosis occurs when mucosa become inflamed and protrude through the wall of the small intestine.

Answer: FALSE
Diff: 3   *Page Ref: 492*

22) Enzymes of the microvilli are called brush border enzymes.

Answer: TRUE
Diff: 2   *Page Ref: 489*

23) Absence of either bile or pancreatic juice indicates that no fat digestion or absorption is occurring. This can lead to blood–clotting problems because the liver needs vitamin K to make prothrombin.

Answer: TRUE

Diff: 3   Page Ref: 491

24) Secretin and cholecystokinin influence the release of both pancreatic juice and bile.

Answer: TRUE

Diff: 2   Page Ref: 491

25) Fats are absorbed by active transport in the small intestine.

Answer: FALSE

Diff: 2   Page Ref: 492

26) Mass movements are slow–moving contractile waves that move over large areas of the colon three or four times each day.

Answer: TRUE

Diff: 2   Page Ref: 492

27) Sugars and starches are classified as lipids.

Answer: FALSE

Diff: 1   Page Ref: 494

28) Anabolism is the process in which larger molecules are built from smaller ones.

Answer: TRUE

Diff: 2   Page Ref: 495

29) Fat metabolism can result in acidosis (ketoacidosis).

Answer: TRUE

Diff: 2   Page Ref: 498

30) Optimal health of tissues is achieved when HDL and LDL are present in equal amounts within the bloodstream.

Answer: FALSE

Diff: 2   Page Ref: 502

31) The body's thermostat, which constantly regulates body temperature, is located within the hypothalamus.

Answer: TRUE

Diff: 1   Page Ref: 504

32) Watery stools that result when food residue is rushed through the large intestine before sufficient water has been reabsorbed, causing dehydration and electrolyte imbalance, is called constipation.

Answer: FALSE

Diff: 1   Page Ref: 493

Matching

Match the following nutrients with their associated digestive enzymes:

1) Proteins

Diff: 2   Page Ref: 485

2) Lactose

Diff: 2   Page Ref: 484

3) Starch

Diff: 2   Page Ref: 485

4) Fat

Diff: 2   Page Ref: 490

5) Nucleic acids

Diff: 2   Page Ref: 490

A) lipase

B) pepsinogen

C) hydrochloric acid

D) nuclease

E) bile

F) lactase

G) amylase

H) pepsinogens

1) H   2) F   3) G   4) A   5) D

Identify the digestive organ that is primarily associated with the following digestive function:

6) Primary site of water absorption

Diff: 2   Page Ref: 492

7) Site where starch digestion begins

Diff: 2   Page Ref: 485

8) Tube through which food is propelled but no digestion takes place

Diff: 2   Page Ref: 485

9) Site where the beginning of protein digestion occurs

Diff: 2   Page Ref: 475; 485

10) Site where pancreatic enzymes and bile enter the alimentary canal

Diff: 2   Page Ref: 476

11) Site of vitamin K synthesis by bacteria

Diff: 2   Page Ref: 492

12) Site of initiation of the defecation reflex

Diff: 2   Page Ref: 492

A) small intestine

B) mouth

C) anus

D) esophagus

E) duodenum

F) large intestine

G) stomach

H) rectum

I) ileum

6) F   7) B   8) D   9) G   10) E   11) F
12) H

Match the following terms or phrases with the appropriate nutrient:

13) Glucose and glycogen

    Diff: 1   Page Ref: 496; 500

14) Amino acids

    Diff: 1   Page Ref: 494–495

15) Coenzymes

    Diff: 1   Page Ref: 495

16) Calcium, phosphorus, potassium

    Diff: 1   Page Ref: 495

17) Triglycerides

    Diff: 1   Page Ref: 494

18) Fiber

    Diff: 1   Page Ref: 494

A) minerals

B) lipids

C) vitamins

D) proteins

E) carbohydrates

13) E   14) D   15) C   16) A   17) B   18) E

Essay

1) Describe the four layers of the GI tract.

Answer: 1. Mucosa is the moist innermost layer; it lines the cavity of the organ.
2. The submucosa is found beneath the mucosa layer. It contains blood vessels, nerve endings, lymph nodules, and lymphatic vessels.
3. The muscular externis is the next layer, which is typically made up of a circular and a longitudinal layer of smooth muscle.
4. The outermost layer is the serosa, which consists of two single layers of cells. The innermost serosa is the visceral peritoneum while the outermost layer is the parietal peritoneum. Between these layers is serous fluid.

    Diff: 1   Page Ref: 472

2) Identify and describe the six major processes involved in gastrointestinal activity.

Answer: Ingestion is the active, voluntary process of placing food into the mouth. Propulsion involves all of the actions involved in moving food along the alimentary canal from the mouth to the anus, including swallowing, peristalsis, segmentation, and mass movements. Mechanical digestion involves all of the activities that break food down into smaller pieces to prepare them for further degradation by enzymes. Chemical digesting, the next step of food breakdown, involves the sequence of steps by which large food molecules are broken down to their building blocks by enzymes. Absorption is the mechanism by which digested end products are moved from the lumen of the GI tract into the blood or lymph. The final process is defecation, which is the elimination of indigestible substances from the body via the anus as feces.

    Diff: 2   Page Ref: 481–484

3) Explain the various processes of food propulsion.

Answer: Deglutition (swallowing) includes two phases, one voluntary and one involuntary. The voluntary phase is called the buccal phase, and it involves movement of the food bolus by the tongue into the pharynx. The involuntary phase is called the pharyngeal–esophageal phase, and it involves blockage of all routes except the esophageal route while the bolus is moved through the pharynx and into the esophagus. This reflex is regulated by the parasympathetic nervous system. Peristalsis is the rhythmic, wavelike motion of the stomach and intestines. It involves waves of contraction that move chyme along, followed by waves of relaxation. Another mechanism of food propulsion is segmentation of the small intestine. Although its chief function is mixing chyme with digestive juices, it also assists in propulsion. Mass movements are another mechanism by which food is moved through the GI tract, which occur three to four times a day, typically just after eating. They are powerful contractions that move over the colon and force contents toward the rectum to be stored until defecation. The presence of feces in the rectum initiates the defecation reflex, which causes the walls of the sigmoid colon and rectum to contract while relaxing the anal sphincters.

Diff: 2   *Page Ref: 481–482*

4) Explain the role of the hormones cholecystokinin and secretin in regulating the release of bile and pancreatic juices.

Answer: When chyme enters the small intestine, it stimulates the mucosa cells to produce the hormones cholecystokinin and secretin. These hormones travel in the bloodstream to their target organs: the pancreas, liver, and gallbladder. The pancreas responds to cholecystokinin by releasing enzyme-rich pancreatic juice and secretin causes the secretion of bicarbonate-rich pancreatic juice. The liver responds to secretin by releasing bile while cholecystokinin stimulates the gallbladder to release stored bile.

Diff: 3   *Page Ref: 491*

5) Explain what vitamins and minerals are and identify their importance to the body.

Answer: Vitamins are water-soluble, fat-soluble, or organic nutrients that the body requires in small amounts. Most function as coenzymes that enable an enzyme to accomplish a particular type of catalysis. Vitamins are found in all major food groups, and a balanced diet is the best way to ensure a full vitamin complement. Minerals are inorganic substances, such as calcium, potassium, and sodium, that the body also requires in adequate supply. The foods highest in mineral content are vegetables, legumes, milk, and some meats.

Diff: 2   *Page Ref: 495*

6) Discuss the anaerobic and aerobic mechanisms by which body cells generate adenosine triphosphate (ATP).

Answer: Cellular respiration includes all of the oxygen-dependent processes by which energy from the breakdown of glucose is captured within chemical bonds which unite adenosine diphosphate (ADP) and inorganic phosphate into the body's preferred metabolic fuel, adenosine triphosphate (ATP). One process, glycolysis, energizes each glucose molecule so that it can be split into two pyruvic acid molecules to yield ATP. The Krebs cycle, located within the mitochondria, produces all the carbon dioxide and water that results during cellular respiration, and it yields a small amount of ATP as well. The electron transport chain, also located within the mitochondria, is the primary producer of ATP. Hydrogen atoms removed during glycolysis and the Krebs cycle are delivered to the protein carriers of the electron transport chain, which form part of the mitochondrial cristae membranes. There the hydrogen atoms are split into their positive ions and negative electrons. The electrons then travel from carrier to carrier in a series of steps that enable phosphate to attach to ADP to form ATP.

Diff: 3   *Page Ref: 496*

7) Explain why there is really no such thing as "good" or "bad" lipoprotein cholesterol.

Answer: Lipoproteins transport cholesterol and fatty acids. Low-density lipoproteins (LDLs) transport cholesterol and other lipids to body cells for use in a variety of ways. If there are large amounts of circulating LDLs, some fatty substances may be deposited on arterial walls, which is the reason they are associated with heart disease risk and have sometimes been labeled "bad." However, they are a necessary transport substance, so the key is to have LDLs in the acceptable range. High-density lipoproteins (HDLs) transport cholesterol from the tissue cells or arteries to the liver for disposal in bile. Because they transport cholesterol away from the arteries, they have sometimes been labeled "good." Again, they are a necessary transport substance, and the key is to have HDLs in the proper ratio with LDLs, so that whatever excess cholesterol is moved in by the LDLs can be moved out again by the HDLs. It is their relative ratio that is important. Both are necessary, and neither should be considered "good" nor "bad."

Diff: 2   *Page Ref: 502*

Short Answer

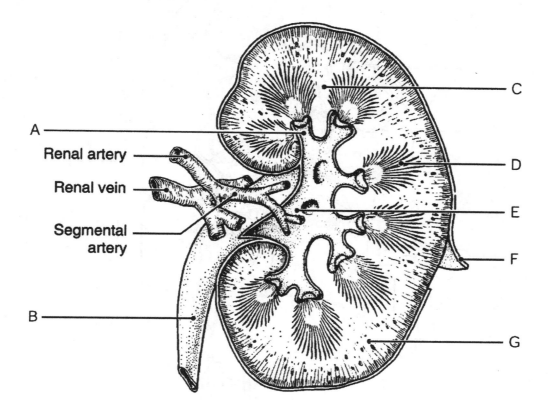

A

Renal artery

Renal vein

Segmental
artery

B

C

D

E

F

G

Figure 15.1

Using Figure 15.1, identify the following:

    1) The ureter is indicated by letter _____.

        Answer: B
        Diff: 1   *Page Ref: 520*

    2) The renal pyramid is indicated by letter _____.

        Answer: D
        Diff: 1   *Page Ref: 520*

    3) The fibrous capsule is indicated by letter _____.

        Answer: F
        Diff: 1   *Page Ref: 520*

    4) The renal column is indicated by letter _____.

        Answer: C
        Diff: 1   *Page Ref: 520*

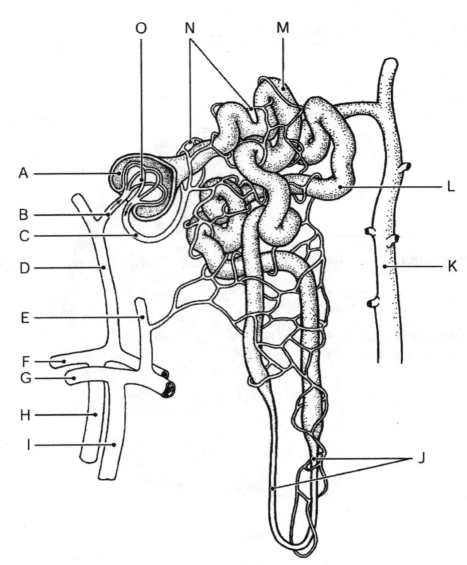

Figure 15.2

Using Figure 15.2, identify the following:

5) The loop of Henle is indicated by letter _____.

Answer: J
Diff: 1   Page Ref: 522

6) The collecting duct is indicated by letter _____.

Answer: K
Diff: 1   Page Ref: 522

7) The glomerular capsule (Bowman's capsule) is indicated by letter _____.

Answer: A
Diff: 1   Page Ref: 522

8) The proximal convoluted tubule is indicated by letter _____.

Answer: M
Diff: 1   Page Ref: 522

9) The afferent arteriole is indicated by letter _____.

Answer: B
Diff: 1   Page Ref: 522

10) The arcuate vein is indicated by letter _____.

Answer: G
Diff: 1   Page Ref: 522

11) The glomerulus is indicated by letter _____.

Answer: O
Diff: 1   Page Ref: 522

Fill in the blank or provide a short answer:

12) Each kidney is surrounded and held in place against the muscles of the trunk wall by its _____.

Answer: renal fascia
Diff: 2   Page Ref: 519

13) There are three regions of the kidney; the outermost region is known as the _____.

Answer: renal cortex
Diff: 1   Page Ref: 520

14) Renal pyramids are separated by extensions of cortex–like tissue called the _____.

Answer: renal columns
Diff: 2   Page Ref: 521

15) As blood flows toward the kidney, it travels from the renal artery into vessels called the _____.

Answer: segmental arteries
Diff: 3   Page Ref: 521

16) The process of filtration occurs in a specific structure in the nephron called the _____.

Answer: glomerulus
Diff: 2   Page Ref: 523

17) A urinary output of less than 100 mL per day is called _____.

Answer: anuria
Diff: 1   Page Ref: 524

18) The pigment resulting from the destruction of hemoglobin that gives freshly–voided urine its pale yellow color is called _____.

Answer: urochrome
Diff: 2   Page Ref: 524

19) A vegetarian diet is said to be a(n) _____ diet because it makes urine extremely alkaline as the kidneys excrete excess bases.

Answer: alkaline–ash
Diff: 2   Page Ref: 525

20) The condition that results when red blood cells are abnormally present in urine is called
_____.

Answer: hematuria
Diff: 2   Page Ref: 528

21) Specific gravity is the term used to compare how much heavier urine is than _____.

Answer: distilled water
Diff: 1   Page Ref: 525

22) Another term for kidney stones, which form when urine becomes extremely concentrated, is
_____.

Answer: renal calculi
Diff: 2   Page Ref: 528

23) The smooth triangular region of the bladder base that is outlined by the openings of the two
ureters and the urethra is called the _____.

Answer: trigone
Diff: 2   Page Ref: 528

24) Urinary bladder inflammation often caused by bacterial infection is called _____.

Answer: cystitis
Diff: 1   Page Ref: 530

25) The involuntary sphincter that keeps the urethra closed when urine is not being passed is
called the _____.

Answer: internal urethral sphincter
Diff: 1   Page Ref: 529

26) The inability to voluntarily control the external urethral sphincter is known as _____.

Answer: incontinence
Diff: 1   Page Ref: 530

27) Voiding, urination, and _____ are terms that indicate the passage of urine from the
bladder.

Answer: micturition
Diff: 2   Page Ref: 530

28) About two-thirds of body fluid is found within living cells; this fluid is called the _____.

Answer: intracellular fluid (ICF)
Diff: 2   Page Ref: 531

29) Sodium ion content of the extracellular fluid (ECF) is largely regulated by an adrenal cortex
hormone called _____.

Answer: aldosterone
Diff: 3   Page Ref: 533

30) Highly sensitive cells within the hypothalamus that react to changes in blood composition and
cause the release of antidiuretic hormone (ADH) when appropriate are called _____.

Answer: osmoreceptors
Diff: 3   Page Ref: 532

31) The abnormal condition that results from the lack of ADH release, causing huge amounts of very dilute urine to be voided, is called _____.

Answer: diabetes insipidus
Diff: 2   Page Ref: 533

32) The primary urinary symptom of Addison's disease (hypoaldosteronism) is called _____.

Answer: polyuria
Diff: 3   Page Ref: 535

33) Arterial blood pH between 7.35 and 7.0 is called _____.

Answer: physiological acidosis
Diff: 3   Page Ref: 535

34) A strong acid will dissociate and liberate more _____ ions in water than a weak acid.

Answer: hydrogen (H^+)
Diff: 2   Page Ref: 536

35) The kidneys can help maintain a rising blood pH by excreting _____ ions and reabsorbing _____ ions by the tubule cells.

Answer: bicarbonate; hydrogen
Diff: 3   Page Ref: 537

36) The need to urinate frequently at night, which plagues over 50% of the elderly, is called _____.

Answer: nocturia
Diff: 2   Page Ref: 538

37) Untreated streptococcal infections in childhood that can lead to the kidney infection characterized by antigen–antibody complexes clogging the glomerular filters is known as _____.

Answer: glomerulonephritis
Diff: 3   Page Ref: 538

38) A feeling that it is necessary to void, which is experienced more regularly in the elderly, is known as _____.

Answer: urgency
Diff: 3   Page Ref: 538

Multiple Choice

1) Which one of the following is NOT one of the functions of the kidneys:
    A) manufacture urine
    B) convert vitamin D from its inactive to its active form
    C) dispose of metabolic waste products
    D) produce hormones that assist in digestion
    E) regulate blood volume

Answer: D
Diff: 1   Page Ref: 518

2) Which of the following is NOT an organ found in the urinary system:
   A) kidney
   B) ureter
   C) pancreas
   D) urinary bladder
   E) urethra

   Answer: C
   Diff: 1   *Page Ref: 518*

3) Which one of the following terms describes the location of the kidneys:
   A) suprarenal
   B) retroperineal
   C) adrenal
   D) intraperitoneal
   E) retroperitoneal

   Answer: E
   Diff: 1   *Page Ref: 518*

4) The kidneys are aided in the excretion of fluids by the:
   A) lungs
   B) skin
   C) hair
   D) lungs and skin
   E) skin and hair

   Answer: D
   Diff: 1   *Page Ref: 518*

5) The triangular regions of the kidneys that are striped in appearance and separated by the renal columns are the:
   A) renal cortex
   B) renal medulla
   C) renal pyramids
   D) renal pelvis
   E) calyces

   Answer: C
   Diff: 1   *Page Ref: 521*

6) As venous blood is drained from the kidney, which path does it follow:
   A) cortical radiate veins, arcuate veins, interlobar veins, renal vein
   B) renal vein, interlobar veins, segmental veins, arcuate veins
   C) arcuate veins, cortical radiate veins, interlobar veins, renal vein
   D) renal vein, segmental veins, interlobar veins, arcuate veins, cortical radiate veins
   E) cortical radiate veins, arcuate veins, interlobar veins, segmental veins, renal vein

   Answer: A
   Diff: 3   *Page Ref: 521*

7) The enlarged, cup-shaped closed end of the renal tubule that completely surrounds the glomerulus is called the:
   A) collecting duct
   B) proximal convoluted tubule
   C) loop of Henle
   D) Bowman's capsule
   E) distal convoluted tubule

Answer: D
Diff: 1   Page Ref: 521

8) Each kidney contains about:
   A) 100,000 nephrons
   B) 500,000 nephrons
   C) 1 million nephrons
   D) 2 million nephrons
   E) 3 million nephrons

Answer: C
Diff: 1   Page Ref: 521

9) Starting from the glomerular capsule, the correct order of the renal tubule regions is:
   A) proximal convoluted tubule, distal convoluted tubule, loop of Henle
   B) distal convoluted tubule, loop of Henle, proximal convoluted tubule
   C) loop of Henle, proximal convoluted tubule, distal convoluted tubule
   D) proximal convoluted tubule, loop of Henle, distal convoluted tubule
   E) distal convoluted tubule, proximal convoluted tubule, loop of Henle

Answer: D
Diff: 1   Page Ref: 521

10) The portion of the renal tubule that completely surrounds the glomerulus is the:
    A) collecting duct
    B) proximal convoluted tubule (PCT)
    C) glomerular (Bowman's) capsule
    D) distal convoluted tubule (DCT)
    E) loop of Henle

Answer: C
Diff: 2   Page Ref: 521

11) Most nephrons are located within the renal:
    A) pelvis
    B) calyces
    C) medulla
    D) pyramids
    E) cortex

Answer: E
Diff: 2   Page Ref: 523

12) The percentage of filtrate eventually reabsorbed into the bloodstream is closest to:
   A) 10%
   B) 25%
   C) 50%
   D) 80%
   E) 99%

   Answer: E
   Diff: 2   Page Ref: 523

13) Of the capillary beds associated with each nephron, the one that is both fed and drained by arterioles is the:
   A) peritubular capillaries
   B) pyramidal capillaries
   C) glomerulus
   D) Henle capillaries
   E) Bowman's capillaries

   Answer: C
   Diff: 3   Page Ref: 523

14) The peritubular capillaries arise from the _____, which drains the glomerulus.
   A) afferent arteriole
   B) efferent arteriole
   C) Bowman's capsule
   D) loop of Henle
   E) glomerulus

   Answer: B
   Diff: 3   Page Ref: 523

15) The nonselective, passive process performed by the glomerulus that forms blood plasma without blood proteins is called:
   A) absorption
   B) secretion
   C) filtration
   D) tubular reabsorption
   E) glomerular reabsorption

   Answer: C
   Diff: 2   Page Ref: 523; 524

16) Uric acid, a nitrogenous waste product, results from the metabolism of:
   A) creatinine
   B) nucleic acids
   C) proteins
   D) amino acids
   E) salt

   Answer: B
   Diff: 2   Page Ref: 524

17) Which one of the following is NOT a substance typically reabsorbed by the tubules under normal healthy conditions:
   A) glucose
   B) urea
   C) amino acids
   D) sodium
   E) water

Answer: B
Diff: 2   Page Ref: 524

18) Which one of the following is NOT true of urine under normal healthy conditions:
   A) it is sterile
   B) it is slightly alkaline
   C) it is more dense than water
   D) it is slightly aromatic
   E) it typically contains ammonia

Answer: B
Diff: 2   Page Ref: 524–525; 527

19) Which one of the following substances is normally found in urine:
   A) blood proteins
   B) red blood cells
   C) hemoglobin
   D) white blood cells
   E) creatinine

Answer: E
Diff: 2   Page Ref: 524; 527

20) The presence of pus in urine is called:
   A) glycosuria
   B) pyuria
   C) bilirubinuria
   D) hematuria
   E) proteinuria

Answer: B
Diff: 2   Page Ref: 527

21) Dilute urine would have a specific gravity closest to:
   A) 0.005
   B) 1.001
   C) 1.010
   D) 1.020
   E) 1.030

Answer: B
Diff: 2   Page Ref: 525

22) The tube connecting the renal hilus of the kidney to the bladder is the:
   A) urethra
   B) proximal convoluted tubule
   C) distal convoluted tubule
   D) ureter
   E) collecting duct

   Answer: D
   Diff: 2   Page Ref: 528

23) The noninvasive treatment for kidney stones that uses ultrasound waves to shatter calculi is called:
   A) lithotripsy
   B) lithiasis
   C) lithectomy
   D) lithotomy
   E) lithoscopy

   Answer: A
   Diff: 2   Page Ref: 528

24) The bladder is able to expand as urine accumulates within it due to the presence of:
   A) rugae
   B) transitional epithelium
   C) segmentation
   D) pseudostratified epithelium
   E) sphincters

   Answer: B
   Diff: 2   Page Ref: 529

25) Urine is transported from the bladder to the outside of the body by the:
   A) ureter
   B) trigone
   C) prostate gland
   D) urethra
   E) collecting duct

   Answer: D
   Diff: 2   Page Ref: 529

26) The average adult bladder is moderately full with _____ of urine within it.
   A) 100 mL
   B) 500 mL
   C) 1 liter
   D) 2 liters
   E) 1 gallon

   Answer: B
   Diff: 2   Page Ref: 529

27) The voluntarily controlled sphincter fashioned by skeletal muscle at the point where the urethra passes through the pelvic floor is called the:
   A) internal urethral sphincter
   B) internal anal sphincter
   C) external urethral sphincter
   D) trigone
   E) detrusor sphincter

Answer: C
Diff: 2   Page Ref: 529

28) The process of emptying the bladder is referred to as voiding or:
   A) tubular secretion
   B) filtration
   C) tubular reabsorption
   D) incontinence
   E) micturition

Answer: E
Diff: 2   Page Ref: 530

29) Which one of the following is NOT true of incontinence:
   A) it occurs when we are unable to voluntarily control the external sphincter
   B) it is normal in children 2 years old or younger
   C) it is normal in older children who sleep soundly
   D) it can result from pressure on the bladder
   E) it is never considered normal

Answer: E
Diff: 2   Page Ref: 530

30) Enlargement of the prostate that surrounds the neck of the bladder in adult men is called
   _____ , which may cause voiding difficulty.
   A) atrophy
   B) dystrophy
   C) hyperplasia
   D) hypoplasia
   E) eutrophy

Answer: C
Diff: 2   Page Ref: 530

31) In one 24-hour period, the kidneys of an average-sized healthy adult filter approximately
   _____ through their glomeruli into the tubules.
   A) 10-15 liters of blood plasma
   B) 50-75 liters of blood plasma
   C) 100-125 liters of blood plasma
   D) 150-180 liters of blood plasma
   E) 200-240 liters of blood plasma

Answer: D
Diff: 3   Page Ref: 524

32) In contrasting urine and filtrate by the time it reaches the collecting ducts, it could be said that:
   A) they contain essentially the same concentration of nutrients
   B) they contain essentially the same amount of water
   C) filtrate contains almost everything that blood plasma does
   D) urine contains almost everything that blood plasma does
   E) filtrate contains more unnecessary substances than urine does

Answer: C
Diff: 3   *Page Ref: 523–524*

33) Which one of the following is NOT one of the major roles of the kidneys in normal healthy adults:
   A) excretion of nitrogen–containing wastes
   B) maintenance of water balance of the blood
   C) maintenance of electrolyte balance of the blood
   D) conversion of ammonia to bicarbonate ion
   E) ensuring proper blood pH

Answer: D
Diff: 3   *Page Ref: 531*

34) In a healthy young adult female, water accounts for:
   A) one–quarter of body weight
   B) less than one–half of body weight
   C) approximately one–half of body weight
   D) three–quarters of body weight
   E) 99% of body weight

Answer: C
Diff: 2   *Page Ref: 531*

35) Extracellular fluid is found everywhere in the body EXCEPT:
   A) within living cells
   B) blood plasma
   C) interstitial fluid
   D) cerebrospinal fluid
   E) humors of the eye and lymph

Answer: A
Diff: 1   *Page Ref: 531*

36) The main hormone that acts on the kidneys to regulate sodium ion concentration of the extracellullar fluid (ECF) is:
   A) ADH
   B) renin
   C) secretin
   D) aldosterone
   E) epinephrine

Answer: D
Diff: 3   *Page Ref: 533*

37) Antidiuretic hormone prevents excessive water loss by promoting water reabsorption in the:
   A) glomerulus
   B) proximal convoluted tubule
   C) distal convoluted tubule
   D) collecting duct
   E) bladder

   Answer: D
   Diff: 3   Page Ref: 533

38) A simple rule concerning water and electrolyte regulation is:
   A) salt passively follows water
   B) salt actively follows water
   C) potassium passively follows sodium
   D) water passively follows salt
   E) water actively follows salt

   Answer: D
   Diff: 2   Page Ref: 535

39) The results of the renin–angiotensin mechanism mediated by the juxtaglomerular apparatus of the renal tubules include all of the following EXCEPT:
   A) vasoconstriction
   B) increased peripheral resistance
   C) blood volume increase
   D) blood pressure increase
   E) suppression of aldosterone

   Answer: E
   Diff: 3   Page Ref: 535

40) The proper pH for the blood is:
   A) 6.8–6.9
   B) 7.0–7.35
   C) 7.35–7.45
   D) 7.5–8.0
   E) 6.5–8.0

   Answer: C
   Diff: 2   Page Ref: 535

41) The chemical buffer system that includes carbonic acid and its salt, which ties up the H^+ released by strong acids, is called the:
   A) phosphate buffer system
   B) protein buffer system
   C) ionic buffer system
   D) bicarbonate buffer system
   E) carbonic buffer system

   Answer: D
   Diff: 2   Page Ref: 536

42) The chemically buffered combination of strong acids that dissociate completely in water with weak bases such as hydroxides leads to a:
   A) weak acid and a salt
   B) weak acid and a strong base
   C) strong base and a salt
   D) weak base and water
   E) weak base and salt
   Answer: A
   Diff: 3   *Page Ref: 536*

43) When carbon dioxide enters the blood from tissue cells, it is converted to _____ for transport within blood plasma.
   A) sodium hydroxide
   B) ammonia
   C) carbonic anhydrase
   D) bicarbonate ion
   E) sodium bicarbonate
   Answer: D
   Diff: 2   *Page Ref: 537*

44) When blood pH begins to rise, the respiratory control centers in the brain are:
   A) accelerated
   B) depressed
   C) not effected
   D) shut off
   E) controlled by the kidneys
   Answer: B
   Diff: 2   *Page Ref: 537*

45) The most potent of all mechanisms and substances that the body uses to regulate blood pH are:
   A) the respiratory system controls
   B) the kidneys
   C) hormones
   D) the buffer system
   E) enzymes
   Answer: B
   Diff: 2   *Page Ref: 537*

46) Functional kidneys develop within the womb by the third month after conception from the _____ set of tubule systems.
   A) first
   B) second
   C) third
   D) fourth
   E) fifth
   Answer: C
   Diff: 3   *Page Ref: 538*

47) The degenerative condition in which blisterlike sacs (cysts) containing urine form on the kidneys and obstruct urine drainage is called:
   A) cystitis
   B) dysuria
   C) hypospadias
   D) epispadias
   E) polycystic kidney
Answer: E
Diff: 2   Page Ref: 538

48) Hypospadias is a condition of male children that involves:
   A) atrophied prostate
   B) opening of the urethra on the ventral surface of the penis
   C) cysts on the kidneys
   D) closing of the foreskin over the end of the penis
   E) inflammation of the glomerulus
Answer: B
Diff: 2   Page Ref: 538

49) The average output of urine for a normal healthy adult is:
   A) 500 mL/day
   B) 1000 mL/day
   C) 1500 mL/day
   D) 2000 mL/day
   E) 2500 mL/day
Answer: C
Diff: 3   Page Ref: 538

50) Control of the voluntary urethral sphincter in normal children is related to:
   A) intelligence
   B) nervous system development
   C) enzymatic regulation
   D) hormone regulation
   E) muscular development
Answer: B
Diff: 2   Page Ref: 538

51) From childhood through late middle age, one of the most common bacteria to infect and inflame the urinary tract and cause urethritis and cystitis is:
   A) streptococcus
   B) staphylococcus
   C) *Escherichia coli*
   D) *Mycobacterium tuberculosis*
   E) *Clostridium botulinum*
Answer: C
Diff: 2   Page Ref: 538

True/False

1) The medial indentation of the kidney where several structures such as the ureters, renal blood vessels, and nerves enter and exit the kidney is called the hilus.

Answer: TRUE
Diff: 1   *Page Ref: 519*

2) The tiny filtering structures of the kidneys are called nephrons.

Answer: TRUE
Diff: 1   *Page Ref: 521*

3) The lumen surfaces of the tubule cells within the proximal convoluted tubule are covered with microvilli.

Answer: TRUE
Diff: 2   *Page Ref: 521*

4) The region of the renal tubule closest to the glomerular capsule is the distal convoluted tubule.

Answer: FALSE
Diff: 2   *Page Ref: 521*

5) The peritubular capillary bed arises from the afferent arteriole.

Answer: FALSE
Diff: 3   *Page Ref: 523*

6) Blood proteins and blood cells are too large to pass through the filtration membrane and should not be found in filtrate.

Answer: TRUE
Diff: 2   *Page Ref: 524*

7) Tubular reabsorption begins in the glomerulus.

Answer: FALSE
Diff: 2   *Page Ref: 524*

8) Nitrogenous waste products such as urea, uric acid, and creatinine are excreted from the body in urine rather than reabsorbed.

Answer: TRUE
Diff: 3   *Page Ref: 524*

9) The pigment that gives urine its characteristic yellow color is urochrome.

Answer: TRUE
Diff: 2   *Page Ref: 524*

10) The specific gravity of urine is typically lower than the specific gravity of pure water.

Answer: FALSE
Diff: 1   *Page Ref: 525*

11) Tubular secretion, which seems to be important for removal of substances not already in the filtrate, is essentially reabsorption in reverse.

Answer: TRUE
Diff: 1   *Page Ref: 524*

12) Urine moves down the ureters into the bladder due to gravitational pull alone.
   Answer: FALSE
   Diff: 2   *Page Ref: 528*

13) The internal urethral sphincter is involuntary.
   Answer: TRUE
   Diff: 1   *Page Ref: 529*

14) The urethra, which carries urine exiting the bladder by peristalsis, is typically shorter in females than in males.
   Answer: TRUE
   Diff: 1   *Page Ref: 529*

15) Following the micturition reflex, it is impossible to postpone bladder emptying.
   Answer: FALSE
   Diff: 1   *Page Ref: 530*

16) The fluid stored inside cells is referred to as extracellular fluid (ECF).
   Answer: FALSE
   Diff: 2   *Page Ref: 531*

17) The movement of water from one fluid compartment to another has no effect on blood volume and blood pressure.
   Answer: FALSE
   Diff: 3   *Page Ref: 532*

18) Antidiuretic hormone (ADH) causes increased water loss through the urine.
   Answer: FALSE
   Diff: 2   *Page Ref: 532–533*

19) The most important trigger for aldosterone release is the renin–angiotensin mechanism, mediated by the renal tubules.
   Answer: TRUE
   Diff: 2   *Page Ref: 535*

20) A person with arterial blood pH above 7.45 is said to have acidosis.
   Answer: FALSE
   Diff: 1   *Page Ref: 535*

21) The kidneys help maintain acid–base balance of the blood by excreting bicarbonate ions.
   Answer: TRUE
   Diff: 2   *Page Ref: 537*

22) When blood pH becomes too acidic, the tubule cells of the kidneys excrete bicarbonate ions and retain hydrogen ions.
   Answer: FALSE
   Diff: 3   *Page Ref: 537*

23) Sexually transmitted diseases (STDs) are primarily infections of the reproductive tracts but may also cause urinary tract infections.

Answer: TRUE
Diff: 1   *Page Ref: 538*

24) Incontinence is often the final outcome of the urinary system during the aging process.

Answer: TRUE
Diff: 2   *Page Ref: 538; 540*

Matching

Identify the substances within the urine and their possible causes with the name of the associated condition:

1) RBCs in the urine due to trauma or infection
   Diff: 2   *Page Ref: 528*

2) Hemoglobin in the urine due to hemolytic anemia or a transfusion reaction
   Diff: 2   *Page Ref: 528*

3) Glucose in the urine due to diabetes mellitus
   Diff: 2   *Page Ref: 528*

4) Bile pigment in the urine due to hepatitis
   Diff: 2   *Page Ref: 528*

5) Pus containing WBCs and bacteria in the urine due to urinary tract infection
   Diff: 2   *Page Ref: 528*

6) Proteins in the urine due to pregnancy or excessive exercise
   Diff: 2   *Page Ref: 528*

A) dysuria

B) anuria

C) bilirubinuria

D) hematuria

E) pyuria

F) hemoglobinuria

G) uremia

H) proteinuria

I) glycosuria

1) D   2) F   3) I   4) C   5) E   6) H

Identify the urinary structure with its associated description:

7) Cup-shaped extensions of the pelvis

Diff: 2   Page Ref: 521

8) Outer, lighter region of the kidney

Diff: 2   Page Ref: 520

9) Vessels supplying each kidney with blood to be filtered

Diff: 2   Page Ref: 521

10) Cortex–like extensions that separate the pyramids

Diff: 2   Page Ref: 521

11) Darker, reddish–brown internal area of the kidney

Diff: 2   Page Ref: 521

12) Triangular regions with a striped appearance

Diff: 2   Page Ref: 521

13) Flat, basinlike cavity medial to the hilus of the kidney

Diff: 2   Page Ref: 521

A) renal cortex

B) renal pyramids

C) renal medulla

D) renal columns

E) renal artery

F) renal pelvis

G) pyramids

H) calyces

I) renal vein

7) H   8) A   9) E   10) D   11) C   12) B

13) F

Identify these organs of the urinary system with their associated descriptions:

14) Tube that drains urine from the kidney to the bladder

Diff: 2   Page Ref: 528

A) bladder

B) urethra

C) ureter

15) Muscular sac suitable for temporary urine storage

Diff: 2   Page Ref: 528

16) Transports urine and sperm in males

Diff: 2   Page Ref: 530

17) In males, this organ is surrounded by the prostate

Diff: 2   Page Ref: 528

18) Contains an area called the trigone formed by the openings of the ureters and urethra

Diff: 2   Page Ref: 528–529

19) Inflammation of this organ is called cystitis

Diff: 2   Page Ref: 529–530

14) C   15) A   16) B   17) A   18) A   19) A

Essay

1) Identify and describe the three major processes involved in urine formation.

Answer: Filtration is a nonselective, passive process with the glomerulus acting as the filter. The filtrate formed is essentially blood plasma without blood proteins, which are too large to pass through the filtration membrane into the renal tubule. Reabsorption is the process by which the body reclaims substances within the filtrate that it wants to keep. Most reabsorption is an active process using membrane carriers. Substances that are typically reabsorbed include amino acids, glucose, and ions. Most reabsorption occurs in the proximal convoluted tubules. Secretion is the opposite process. With secretion, substances such as hydrogen ions, potassium ions, and creatinine are removed from the peritubular capillaries into the tubules to be eliminated in urine.

Diff: 2   Page Ref: 524

2) Describe the normal characteristics of freshly-voided urine in a healthy adult.

Answer: Urine is a pale, straw-colored liquid that progressively becomes a darker yellow color as it becomes more concentrated. The yellow color is a result of the presence of urochrome pigment, a by-product of hemoglobin breakdown. Urine is more dense than water with a specific gravity of 1.001 to 1.035. Urine is sterile and slightly aromatic and has an acidic pH of around 6. Urine normally contains sodium and potassium ions, urea, uric acid, creatinine, ammonia, and bicarbonate ions, as well as other ions the body needs to dispose of.

Diff: 2   *Page Ref: 524-525; 527*

3) Describe and explain urethral control and concepts related to incontinence.

Answer: The urethra contains two sphincters. The internal urethral sphincter is involuntary and is formed from a thickening of smooth muscle at the bladder-urethra junction. The second sphincter is the external urethral sphincter, made from skeletal muscle and under voluntary control. Control of the external urethral sphincter often develops at around 2 years of age. Prior to that time, the child is simply not able to control urination and is incontinent. Other causes for incontinence include emotional problems, pressure on the bladder, such as with pregnancy, stroke, spinal cord injury, and the aging process.

Diff: 2   *Page Ref: 538; 540*

4) Contrast the roles of the ureters and urethra in the urinary system.

Answer: The ureters are tubes that connect the kidneys to the bladder. Each ureter transports urine to the bladder. Both gravity and peristalsis aid in the movement of urine.
The urethra is a tube that transports urine from the bladder to the outside of the body. The passage of urine from the bladder into the urethra is controlled by two sphincters: the internal, involuntary sphincter and the external, voluntary sphincter.

Diff: 1   *Page Ref: 528-530*

5) Explain the renin-angiotensin mechanism.

Answer: The renin-angiotensin mechanism is the most important trigger for the release of aldosterone. It is mediated by the juxtaglomerular (JG) apparatus of the renal tubules. The JG apparatus consists of modified smooth muscle cells that are stimulated by low blood pressure within the afferent arteriole or changes in solute content of the filtrate. The JG cells respond to these changes by releasing renin into the blood. Renin catalyzes reactions that lead to angiotensin II production, which then acts directly on the blood vessels to cause vasoconstriction as well as aldosterone release. Aldosterone then causes the reabsorption of sodium and water, leading to increased blood volume and blood pressure.

Diff: 3   *Page Ref: 535*

6) Describe the bicarbonate buffer system and explain its importance in regulating pH changes.

Answer: The bicarbonate buffer system is one of three major chemical buffer systems in normal humans. The buffer systems each help to maintain pH within the body's fluid compartments, and since they act within a fraction of a second, they are the first line of defense in resisting abnormal pH changes. The bicarbonate buffer system is a mixture of carbonic acid and sodium bicarbonate. Carbonic acid is a weak acid which remains relatively intact in the presence of a strong acid. Its salt, sodium bicarbonate, acts as a weak base in the presence of a strong acid, such as hydrochloric acid, tying up the H^+ released and forming carbonic acid. Because the strong acid is changed to a weak acid, the pH of the solution is lowered slightly. If a strong base like sodium hydroxide is added to a solution containing the bicarbonate buffer system, sodium bicarbonate will not dissociate further, but carbonic acid will. More hydrogen ions will be released to bind with the hydroxyl ions, with the net result being the replacement of a strong base by a weak one. The pH of the solution will then rise slightly.

Diff: 3   *Page Ref: 536–537*

Chapter 16 The Reproductive System

Short Answer

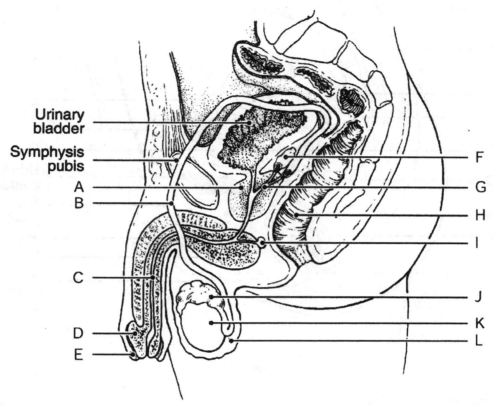

Urinary
bladder

Symphysis
pubis

A
B

C

D
E

F
G
H
I

J
K
L

Figure 16.1

Using Figure 16.1, identify the following:

1) The testis is indicated by letter _____.

Answer: K
Diff: 1   Page Ref: 547

2) The ductus (vas) deferens is indicated by letter _____.

Answer: B
Diff: 1   Page Ref: 547

3) The seminal vesicle is indicated by letter _____.

Answer: F
Diff: 1   Page Ref: 547

4) The prepuce is indicated by letter _____.

Answer: E
Diff: 1   Page Ref: 547

5) The urethra is indicated by letter _____.

Answer: C
Diff: 1   Page Ref: 547

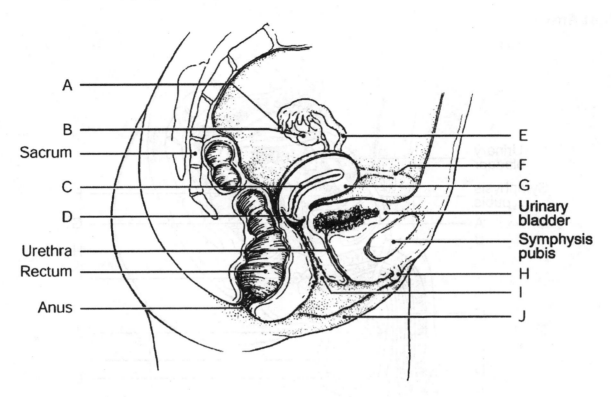

Figure 16.2

Using Figure 16.2, identify the following:

6) The uterine (fallopian) tube is indicated by letter _____.

Answer: E
Diff: 1   Page Ref: 554

7) The ovary is indicated by letter _____.

Answer: B
Diff: 1   Page Ref: 554

8) The clitoris is indicated by letter _____.

Answer: H
Diff: 1   Page Ref: 554

9) The fimbriae are indicated by letter _____.

Answer: A
Diff: 1   Page Ref: 554

10) The round ligament is indicated by letter _____.

Answer: F
Diff: 1   Page Ref: 554

Fill in the blank or provide a short answer:

11) The fibrous "white coat" connective tissue capsule surrounding each testis is called the
_____.

Answer: tunica albuginea
Diff: 2   Page Ref: 546

12) The male sterilization birth control procedure that involves cauterization of the ductus deferens
is called _____.

Answer: vasectomy
Diff: 1   Page Ref: 548

13) The glands that produce a thick, yellowish secretion which nourishes and activates sperm are
the _____.

Answer: seminal vesicles
Diff: 1   Page Ref: 548

14) The type of sugar that is found in semen and provides essentially all the energy fuel for sperm
is called _____.

Answer: fructose
Diff: 2   Page Ref: 548

15) The enlarged tip of the penis is called the _____.

Answer: glans penis
Diff: 1   Page Ref: 549

16) Another term for the foreskin that is surgically removed during circumcision is the _____.

Answer: prepuce
Diff: 2   Page Ref: 549

17) The helmet–like region of the sperm that is similar to a large lysosome and assists penetration
of the egg is called the _____.

Answer: acrosome
Diff: 2   Page Ref: 551

18) The entire process of spermatogenesis takes _____ days.

Answer: 64 to 72
Diff: 1   Page Ref: 552

19) The hormone testosterone is produced by the _____ cells of the testes.

Answer: interstitial
Diff: 2   Page Ref: 552

20) Tiny saclike structures within the ovaries in which oocytes are found are called _____.

Answer: ovarian follicles
Diff: 2   Page Ref: 553

21) A mature ovarian follicle that is ready to be ejected from an ovary is called a _____.

Answer: Graafian (or vesicular) follicle
Diff: 2   Page Ref: 553

22) The Graafian (vesicular) follicle, which is ruptured following ovulation, is called the
_____.

Answer: corpus luteum
Diff: 3   Page Ref: 553–554

23) The finger-like projections that partially surround the ovary at the distal end of each uterine
tube is called _____.

Answer: fimbriae
Diff: 2   Page Ref: 554

24) The bacteria from gonorrhea and other infections can spread to the peritoneal cavity. Unless
treated promptly, the infection condition can cause _____, which is a major cause of
female infertility.

Answer: pelvic inflammatory disease
Diff: 2   Page Ref: 555

25) The ligament that anchors the anterior portion of the uterus is called the _____.

Answer: round ligament
Diff: 2   Page Ref: 555

26) The innermost layer of the uterus is a mucosa layer called the _____.

Answer: endometrium
Diff: 2   Page Ref: 556

27) Burrowing of the fertilized egg into the endometrium lining of the uterus is called _____.

Answer: implantation
Diff: 1   Page Ref: 556

28) The thin fold of mucosa that partially closes the distal end of the vagina before the first
experience of sexual intercourse is called the _____.

Answer: hymen
Diff: 2   Page Ref: 556

29) The labia majora enclose the region known as the _____, which contains the external
opening of the urethra.

Answer: vestibule
Diff: 2   Page Ref: 556

30) The process of creating female gametes is called _____.

Answer: oogenesis
Diff: 2   Page Ref: 557

31) The hormone that promotes a small number of primary follicles within the ovary to grow and
mature each month is _____.

Answer: follicle-stimulating hormone (FSH)
Diff: 2   Page Ref: 557

32) The ovum has _____ chromosomes.

Answer: 23
Diff: 2   Page Ref: 558

33) The follicle–cell capsule surrounding an ovulated secondary oocyte is called the _____.

Answer: corona radiata
Diff: 3   *Page Ref: 557*

34) The hormone produced by the corpus luteum that helps maintain pregnancy is called

_____.

Answer: progesterone
Diff: 2   *Page Ref: 561*

35) Days 1–5 of the menstrual cycle are the first phase known as the _____ phase.

Answer: menstrual
Diff: 1   *Page Ref: 559*

36) Mammary glands are modified _____ glands.

Answer: sweat
Diff: 2   *Page Ref: 561*

37) The process by which the acrosome membranes of sperm break down is known as the

_____.

Answer: acrosomal reaction
Diff: 2   *Page Ref: 563*

38) A fertilized egg, which represents the first cell of a new individual, is called a _____.

Answer: zygote
Diff: 2   *Page Ref: 564*

39) The early stage of embryonic development during which rapid mitotic cell divisions occur as the zygote travels down the uterine tube is called _____.

Answer: cleavage
Diff: 2   *Page Ref: 565*

40) The primary germ layer that gives rise to the nervous system and epidermis of the skin is called the _____.

Answer: ectoderm
Diff: 3   *Page Ref: 565*

41) The hormone that causes pelvic ligaments and the pubic symphysis to relax, widen, and become more flexible is called _____.

Answer: relaxin
Diff: 2   *Page Ref: 567*

42) The series of events that expel the infant from the uterus are referred to collectively as

_____.

Answer: labor
Diff: 2   *Page Ref: 569*

43) The first stage of labor is known as the _____ stage.

Answer: dilation
Diff: 2   *Page Ref: 570*

44) The placenta and its attached fetal membranes, expelled from the uterus during the placental stage of labor, are collectively referred to as the _____.

Answer: afterbirth
Diff: 2   *Page Ref: 571*

45) Individuals who possess both ovarian and testicular tissues are called _____.

Answer: hermaphrodites
Diff: 1   *Page Ref: 573*

46) The cessation of ovulation and menses for an entire year is called _____.

Answer: menopause
Diff: 2   *Page Ref: 576*

Multiple Choice

1) The male gonads have both sperm–producing and testosterone–producing functions and are called:
   A) testes
   B) sperm
   C) ovaries
   D) ovum
   E) gametes

Answer: A
Diff: 1   *Page Ref: 546*

2) The fibrous connective tissue enclosing each testis is the:
   A) seminiferous tubule
   B) tunica albuginea
   C) interstitial cells
   D) ductus deferens
   E) spermatic cord

Answer: B
Diff: 2   *Page Ref: 546*

3) The exocrine function of the male testes is:
   A) testosterone production
   B) ovum fertilization
   C) sperm production
   D) embryo nutrition
   E) estrogen production

Answer: C
Diff: 1   *Page Ref: 546*

4) The actual "sperm–forming factories" of the male reproductive system that empty sperm into the rete testes are called the:
   A) interstitial cells
   B) epididymis
   C) ductus deferens
   D) bulbourethral glands
   E) seminiferous tubules

Answer: E
Diff: 1   Page Ref: 546

5) Androgens such as testosterone are produced by the:
   A) seminiferous tubules
   B) interstitial cells
   C) epididymis
   D) bulbourethral glands
   E) prostate

Answer: B
Diff: 2   Page Ref: 546

6) The correct descending order of the male duct system (from inside to outside) is:
   A) epididymis, ductus deferens, urethra, ejaculatory duct
   B) ejaculatory duct, epididymis, ductus deferens, urethra
   C) ductus deferens, epididymis, ejaculatory duct, urethra
   D) epididymis, ductus deferens, ejaculatory duct, urethra
   E) ejaculatory duct, ductus deferens, epididymis, urethra

Answer: D
Diff: 2   Page Ref: 546; 548

7) Maturing sperm gain their ability to swim while in the:
   A) seminiferous tubules
   B) epididymis
   C) ductus deferens
   D) ejaculatory duct
   E) urethra

Answer: B
Diff: 2   Page Ref: 546

8) Which one of the following is NOT true of the spermatic cord:
   A) it is a connective tissue sheath
   B) it encloses the ductus deferens
   C) it encloses the epididymis
   D) it contains nerves
   E) it contains blood vessels

Answer: C
Diff: 2   Page Ref: 546

9) The middle part of the male urethra that extends from the prostate to the penis is called the:
   A) prostatic urethra
   B) membranous urethra
   C) spongy urethra
   D) penile urethra
   E) bulbourethra

   Answer: B
   Diff: 2   Page Ref: 548

10) Which one of the following is NOT a component of semen:
   A) sperm
   B) seminal fluid
   C) prostatic fluid
   D) bulbourethral fluid
   E) epididymal fluid

   Answer: E
   Diff: 2   Page Ref: 548–549

11) Thick, clear mucus that cleanses the urethra of acidic urine is produced by the:
   A) testes
   B) seminal vesicles
   C) prostate
   D) bulbourethral glands
   E) epididymis

   Answer: D
   Diff: 3   Page Ref: 549

12) Milky-colored fluid secreted from the prostate:
   A) nourish sperm
   B) activate sperm
   C) cleanse the urethra
   D) neutralize urine
   E) are endocrine only

   Answer: B
   Diff: 2   Page Ref: 548

13) Normal healthy semen has an approximate pH level of:
   A) 3.5–4
   B) 4.0–5.7
   C) 6.0–7.0
   D) 7.2–7.6
   E) 8.5–9.0

   Answer: D
   Diff: 2   Page Ref: 549

14) Pregnancy is generally improbable with a sperm count:
   A) under 20,000 per milliliter
   B) under 1 million per milliliter
   C) under 5 million per milliliter
   D) under 20 million per milliliter
   E) under 100 million per milliliter

Answer: D
Diff: 2   Page Ref: 549

15) Spermatogenesis begins:
   A) prior to birth
   B) at birth
   C) during puberty
   D) during adulthood
   E) during old age

Answer: C
Diff: 1   Page Ref: 550

16) The primitive stem cell of spermatogenesis, which is found on the periphery of each
seminiferous tubule, is called:
   A) spermatogonia
   B) spermatid
   C) primary spermatocyte
   D) secondary spermatocyte
   E) sperm

Answer: A
Diff: 2   Page Ref: 550

17) The enlarged tip of the penis is referred to as the:
   A) prepuce
   B) glans penis
   C) shaft
   D) spongy urethra
   E) scrotum

Answer: B
Diff: 1   Page Ref: 549

18) The final outcome of meiosis within both the testicles and the ovaries is:
   A) the formation of two identical daughter cells
   B) one gamete
   C) two gametes
   D) three gametes
   E) four gametes

Answer: E
Diff: 3   Page Ref: 550; 558

19) Each spermatid and ovum have:
   A) 23 pairs of chromosomes
   B) 23 chromosomes
   C) 46 pairs of chromosomes
   D) 46 chromosomes
   E) 2n chromosomes

   Answer: B
   Diff: 3   Page Ref: 550

20) The process in which sperm are streamlined into a head, midpiece, and tail is called:
   A) spermatogenesis
   B) acrosomal reaction
   C) oogenesis
   D) spermiogenesis
   E) ovulation

   Answer: D
   Diff: 2   Page Ref: 551

21) The entire process of spermatogenesis takes approximately:
   A) 25–50 days
   B) 64–72 days
   C) 120 days
   D) 1 year
   E) 15 years

   Answer: B
   Diff: 3   Page Ref: 552

22) Which one of the following is NOT one of the secondary sex characteristics typical of males:
   A) deepening voice
   B) increased growth of body hair
   C) enlargement of skeletal muscle mass
   D) increased sex drive
   E) thickening of bones

   Answer: D
   Diff: 3   Page Ref: 552

23) Fertilization usually occurs in the:
   A) ovary
   B) Graafian follicle
   C) uterine (fallopian) tubes
   D) uterus
   E) vagina

   Answer: C
   Diff: 2   Page Ref: 556

24) The process by which a mature egg is ejected from the ovary is called:
    A) ejaculation
    B) menses
    C) fertilization
    D) ovulation
    E) erection
Answer: D
Diff: 1   *Page Ref: 553*

25) The journey of the oocyte through the uterine tubes to the uterus following ovulation normally takes:
    A) 1 hour
    B) 24 hours
    C) 3–4 days
    D) 1 week
    E) 10 days
Answer: C
Diff: 2   *Page Ref: 555*

26) The superior rounded region of the uterus above the entrance of the uterine tubes is called the:
    A) body
    B) fundus
    C) cervix
    D) corpus
    E) mons pubis
Answer: B
Diff: 1   *Page Ref: 555*

27) The narrow outlet of the uterus that projects into the vagina is called the:
    A) fundus
    B) body
    C) myometrium
    D) cervix
    E) vagina
Answer: D
Diff: 2   *Page Ref: 555*

28) The external female structure that corresponds to the male penis is the:
    A) cervix
    B) vagina
    C) clitoris
    D) perineum
    E) labia majora
Answer: C
Diff: 2   *Page Ref: 556–557*

29) During oogenesis, an oogonium directly gives rise to:
   A) an ovum
   B) a primary oocyte
   C) a secondary oocyte
   D) a first polar body
   E) a second polar body

Answer: B
Diff: 3   *Page Ref: 557*

30) The inner mucosal layer of the uterus that is sloughed off approximately every 28 days is called the:
   A) endometrium
   B) myometrium
   C) perimetrium
   D) epimetrium
   E) hypometrium

Answer: A
Diff: 2   *Page Ref: 556*

31) Which one of the following is a method of birth control available to men only:
   A) condoms
   B) diaphragm
   C) vasectomy
   D) IUD
   E) Norplant®

Answer: C
Diff: 1   *Page Ref: 548; 574–576*

32) Which one of the following is NOT an option for prostate problems:
   A) microwaves to shrink the prostate
   B) surgery
   C) coitus interruptus
   D) drugs such as finasteride
   E) incineration of excess prostate tissue by radiation

Answer: C
Diff: 1   *Page Ref: 548–549; 574–576*

33) The hormone responsible for ovulation is:
   A) estrogen
   B) progesterone
   C) follicle-stimulating hormone
   D) luteinizing hormone
   E) adrenocorticotropic hormone

Answer: D
Diff: 2   *Page Ref: 557*

34) The menstrual cycle is:
   A) 7 days long
   B) 14 days long
   C) 28 days long
   D) 40 days long
   E) 60 days long

Answer: C
Diff: 1   Page Ref: 559

35) Days 15–28 of the menstrual cycle are known as:
   A) the menstrual phase
   B) the secretory phase
   C) menses
   D) secretory phase
   E) implantation

Answer: B
Diff: 2   Page Ref: 559

36) Which one of the following is NOT true of the proliferative state of the menstrual cycle:
   A) it is stimulated by rising estrogen levels
   B) the basal layer of the endometrium regenerates
   C) glands are formed in the endometrium
   D) endometrial blood supply is increased
   E) the endometrium becomes thin and shiny in appearance

Answer: E
Diff: 2   Page Ref: 559

37) Which one of the following is NOT one of the secondary sex characteristics in young women:
   A) enlargement of the accessory organs of reproduction
   B) breast development
   C) appearance of axillary and pubic hair
   D) decreased fat deposits beneath the skin
   E) widening and lightening of the pelvis

Answer: D
Diff: 1   Page Ref: 561

38) The corpus luteum is a special glandular structure of the ovaries that primarily produces:
   A) estrogen
   B) progesterone
   C) testosterone
   D) interstitial cell–stimulating hormone
   E) luteinizing hormone

Answer: B
Diff: 3   Page Ref: 561

39) The mammary glands are:
   A) modified ceruminous glands
   B) modified sebaceous glands
   C) modified sweat glands in both males and females
   D) modified lacrimal glands
   E) modified sweat glands in females only

Answer: C
Diff: 2   Page Ref: 561

40) The clusters of specific glands that produce milk when a woman is lactating are called:
   A) lactiferous ducts
   B) areolar glands
   C) mammary glands
   D) alveolar glands
   E) lactating glands

Answer: D
Diff: 3   Page Ref: 561

41) For women aged 40–49, the American Cancer Society recommends mammography every
_____ to detect breast cancer too small to feel.
   A) year
   B) two years
   C) three years
   D) four years
   E) five years

Answer: B
Diff: 2   Page Ref: 562

42) For a sperm cell to fertilize an ovum, sexual intercourse must occur no more than _____
hours before ovulation.
   A) 12
   B) 24
   C) 48
   D) 72
   E) 90

Answer: C
Diff: 3   Page Ref: 563

43) A fertilized egg is known as a:
   A) primary oocyte
   B) zygote
   C) morula
   D) blastocyte
   E) secondary oocyte

Answer: B
Diff: 1   Page Ref: 564

44) The tiny ball of 16 cells found freely floating in the uterine cavity is called a:
   A) blastocyte
   B) zygote
   C) morula
   D) placenta ·
   E) trophoblast

Answer: C
Diff: 1   Page Ref: 565

45) The primary germ layer that gives rise to the mucosae and associated glands is the:
   A) ectoderm
   B) blastocyst
   C) mesoderm
   D) endoderm
   E) morula

Answer: D
Diff: 2   Page Ref: 566

46) Many home pregnancy tests assay for _____ within a woman's urine.
   A) human chorionic gonadotropin
   B) estrogen
   C) progesterone
   D) luteinizing hormone
   E) testosterone

Answer: A
Diff: 2   Page Ref: 565

47) The placenta is usually functioning to deliver nutrients and oxygen to, and remove waste from, the embryonic blood by the _____ of pregnancy.
   A) first week
   B) second week
   C) third week
   D) fourth week
   E) fifth week

Answer: C
Diff: 2   Page Ref: 566

48) All the organ systems are laid down, at least in rudimentary form, and the embryo looks distinctly human by the _____ of embryonic development.
   A) first week
   B) second week
   C) fourth week
   D) eighth week
   E) twelfth week

Answer: D
Diff: 3   Page Ref: 566

49) The hormone produced by the placenta that causes the pelvic ligaments and pubic symphysis to relax, widen, and become more flexible to ease birth passage is called:
   A) renin
   B) relaxin
   C) progesterone
   D) chorion
   E) gonadotropin

Answer: B
Diff: 3   Page Ref: 567

50) Parturition is another term for:
   A) menopause
   B) menses
   C) fertilization
   D) menstruation
   E) childbirth

Answer: E
Diff: 2   Page Ref: 569

51) The normal period of human gestation is calculated as _____ from the last menstrual period.
   A) 265 days
   B) 9 calendar months
   C) 9 lunar months
   D) 280 days
   E) 295 days

Answer: D
Diff: 2   Page Ref: 569

52) Irregular uterine contractions called Braxton Hicks:
   A) signal impending labor
   B) are also known as false labor
   C) are a symptom of placenta previa
   D) are a symptom of abruptio placenta
   E) are a symptom of toxemia

Answer: B
Diff: 2   Page Ref: 569

53) Labor is initiated by prostaglandins and _____.
   A) renin
   B) relaxin
   C) oxytocin
   D) progesterone
   E) human chorionic gonadotropin

Answer: C
Diff: 2   Page Ref: 569

54) The stage of labor that involves the delivery of the infant is the:
   A) dilation stage
   B) expulsion stage
   C) secretory phase
   D) placental stage
   E) postpartum stage

Answer: B
Diff: 1   Page Ref: 570

55) Male sex chromosomes are represented by:
   A) XX
   B) XO
   C) XY
   D) XZ
   E) YY

Answer: C
Diff: 1   Page Ref: 571

56) The first menstrual period, which usually occurs at approximately age 13, is called:
   A) menses
   B) menstruation
   C) menopause
   D) menarche
   E) menogen

Answer: D
Diff: 2   Page Ref: 573

57) Menopause, which ends childbirth ability, is considered to have occurred when a woman:
   A) misses her first period
   B) misses two periods in a row
   C) turns 50
   D) has gone a year without menstruation
   E) has had a hysterectomy

Answer: D
Diff: 2   Page Ref: 576

True/False

1) The trip through the coiled 20–foot (6 meter) long epididymis takes about 20 days.
Answer: TRUE
Diff: 2   Page Ref: 546

2) The rete testis connects the epididymis to the ductus deferens.
Answer: FALSE
Diff: 2   Page Ref: 546

3) The smooth muscle walls of the ductus deferens (also called vas deferens) create peristaltic waves that rapidly squeeze the sperm forward.
Answer: TRUE
Diff: 1   Page Ref: 546; 548

4) Urine and sperm are able to pass through the urethra at the same time.
   Answer: FALSE
   Diff: 1   Page Ref: 548

5) The portion of the male urethra that is surrounded by the prostate is called the membranous urethra.
   Answer: FALSE
   Diff: 1   Page Ref: 548

6) Prostatic cancer is the common reason men consult a urologist because it is the leading type of cancer in adult men.
   Answer: FALSE
   Diff: 1   Page Ref: 548

7) The bulbourethral glands are located inferior to the prostate gland and produce a clear mucous secretion that aids lubrication during sexual intercourse.
   Answer: TRUE
   Diff: 1   Page Ref: 549

8) Sperm swim faster in an alkaline environment and are more sluggish in an acidic environment.
   Answer: TRUE
   Diff: 2   Page Ref: 549

9) Viable sperm cannot be produced at below body temperature.
   Answer: FALSE
   Diff: 1   Page Ref: 549

10) An erection results from blood filling the spongy erectile tissues of the penis.
    Answer: TRUE
    Diff: 1   Page Ref: 549

11) One primary spermatocyte will undergo meiosis to ultimately form four sperm.
    Answer: TRUE
    Diff: 3   Page Ref: 551

12) Spermatids have 46 chromosomes.
    Answer: FALSE
    Diff: 2   Page Ref: 551

13) The acrosome helps a sperm penetrate the follicle cells that surround the egg.
    Answer: TRUE
    Diff: 2   Page Ref: 551–552

14) The hormone that causes secondary sex characteristics in males is progesterone.
    Answer: FALSE
    Diff: 2   Page Ref: 552

15) Ovaries are the size and shape of almonds and contain many tiny saclike structures called ovarian follicles, each of which consists of an immature egg surrounded by one or more layers of follicle cells.

Answer: TRUE
Diff: 1   *Page Ref: 553*

16) After ovulation, the egg is transformed into a corpus luteum.

Answer: FALSE
Diff: 2   *Page Ref: 553–554*

17) Oocytes are carried toward the uterus by both cilia and peristalsis.

Answer: TRUE
Diff: 1   *Page Ref: 554–555*

18) The innermost layer of the uterus is called the myometrium.

Answer: FALSE
Diff: 1   *Page Ref: 556*

19) When a woman is not pregnant, the endometrial lining of the uterus is sloughed off about every 28 days.

Answer: TRUE
Diff: 2   *Page Ref: 556*

20) Detection of uterine cancer is best accomplished by a yearly Pap smear.

Answer: FALSE
Diff: 2   *Page Ref: 556*

21) The external genitalia of a female is also called the vulva.

Answer: TRUE
Diff: 1   *Page Ref: 556*

22) The diamond–shaped region of a female's external genitalia found between the anterior end of the labial folds, the anus posteriorly, and the ischial tuberosities is called the perineum.

Answer: TRUE
Diff: 3   *Page Ref: 557*

23) The cyclic changes that occur monthly in the ovary constitute the ovarian cycle.

Answer: TRUE
Diff: 2   *Page Ref: 557*

24) A primary oocyte undergoes meiosis and produces a secondary oocyte and a polar body.

Answer: TRUE
Diff: 3   *Page Ref: 557*

25) Ovulation occurs during the secretory phase of the menstrual cycle.

Answer: FALSE
Diff: 2   *Page Ref: 559; 561*

26) Estrogens cause the appearance of secondary sex characteristics in females.

Answer: TRUE
Diff: 1   *Page Ref: 561*

27) Penetration of the secondary oocyte by a sperm stimulates its nucleus to undergo the second meiotic division.

Answer: TRUE
Diff: 3   Page Ref: 564

28) Ovulation usually occurs on or about day 14 of the menstrual cycle.

Answer: TRUE
Diff: 1   Page Ref: 559–560

29) Breast cancer is a leading cause of death in American women, with self-examination and mammography being the best forms of early detection.

Answer: TRUE
Diff: 1   Page Ref: 561–562

30) The rapid mitotic cell division that occurs after the fertilization of an egg is known as cleavage.

Answer: TRUE
Diff: 2   Page Ref: 565

31) The two functional areas of the blastocyst are the morula and the trophoblast.

Answer: FALSE
Diff: 3   Page Ref: 565

32) The endoderm gives rise to the nervous system and the epidermis of the skin.

Answer: FALSE
Diff: 2   Page Ref: 565

33) Beginning at the ninth week of development, the embryo is referred to as a fetus.

Answer: TRUE
Diff: 2   Page Ref: 566

34) False labor is caused by Braxton Hicks contractions.

Answer: TRUE
Diff: 2   Page Ref: 569

35) The cervix typically dilates to about 10 cm during the dilation stage of labor.

Answer: TRUE
Diff: 2   Page Ref: 570

36) The placenta and its attached fetal membranes, delivered during the placental stage of labor, are called the afterbirth.

Answer: TRUE
Diff: 3   Page Ref: 571

37) Menopause generally occurs between ages 10 and 15 in females.

Answer: FALSE
Diff: 2   Page Ref: 573

Matching

Identify the time period at which fetal development changes or accomplishments occur:

1) All body systems are present in at least rudimentary form

   Diff: 2   Page Ref: 568

2) Vernix caseosa covers body and lanugo covers skin

   Diff: 2   Page Ref: 569

3) Eyes are open and myelination of spinal cord begins

   Diff: 2   Page Ref: 569

4) Sex is readily detected from the genitals

   Diff: 2   Page Ref: 568

5) Quickening (mother feels spontaneous muscular activity of fetus) occurs

   Diff: 2   Page Ref: 569

6) Limbs are present even though they might still be webbed

   Diff: 2   Page Ref: 568

7) Heart is actively pumping blood

   Diff: 2   Page Ref: 568

8) Facial features are present in crude form

   Diff: 2   Page Ref: 568

9) Fingernails and toenails are present and skin is wrinkled and red

   Diff: 2   Page Ref: 569

10) Head is nearly as large as body and major brain regions are present

   Diff: 2   Page Ref: 569

A) 21–30 weeks

B) 13–16 weeks

C) 4 weeks

D) 17–20 weeks

E) 16 weeks

F) 12 weeks

G) 8 weeks

H) 9–12 weeks

11) General sensory organs are present and blinking motion of eyes occur

Diff: 2   Page Ref: 568

12) Fetal position is assumed because of space restrictions

Diff: 2   Page Ref: 569

1) G	2) D	3) A	4) F	5) D	6) G
7) C	8) H	9) A	10) A	11) B	12) D

Match each description with the appropriate male reproductive structure:

13) Duct connecting epididymis to ejaculatory duct

Diff: 2   Page Ref: 546

14) Organ that produces testosterone

Diff: 2   Page Ref: 546

15) Tube that transports either urine or sperm to the exterior of the body

Diff: 2   Page Ref: 548

16) Gland that produces a thick, yellowish secretion

Diff: 2   Page Ref: 548

17) Sac of skin found hanging outside the abdominal cavity

Diff: 2   Page Ref: 549

A) seminal vesicles

B) scrotum

C) prostate

D) ductus (vas) deferens

E) ejaculatory duct

F) testis

G) penis

H) urethra

13) D	14) F	15) H	16) A	17) B

Match each description with the appropriate female reproductive structure:

18) Birth canal

    Diff: 2   *Page Ref: 556*

    A) clitoris

    B) uterus

19) Organ that is the typical site
    of implantation of a fertilized
    egg

    Diff: 2   *Page Ref: 555–556*

    C) uterine (fallopian) tube

    D) labia minora

20) Duct that transports a
    fertilized egg

    Diff: 2   *Page Ref: 554*

    E) ovary

    F) vagina

21) Organ that produces eggs

    Diff: 2   *Page Ref: 553*

22) Structure that corresponds to
    the male penis

    Diff: 2   *Page Ref: 556–557*

18) F   19) B   20) C   21) E   22) A

23) Fatty, rounded area overlying
    the pubic symphysis

    Diff: 2   *Page Ref: 556*

    A) mons pubis

23) A

Essay

1) Explain the male duct system by naming each organ and describing the role of each organ involved.

    Answer: The first part of the duct system is the epididymis which connects to the rete testis of the testes on one end and the ductus deferens on the other. Sperm are temporarily stored within the epididymis, where they mature and gain the ability to swim. The next part of the duct system is the ductus deferens, also known as the vas deferens. The ductus deferens propels live sperm from their storage site in the epididymis into the urethra by means of peristalsis. The end of the ductus deferens is called the ejaculatory duct. It passes through the prostate gland and connects with the urethra. The urethra carries sperm to the body exterior.

    Diff: 1   *Page Ref: 546–548*

2) List the three male accessory glands and describe their contributions to the formation of semen.

Answer: 1. The seminal vesicles produce fluid that contributes about 60% of the fluid volume of semen. The secretion is thick, yellowish, and is rich in sugar, vitamin C, prostaglandins, and other substances that nourish and activate the sperm passing through the male's reproductive tract.
2. The prostate produces a milky secretion that also activiates the sperm.
3. The bulbourethral glands produce a thick, clear mucus that drains into the penile urethra to cleanse it of acidic urine. This secretion is the first to be released during sexual excitement and serves as a lubricant during sexual intercourse.

Diff: 2   *Page Ref: 548–549*

3) Describe the process of spermatogenesis.

Answer: Spermatogenesis is sperm production that begins during puberty and continues throughout life. The process is begun by primitive stem cells called spermatogonia. From birth until puberty, spermatogonia undergo mitotic division to increase the number of stem cells. During puberty, FSH causes each division of spermatogonium into one stem cell (type A cell) and one type B cell that becomes a primary spermatocyte. The primary spermatocytes then undergo meiosis to secondary spermatocytes, which then form four spermatids. The spermatids streamline and a tail is formed during spermiogenesis, after which they are mature enough to fertilize an ovum and are called sperm.

Diff: 3   *Page Ref: 550–552*

4) List and describe the three major stages of the menstrual cycle.

Answer: Menses occurs during days 1 through 5 of the menstrual cycle. During this stage, the endometrial lining detaches from the uterine wall and sloughs off. Days 6 through 14 are the proliferative stage wherein rising estrogen levels cause the endometrial lining to regenerate. It becomes thick and velvety again and is highly vascularized. Ovulation occurs on approximately the last day of this stage in response to an LH surge. The secretory stage is from days 15 through 28. During this stage, the corpus luteum produces progesterone, which increases the endometrial blood supply and causes the endometrial glands to increase in size and begin secreting nutrients into the uterine cavity. If fertilization occurs, these nutrients will help sustain the embryo until implantation. If fertilization does not occur, the hormone levels decline and the endometrium spasms, setting the stage for menses to begin again on day 28.

Diff: 3   *Page Ref: 559–561*

5) Describe the events of embryonic development from conception until the fetal stage, including development of the primary germ layers.

Answer: A fertilized egg (zygote) undergoes rapid mitotic cell division in a stage called cleavage. Cleavage provides the building blocks for constructing the embryo, which develops until it has about 100 cells and then hollows out to form a blastocyst. The blastocyst has two areas: the trophoblast and the inner cell mass. The inner cell mass forms the primary germ layers, which are the ectoderm, the endoderm, and the mesoderm. The ectoderm gives rise to the nervous system, the epidermis, and the skin. The endoderm forms the mucosae and associated glands. The mesoderm gives rise to everything else. The trophoblast develops projections called chorionic villi which form the placenta along with tissues from the mother's uterus. By the eighth week, all the organ systems have been laid down and the embryo looks distinctly human. Beginning in the ninth week, the embryo is referred to as a fetus.

Diff: 3   *Page Ref: 565–566*

6) List and describe the three stages of labor.

Answer: Stage 1 is the dilation stage, which extends from the appearance of true contractions until full dilation of the cervix (dilation to about 10 cm in diameter). Usually the amnion ruptures during this stage, which is the longest part of labor and lasts for 6 to 12 hours. Stage 2 is the expulsion stage. It extends from full dilation to delivery of the infant. In this stage, the infant passes through the cervix and vagina to the outside of the body. This stage takes 20 minutes to 2 hours. Stage 3 is the placental stage, which usually lasts about 15 minutes, culminating in delivery of the placenta.

Diff: 2   *Page Ref: 570–571*

GREYSCALE

BIN TRAVELER FORM

Cut By _Aelida E_ Qty _10_ Date _10/22/24_

Scanned By _Keshia_ Qty ~~✗~~ Date _10-22-24_

Scanned Batch IDs

_____   _____   _____

Notes / Exception

_____

_____

_____

_____

_____